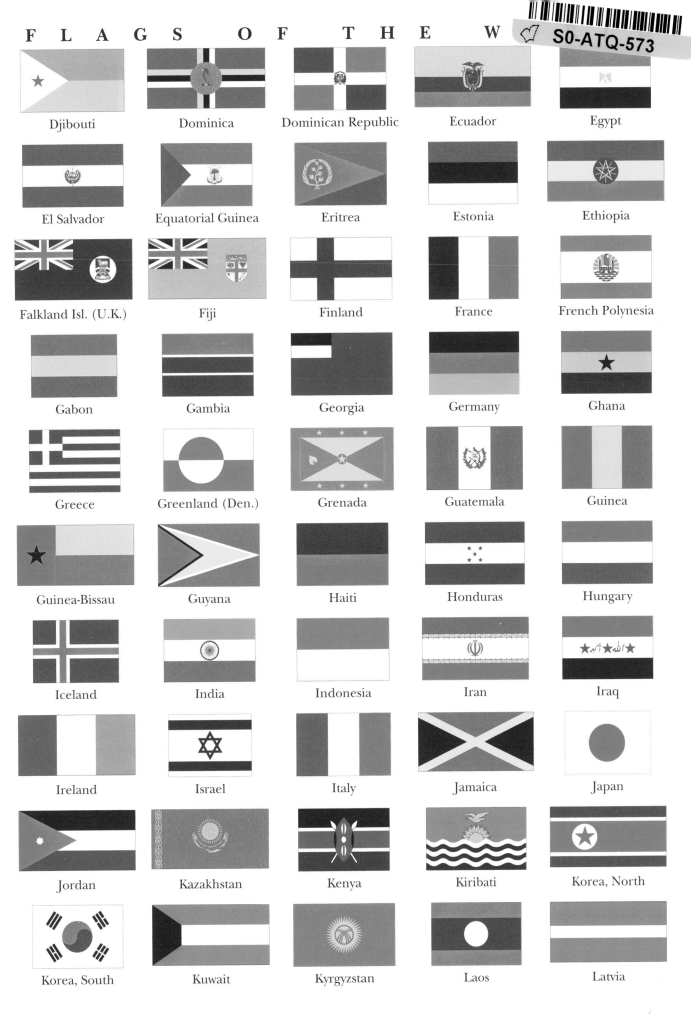

Djibouti

Dominica

Dominican Republic

Ecuador

Egypt

El Salvador

Equatorial Guinea

Eritrea

Estonia

Ethiopia

Falkland Isl. (U.K.)

Fiji

Finland

France

French Polynesia

Gabon

Gambia

Georgia

Germany

Ghana

Greece

Greenland (Den.)

Grenada

Guatemala

Guinea

Guinea-Bissau

Guyana

Haiti

Honduras

Hungary

Iceland

India

Indonesia

Iran

Iraq

Ireland

Israel

Italy

Jamaica

Japan

Jordan

Kazakhstan

Kenya

Kiribati

Korea, North

Korea, South

Kuwait

Kyrgyzstan

Laos

Latvia

WORLD GEOGRAPHY

WORLD GEOGRAPHY

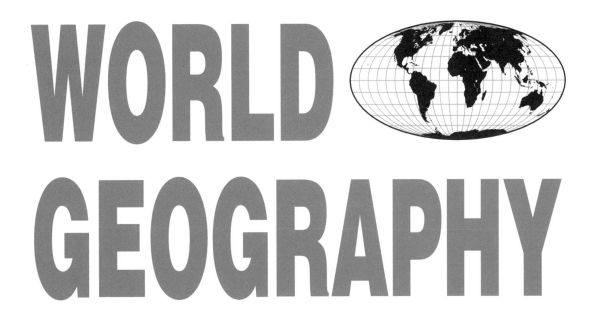

Volume 4

Africa

Editor

Ray Sumner

Long Beach City College

Managing Editor

R. Kent Rasmussen

SALEM PRESS, INC.

Pasadena, California   Hackensack, New Jersey

Editor in Chief: Dawn P. Dawson

Managing Editor: R. Kent Rasmussen   *Research Supervisor:* Jeffry Jensen
Manuscript Editor: Irene Struthers Rush   *Acquisitions Editor:* Mark Rehn
Production Editor: Cynthia Beres   *Page Design and Layout:* James Hutson
Photograph Editor: Philip Bader   *Additional Layout:* William Zimmerman
Assistant Editors: Andrea Miller, Heather Stratton   *Graphics:* Electronic Illustrators Group
Cover Design: Moritz Design, Los Angeles, Calif.

Frontispiece: Africa from space. *(Corbis)*

Library of Congress Cataloging-in-Publication Data

World geography / editor, Ray Sumner ; managing editor, R. Kent Rasmussen.
    p. cm.
    Contents: v. 1. The World. — v. 2. North America and the Caribbean. — v. 3. Central and South America. — v. 4. Africa. — v. 5. Asia. — v. 6. Europe. — v. 7. Antarctica, Australia, and the Pacific. — v. 8. Glossary and Appendices.
    Includes bibliographical references (p.).
    ISBN 0-89356-024-3 (set : alk. paper) — ISBN 0-89356-276-9 (v. 1 : alk. paper) —
ISBN 0-89356-277-7 (v. 2 : alk. paper) — ISBN 0-89356-335-8 (v. 3 : alk. paper) —
ISBN 0-89356-336-6 (v. 4 : alk. paper) — ISBN 0-89356-399-4 (v. 5 : alk. paper) —
ISBN 0-89356-650-0 (v. 6 : alk. paper) — ISBN 0-89356-699-3 (v. 7 : alk. paper) —
ISBN 0-89356-723-X (v. 8 : alk. paper)
    1. Geography—Encyclopedias. I. Sumner, Ray.

G133.W88 2001
910′.3—dc21

2001020281

First Printing

CONTENTS

AFRICA

REGIONS OF AFRICA

PHYSICAL GEOGRAPHY

BIOGEOGRAPHY AND NATURAL RESOURCES

HUMAN GEOGRAPHY

ECONOMIC GEOGRAPHY

GAZETTEER   1133

WORLD GEOGRAPHY

REGIONS OF AFRICA

THE CONTINENT

*Map
Page 961*

Africa is the second largest of the world's great land masses. Together with the large island of Madagascar off its southeast shoreline, Africa covers more than 11.5 million square miles (29.7 million sq. km.), extending from the southern shores of the Mediterranean Sea in the north to the Cape of Good Hope in the south.

PHYSICAL FEATURES. Specialists in plate tectonics and continental drift suggest that in the distant geologic past, Africa was part of the enormous land mass of Gondwanaland. According to this theory, Gondwanaland broke into several segments or plates, one of which, the Indo-Australian plate, moved northward. When it collided with the southeastern edges of the Eurasian plate, the Himalaya Mountains were pushed up by what eventually became India. A second segment of Gondwanaland moved westward to form the continent of Africa.

Tectonic theory argues that Africa's movement has not ended and that the entire continent is pushing against the southern portions of the Eurasian land mass, subjecting the latter to inevitable earthquake dangers. One of the world's most impressive mountain chains, the Atlas Mountains in Northwestern Africa, was thrust upward in an early geologic stage of Africa's continental drift northward. An even more spectacular Eurasian counterpart of tectonic uplift—the European Alps—marks the southwestern lip of the Eurasian plate.

The effect of continental drift on the land mass of Africa formed two immense bodies of water to its west and east—the Southern Atlantic and Indian Oceans. It also created two nearly landlocked seas to its north—the Mediterranean and Red Seas. Other effects of plate tectonics can be traced in land formations within the African continent itself, notably the Great Rift Valley and major zones of former or continuing volcanic activity.

The long oceanic coastlines of Africa, on both the Atlantic and Indian Ocean sides, comprise several geographically distinct subregions bearing specific names. The entrance to the Red Sea is known as the Gulf of Aden, marking the sharp tip called the Horn of Africa, now part of the country of Somalia.

*Horn of
Africa
Page 1161*

The waters between the continent and the island of Mozambique are called the Mozambique Channel. The channel reaches depths of almost 12,000 feet (3,660 meters) between Mozambique proper and the mid-channel Comoros Island archipelago. Probably the best-known geographical subregion at the southern tip of Africa is the Cape of Good Hope, one of the earliest sites of European colonization following Vasco de Gama's historic voyage around the cape into the Indian Ocean in 1498.

*Cape of
Good Hope
Page 1156*

On the Atlantic coast side of Africa, one is struck by the apparent evidence of tectonic theory's claim concerning the continent's former geological connection with what is now the Atlantic coast of South America: The outward bulge of northwest Africa and the curved indentation of the Gulf of Guinea very nearly fit South America's eastern coastline.

*Atlantic
coast
Page 966*

CLIMATIC FEATURES AND VEGETATION ZONES. Although the center of Africa

*Sahara
Page 965*

straddles the equator, the continent's northern portion, bounded by the Mediterranean Sea, extends to 37 degrees north latitude. Cap Bon, in modern Tunisia, thus shares features of the temperate climate zone and vegetation of southern Europe.

Africa's southern tip, at the Cape of Good Hope, reaches as far as 35 degrees south latitude, where Cape Agulhas demonstrates all the features of the temperate climate zone of the Southern Hemisphere. This vastness of geographical extent, coupled with varied conditions brought about by altitude or the coastal effects of ocean currents, means that several broad climate zones characterize different regions. Different climatic conditions bring about notable variations in vegetation, both from north to south and in vast pockets in different geographical regions.

Most of Africa is characterized by one of two climatic zones. Most of the northern half, covered by the Sahara Desert, and the southwest tip, extending between 35 and 23 degrees south latitude, have either semiarid steppe or arid desert conditions. Vast expanses of what climatologists call a tropical continental climate extend from west to east, almost all the way across the continent south of the Sahara into the eastern zone of the Horn of Africa. The Horn itself (specifically modern day Somalia) has a high degree of aridity as a side effect of the northeast trade winds. Thus, it is a desertlike pocket that has much in common with the Saharan zone.

The vast tropical continental zone includes most of the interior, running south from the edges of the Sahara to about 25 degrees south latitude (modern Zimbabwe, just north of South Africa). This re-

Hippopotamus hunting on the Zambezi River during the 1860's. (Eduard Mohr, *To the Victoria Falls of the Zambezi,* 1868)

gion enjoys moderate levels of rainfall, enough to sustain typical savanna plant and animal life.

Savanna vegetation consists of vast stretches of grasslands and medium-sized brush and trees. This is the zone of numerous grazing animal herds and the predators or scavengers that live off victims taken from the herds. Very large animals, notably the elephant, hippopotamus, and rhinoceros, also live in this region of Africa.

Equatorial Africa runs inland from the western coast both north and south of the equator proper, from the level of southern Nigeria in the north and from the northern Angolan coast at about 10 degrees south latitude. The typical patterns of equatorial climate and vegetation—heavy amounts of rainfall and tropical rain forest flora—do not extend as a belt all the way across Africa because of the highland geographical features that run from Ethiopia through East Africa (Kenya and Uganda) down into the southern reaches of the continent. The highland zones share the climatic features and flora and fauna of the savanna regions. They also constitute the most important geological area of Africa associated with early or current volcanic activity.

In areas where mountains are a dominant part of the landscape, they often are natural barriers to rain clouds, creating localized subpatterns in Africa's broad north-to-south climatic zones. One example of this is the island of Madagascar. The central highland range there contributes to a tropical maritime climate, with luxurious vegetation, on the eastern half of the island, where the majority of the rainfall coming from the Indian Ocean falls.

The west's tropical savanna vegetation, on the other hand, is the product of lower levels of rainfall beyond the central mountains. The Great Escarpment running along Africa's southwestern coast, cou-

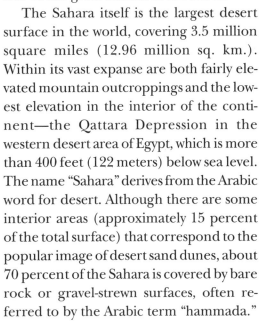

HOW AFRICA GOT ITS NAME

It is claimed that in antiquity, the Greeks called the continent Libya and the Romans called it Africa. The term could have come from the Latin *aprica* ("sunny") or the Greek *aphrike* ("without cold"). Africa referred mainly to the northern coast of the continent that represented a southern extension of Europe. It is believed that the Romans called the area south of their settlements Afriga, or Land of the Afrigs, the name of a Berber settlement south of Carthage.

---

pled with the effects of the Atlantic Ocean's Benguela Current, create an even more extreme pattern. A good portion of Southern Africa's inland climate, especially that of the relatively high Kalahari Desert basin (more than 3,000 feet or about 1,000 meters), is as dry as the interior of the great Sahara in the north.

The Sahara itself is the largest desert surface in the world, covering 3.5 million square miles (12.96 million sq. km.). Within its vast expanse are both fairly elevated mountain outcroppings and the lowest elevation in the interior of the continent—the Qattara Depression in the western desert area of Egypt, which is more than 400 feet (122 meters) below sea level. The name "Sahara" derives from the Arabic word for desert. Although there are some interior areas (approximately 15 percent of the total surface) that correspond to the popular image of desert sand dunes, about 70 percent of the Sahara is covered by bare rock or gravel-strewn surfaces, often referred to by the Arabic term "hammada."

The bareness of large stretches of the Sahara is partly the product of severe strong winds that blow from the northeastern sections of Africa (where high-pressure conditions prevail during most of the year) toward the low-pressure zones of the equa-

Animals Pages 1029-1032

Benguela Current Page 969

torial regions of the continent. These winds do not carry moisture. As they pass into the warmer temperature zones of the desert, the winds warm up themselves, drying out the areas through which they pass. In the somewhat more populated regions on the northern and southern fringes of the Sahara, the seasonal phenomenon of desert wind has been given local names, such as the sirocco, the khamsin, and the harmattan.

Levels of precipitation vary over the vast expanse of the Sahara. To the north and south of the main desert, transitional steppe areas may receive about 10 inches (254 millimeters) of rain annually, which sustains only low shrub growth and some seasonal grasses. The average rainfall for

the core area of the desert never exceeds 5 inches (127 millimeters) per year. When rainfall comes, it is often only after long dry periods, so the hardened surface of the desert cannot absorb the rain. Flash flooding is often the result.

Local geological formations can create a situation that brings the water table close to the surface, resulting in oasis conditions in a restricted area. Because subsurface water follows fissures in the rock formations, green oases may appear in a chain-like sequence over a relatively wide expanse in the middle of otherwise totally arid surroundings.

Two important Atlantic Ocean currents, the Canary Current on the northwest coast and the Benguela Current run-

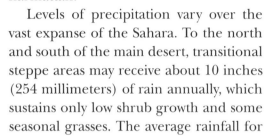

Oasis
Page 973

Sign in Morocco pointing the direction to Timbuktu, Mali, across the Sahara. (Corbis)

ning from the southwest tip along the Namibian coast northward into the Gulf of Guinea, strongly affect the climate of the regions they pass, creating particularly arid conditions along sections of Africa's western coasts. If the enormous arid west-to-east band, including the Sahara, in Northern Africa could be enough to explain the low rainfall of the Northwest coast even without the Canary Current, the Benguela Current is a prime contributor to the aridity of the western half of the southern tip of Africa. Whereas Namibia receives less than 16 inches (400 millimeters) of rain per year, the half of southern South Africa facing the Indian Ocean can receive up to three and a half times that amount.

Rainfall levels less than 16 inches (400 millimeters) are characteristic of all areas of North Africa except the Mediterranean coastal areas of Morocco, Algeria, and Tunisia and the mountainous zones in each of these three Maghreb countries. Rainfall in the broad belt of tropical continental, or savanna, territory south of the Sahara, like the eastern African highlands and countries located south of the equatorial lowland forested areas, is more difficult to predict. It ranges from 16 to 55 inches (400-1,400 millimeters), with averages somewhere between.

The danger of drought in savanna zones, however, is a recurrent fact in African climatology. Rainfall levels in the relatively restricted central equatorial zone, and also the West African coastal areas from Côte d'Ivoire (Ivory Coast) through Nigeria, are almost invariably above 55 inches (1,400 millimeters) annually.

MOUNTAINOUS ZONES. Although the Atlas and Aures ranges of Northern Africa are extensive mountainous systems, no other area on the continent has major chains that could be compared to Asia's Himalayas, South America's Andes, or

North America's Sierras or Rocky Mountains. Geologically speaking, Africa is perhaps the least mountainous continent of the globe.

Deep in the interior of the Saharan zone, in the modern states of Niger, Algeria, and Chad, high desert areas are broken by rather major mountain masses in geographically limited zones. The best known of these are the mountains of Tibesti in Libya and the Ahaggar outcroppings in central Algeria. Elevations in the latter reach nearly 10,000 feet (3,050 meters). Another striking zone of African mountains is found along the long geological split in the earth's crust known as the Great Rift Valley.

MAJOR RIVERS AND DELTAS. Three of the world's longest rivers are found in Africa: the Nile, the Congo and the Niger, located respectively in the northeast, central equatorial, and western Sudanic regions of the continent. The Nile is the longest river in the world, longer than the Amazon in South America. Running more than 4,180 miles (6,065 km.) from its sources in central Africa to the shores of the Mediterranean Sea in Egypt, it drains an area of nearly 1.14 million square miles (3 million sq. km.). Although this total drainage area is significant—measuring only about 190,000 square miles (500,000 sq. km.) less than that of the Mississippi River and more than twice the drainage area of the Niger River—it scarcely matches the Amazon River, which drains more than 2.7 million square miles (7 million sq. km.). Despite its length, the Nile ranks last among the world's ten major rivers in the volume of water it discharges into the sea.

When the two branches of the Nile fan out several miles north of the modern city of Cairo, Egypt, they contribute to a triangular mosaic of canals that for centuries have irrigated the fields of the Nile Delta

Rivers Pages 962, 1164

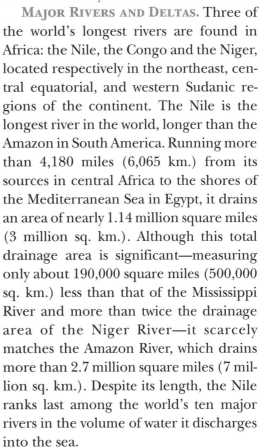

Watershed map Page 972

Drought Page 975

Cairo Page 1155

Caravan
Page 1038

lands. At the terminal points of both branches of the river, the historic ports of Damietta and Rosetta have been visited by traders from ancient to modern times. The smallness of these ports contributed to the growth, from ancient times forward, of the neighboring delta emporium of Alexandria.

This history and familiarity of the Nile delta can be contrasted with the situation of the Niger River delta. Modern maps of the fanlike form of the Niger delta on the coast of Nigeria show the city of Port Harcourt and the island of Bonny near where the easternmost branch of the river enters the Gulf of Guinea. Unlike the two ancient Nile delta cities, Port Harcourt came into existence only in the middle of the nineteenth century, when British explorers realized that the complex marshy wastes along the Nigerian coast were in fact the terminal point of the Niger itself.

As for the sources of the Niger River, early explorers noted another geographical peculiarity. The Niger rises from waters that originate on the eastern slopes of a watershed near the western coasts of Africa, in modern-day Guinea and Mali. The mountainous land mass of the Fouta Jallon, near the modern borders dividing Senegal and Guinea from Mali, explains this division of the watershed so close to the Atlantic Ocean.

Several relatively short rivers due west from the watershed of the Niger flow directly into the Atlantic Ocean. The best known of these is the Gambia River. The Senegal River is the longest river originating near the Niger's own sources but flowing in an entirely different direction. This river flows northwest from its sources in Mali to form the northern border dividing modern Senegal from Mauritania.

The Niger River initially runs northeast from Mali's capital in Bamako until it bends back to the southeast. Two historic cities, Timbuktu and Gao, are located in the area of the Niger Bend. Traditionally, both took advantage of their position along the northernmost reaches of the Niger to become trade termini for caravans across the Sahara.

The Congo River is the earth's fourth-longest. Although only about 370 miles (600 km.) longer than the Niger River, it discharges almost eight times as much water into the Atlantic Ocean—1,400 billion cubic meters annually. The volume of water carried by the Congo River is second only to the Amazon River, for largely the same reasons: Both drain inland equatorial watersheds where heavy rains occur during most of the year. A considerable number of major tributaries feed water into the Congo, including the Aruwimi, Ubangi, and Sangha Rivers north of the Congo's east-to-west course, and the Tshuapa and Kwa Rivers to the south. Each of these major tributaries draws water from several lesser tributaries that cover the central equatorial zone.

The Congo River also differs from the Niger and Nile Rivers in not having a prominent delta formation where it enters the ocean. The twin national capital cities of Kinshasa (formerly Léopoldville) and Brazzaville are located somewhat inland from the coast, separated from it by the famous Livingstone Falls.

The principal rivers that enter the Atlantic Ocean south of the Congo River are less well known. The Cuanza River flows out of the mountain mass to the north of the Kalahari basin, watering the lowlands of modern Angola near its capital at Luanda. Much farther south is the westward-flowing Orange River, fed by the Vaal River. Both of these have their source far away in the drainage system west of the Drakensberg range of South Africa, mountains that nearly reach the shores of the eastern tip of South Africa. The Orange River is the only main river flowing across the southern portion of the arid Kalahari Desert.

The narrow lowland plains along Africa's eastern coasts—running from Durban, South Africa, (located beneath the high peaks of the Drakensberg Range) all the way to the tip of the Horn of Africa in Somalia—are crossed by several rivers that drain into the Indian Ocean. The most important of these is the Zambezi River, whose sources lie deep in the interior. The Zambezi reaches the Indian Ocean on the coast of Mozambique. One of its tributaries, the Luangua River, flows generally southward away from a point midway between Lakes Malawi and Tanganyika, both located in the long Great Rift Valley region. Neither lake receives water from the Luangua River, despite their closeness to it.

North of Mozambique, several shorter rivers empty into the Indian Ocean. The Tana River flows directly from the slopes of Mount Kenya to the shoreline north of the Kenyan city of Mombasa.

Finally, the lengthy Webi Shebali flows directly out of the mountain massifs of Ethiopia and heads toward the Indian Ocean near Somalia's capital city of Mogadishu. Just short of the ocean, it bends southward to follow the coast (its name changing to a near identical Somali version, Uebi Scebeli) and dissipates in the arid lowlands without actually flowing into the ocean.

MAJOR INLAND LAKES. Several inland lakes in Africa are big enough to be seen on most maps of the entire continent. Located in the arid interior of the Sahara, Lake Chad is the only major body of water in the northern third of Africa. It lies in the center of a major inland basin called the Bodele Depression, and receives drainage from an immense area reaching as far northwest as the Ahaggar Mountains

in Algeria and the Adamawa Plateau in Cameroon to the south. Two rivers flow westward toward it from the Maraone Highlands and Ennedi Hills in Chad, although their waters do not always reach as far as the present lake. Waters from two important rivers to its southeast, the Logone (originating in the Adamawa Plateau) and Chiari Rivers, are more certain sources of runoff. In earlier geological times, the expanse of Lake Chad was much greater.

In the eastern third of the continent, where the north-south geological effects of the Great Rift Valley are evident, one finds not only Lake Victoria at the level of the equator between the two eastern branches of the Great Rift Valley but also the long, narrow waters of Lakes Tanganyika and Malawi. The complexity of geological structures in the area around Lake Victoria makes this region a center of volcanic activity, and therefore the home of some of Africa's most best-known mountain peaks.

MINERAL WEALTH. The richest zones of mineral wealth are found south of the equator, especially in the area running from the southeastern corner of Congo-Kinshasa (Democratic Republic of the Congo; formerly Zaire) through Zimbabwe and along the eastern zones of South Africa.

South Africa is one of the world's major sources of gold and diamond mining. Some of the same areas of South Africa offer major possibilities for mining coal. Other mining products that have commercial export potential include copper, antimony, chrome, asbestos, tin, and platinum.

Beyond Southern Africa, mining, on a somewhat smaller scale, is an essential part of the export economy of several other regions. In Northwest and West Africa, Mauritania, the Côte d'Ivoire (Ivory Coast), Nigeria, and Angola all extract and exploit some minerals. In restricted areas, notably in the Congo region and Gabon in Equatorial Africa, sources of uranium are of considerable importance to the world market.

Cape Town
Page 962

After the gold and diamonds of South Africa, the most important resources extracted from the ground beneath Africa are petroleum and its byproducts. The biggest producers of petroleum in Africa are Libya, Algeria, and Nigeria. In the last quarter of the twentieth century, Egypt's Red Sea zone, together with several states along the central West African coast (most notably Angola) became secondary petroleum-producing areas.

Johan-
nesburg
Page 1161

AGRICULTURE. Certain areas of Africa have moved toward agricultural crop diversification in response to demands in the world market. Nevertheless, the continent can be divided into general regions of predominant staple crops, which provide the basic subsistence food sources in those regions. Production of those crops depends in large measure on broad climatic conditions. Maize (corn) can be grown as a staple crop only in the southern third of Africa, whereas wheat (which requires predictable seasonal rains) is restricted to regions north of the Sahara. The arid Saharan zone, stretching eastward to the Horn of Africa (Ethiopia and Somalia), can only support sorghum and millet. The wettest regions of Africa, mainly the coastlands of the Gulf of Guinea and Equatorial Africa itself, depend primarily on root crops such as potatoes, yams, and manioc as staples.

Sorghum
Page 1033

MAJOR CITIES. Most of Africa's major cities are of relatively recent origin, and their striking growth in the last half of the twentieth century is a reflection of several demographic factors. Economic conditions, especially the attraction of unemployed rural masses to presumed job markets in the cities, have created many zones of extensive crowding on the outskirts of relatively undeveloped urban systems. Almost every African capital city shares this characteristic.

A few major cities have longer histories and have developed the recognizable attributes of major urban centers. Among these, the South African cities of Cape Town and Johannesburg owe much of their original development to the heavy emphasis placed on concentrating economic infrastructure during the long period of European colonial rule. Both, however, show signs of central urban modernity, surrounded on all sides by overwhelming problems created by the rural-to-urban migration of large numbers of Africans. Some urban migrants came under the strictly controlled conditions of the segregationist apartheid period, others under the largely uncontrollable conditions in the period following the transition to African majority rule in South Africa in the 1990's.

Another giant urban complex with a long history is on the opposite end of the continent. Cairo, in Egypt, founded in 969 C.E., has become Africa's most populated city. As has occurred in many other less massive African urban centers, Cairo's population explosion occurred mainly in the second half of the twentieth century.

Byron Cannon

FOR FURTHER STUDY

Carlson, Lucile. *Africa's Lands and Nations.* New York: McGraw Hill, 1967

Grove, A. T. *The Changing Geography of Africa.* 2d ed. Oxford, England: Oxford University Press, 1993.

Peters, Sunday W. *Regional Geology of Africa.* Berlin: Springer-Verlag, 1991.

Reader, John. *Africa: A Biography of the Continent.* New York: Alfred A. Knopf, 1997.

White, Richard. *Africa in Focus.* London: Macmillan Press, 1990.

THE OFFSHORE ISLANDS

The islands that lie off the coast of Africa fall into five geographical groups: Macronesia, the Gulf of Guinea, the isolated islands of the mid-Atlantic range, off Africa's east coast, and in the Indian Ocean. From tiny, barren Ascension in the Atlantic Ocean to enormous Madagascar in the Indian Ocean, they display almost as much variety as the continent itself. However, they have several factors in common. All were colonized by European nations, and most have suffered from a lack of resources. Many have relied on a plantation-style economy stressing only one or two crops, making them vulnerable to shifts in world markets. Tourism has provided several islands with an economic boost, but tourists can threaten the very cultures that attract them.

MACRONESIA. Islands lying off the northwest and west coasts of Africa include Madeira, the Canary Islands to the south, and Cape Verde farther south still. Along with the Azores, which lie in the North Atlantic more than 850 miles (13,675 km.) west of Portugal, these islands are known as Macronesia, a term derived from the Greek words for "large" and "island." All are the peaks of volcanoes, several of which remain active.

Madeira lies about 350 miles (563 km.) from the African coast of Morocco. The Canary Islands are much closer to Africa, and, when the weather is clear, an observer on the island of Fuerteventura can see the coast of southern Morocco. The islands of Cape Verde lie much farther south, about 300 miles (480 km.) off the coast of West Africa.

Lack of rainfall is a problem in most of Macronesia. Only two of the Canary Islands have rivers that run year-round, and the two islands nearest Africa resemble the arid North African coast opposite them. Settlers in Madeira and the Canaries have built complex systems of canals and tunnels to distribute water evenly, enabling many temperate and subtropical fruits and vegetables to be grown. The islands of Cape Verde are barren and chronically short of water.

Cape Verde
Page 1156

Only the Canary Islands seem to have been inhabited when European explorers reached them, although all may have been visited from time to time by early seafarers. Today, Madeira is a part of Portugal and the Canary Islands are part of Spain. These islands are visited by large numbers of tourists, and the residents of the Canary Islands enjoy a middle-income economy. Once a Portuguese colony and an important stop for ships, Cape Verde became independent in 1975. As a result of its harsh climate and lack of resources, it has never recovered the modest economic status it once enjoyed.

THE GULF OF GUINEA. Under the bulge of West Africa, a chain of volcanic islands stretches southwestward in an almost straight line into the Gulf of Guinea, a continuation of a range that includes Mount Cameroon on the continent. Nearest Africa is Bioko, an important part of the nation of Equatorial Guinea and site of its capital, Malabo. Next in line and extending to the equator are the islands that make up the nation of São Tomé and Príncipe. At the end of the chain lies tiny Annobón, also part of Equatorial Guinea.

Canary
Islands
Page 1155

AFRICA'S ISLANDS BECOME FREE

Africa's history has been immeasurably influenced by the intervention of European countries, many of which occupied African lands—usually forcibly—and enslaved the indigenous peoples. Although independence has not necessarily brought freedom or economic progress to Africa, it has returned the fate of the continent to its own people. Following are the dates on which and the countries from which Africa's islands gained their independence:

1960   Madagascar becomes independent of France.

1963   Zanzibar becomes independent of Great Britain; a year later it joins Tanganyika to form the United Republic of Tanzania.

1968   Equatorial Guinea (including Annobón and Bioko) becomes independent of Spain.

1968   Mauritius becomes independent of Great Britain.

1975   Cape Verde becomes independent of Portugal.

1975   Comoros becomes independent of France.

1975   São Tomé and Príncipe becomes independent of Portugal.

1976   Seychelles becomes independent of Great Britain.

The climate of these islands is tropical wet, and all are renowned for their spectacular beauty. However, the islands can be unhealthy, especially for those not raised in the region, and malaria and tuberculosis are endemic in Bioko. Crops such as cocoa and coffee have sustained the islands' economies from time to time, although both countries had to import most of their food by the end of the twentieth century.

Sparsely populated when the Portuguese arrived in the fifteenth century, the islands in the Gulf of Guinea have been colonies of Spain or Portugal for most of their modern history. Bioko and São Tomé were important slave-trading stations, and even after the abolition of slavery, forced labor remained the norm in São Tomé and Príncipe, as it did in much of Portuguese Africa. By the late 1990's, a series of repressive governments had virtually destroyed the economy and infrastructure of Equatorial Guinea.

THREE ISOLATED ISLANDS. Rising from the undersea range of mountains known as the Mid-Atlantic Ridge are the three isolated islands of Ascension, St. Helena, and Tristan da Cunha. All three islands are volcanic, but only the last has experienced an active eruption in recent times. Ascension and St. Helena lie in the Tropics; the former island is relatively barren, but the latter was heavily forested until imported goats destroyed much of its vegetation.

Tristan da Cunha lies far to the south, 1,600 miles (2,575 km.) from St. Helena. Uninhabited until their discovery in the early sixteenth century by Portuguese explorers, the islands have sometimes benefited from their isolation. Ships routinely stopped at St. Helena for fresh water in the nineteenth century, and the island was chosen by the British as a place of exile for defeated French emperor Napoleon Bonaparte. Ascension has become an important telecommunications center. It and Tristan da Cunha are dependencies of

St. Helena; St. Helena is a dependency of Great Britain.

OFF AFRICA'S EAST COAST. Africa's largest island, Madagascar is the fourth-largest island in the world—after Greenland, New Guinea, and Borneo. Nearby are the Comoros, islands lying at the northern end of the Mozambique Channel between Madagascar and the nation of Mozambique. Farther north still and hugging the coast of Africa are the small islands of Zanzibar and Pemba, both part of the nation of Tanzania. Lying east of the "horn" of East Africa is the island of Socotra, part of the Arabian country of Yemen.

Geologists believe that Madagascar was once connected to Africa and India as part of the prehistoric continent of Gondwanaland. The island apparently became separated during the late Cretaceous period, some 65 million years ago, allowing many unique plants and animals to evolve. The first human inhabitants of Madagascar arrived more than 2,000 years ago and ap-

parently had a wide range of origins, from Indonesia and Malaya to Africa itself.

Because of its size and geography, Madagascar has a variety of climates. The island's east coast experiences a hot, wet monsoon season from November through April, although its southwestern region remains almost perpetually dry. Comoros experiences the same monsoon on a more uniform basis. Rice is grown for domestic consumption in both nations, and burning of forests for its cultivation has led to serious soil erosion on Madagascar. Madagascar and Comoros grow such crops as coffee for export, and are important sources of flavorings and spices such as vanilla and cloves. Comoros is the world's second-largest producer of vanilla and the largest producer of ylang-ylang, a fragrant ingredient of perfume.

Colonized by the French in the nineteenth century, Madagascar became independent in 1960 and Comoros in 1975. Both countries face dire economic prob-

Lemurs
Page 963

Wooden boats called "dhows" are anchored in front of the Old Grand Mosque in Moroni, the capital of the Comoro archipelago, in mid-2000. (AP/Wide World Photos)

lems. Comoros has few natural resources, and it and Madagascar are among the poorest countries in Africa.

Zanzibar
Page 1168

Low-lying and once disease-ridden, Zanzibar has few resources of its own, but its position on the coast of East Africa has enabled it to profit as a trading depot for the region. Once the center of the East African slave trade, Zanzibar was persuaded by the British to abolish the trade in 1873. The British subsequently declared a protectorate over the island, which regained its independence in 1963. The following year, Zanzibar joined Tanganyika to become the nation of Tanzania.

In the Indian Ocean, a handful of islands lie scattered east of Madagascar. These include the Mascarene Islands—Mauritius, Rodrigues, and Réunion—just north of the tropic of Capricorn, and the nation of Seychelles, located just south of the equator. The Mascarenes are volcanic, and a volcano on Réunion remains active. The islands of Seychelles are largely granite, although the group includes a number of low-lying coral atolls, most of them uninhabited.

Seychelles
Page 963

All the islands in this region have a tropical monsoonal climate. Like Madagascar and Comoros, they are home to many unique and often fragile species of plants and animals. The *coco de mer,* at 49 pounds (22 kilograms) the heaviest seed in the world, grows on a species of palm in Seychelles. The dodo, a large flightless bird, was found on Mauritius until it was slaughtered to extinction for its meat.

Although they were undoubtedly known to traders and seafarers, the Mascarenes and Seychelles remained largely uninhabited until settled a few centuries ago by Europeans—Mauritius in the late sixteenth century, Réunion in the mid-seventeenth century, and Seychelles in the mid-eighteenth century. Their populations today are descendants not only of their original settlers but of slaves and traders drawn from throughout the Indian Ocean area.

Mauritius and Seychelles received their independence from Great Britain in 1968 and 1976, respectively. Réunion remains a self-governing overseas department of France. Although sugarcane has long been a traditional crop on Mauritius and Réunion, tourism has begun to play an increasingly important role on all the islands.

Grove Koger

FOR FURTHER STUDY

Blackburn, Julia. *The Emperor's Last Island: A Journey to St. Helena.* New York: Pantheon, 1991.

Bowermaster, Jon. "Is This the Last Outpost of Innocence?" (São Tomé and Príncipe). *Conde Nast Traveler* 29, no. 12 (December, 1994): 140-143, 156, 158.

Gran Canaria, Lanzarote, Fuerteventura: The Eastern Canaries. Singapore: APA Publications; New York: Prentice Hall Travel, 1998.

Irwin, Aisling, and Colum Wilson. *Cape Verde Islands: The Bradt Travel Guide.* Old Saybrook, Conn.: Globe Pequot Press, 1998.

Library of Congress. Federal Research Division. *Indian Ocean: Five Island Countries (Madagascar, Mauritius, Comoros, Seychelles, Maldives).* Washington, D.C.: Government Printing Office, 1995.

Madeira. New York: Prentice Hall Travel, 1998.

Preston-Mafham, Ken. *Madagascar: A Natural History.* New York: Facts on File, 1991.

Romey, William D. "Stop-off at Tristan da Cunha." *Focus* 45, no. 2 (Summer-Fall, 1998): 28.

Singh, Sarina. *Mauritius, Réunion and Seychelles.* Oakland, Calif.: Lonely Planet Publications, 1998.

Tenerife and the Western Canary Islands. New York: Prentice Hall Travel, 1998.

PHYSICAL GEOGRAPHY

PHYSIOGRAPHY

*Map
Page 964*

The world's second-largest continent, after Asia, Africa covers 11.7 million square miles (30.3 million sq. km.) It is surrounded by the Arabian Sea and Indian Ocean to the east and south, the Atlantic Ocean on the west, and the Mediterranean Sea on the north. The estimate of its size includes major offshore islands, especially the immense island of Madagascar, whose surface covers 226,658 square miles (587,725 sq. km.). Other significant island complexes are Zanzibar and Pemba, plus the Comoro and Seychelles Islands off Africa's eastern coast, and the Canary and Madeira Islands in the Atlantic off northwest Africa. Individual islands close to the western coast include São Tomé, Príncipe, Annoban, and Fernando Po in the Gulf of Guinea.

Africa is traditionally divided into five main regions: North Africa, East Africa, West Africa, Central Africa, and Southern Africa. It is relatively easy to describe these regions in general terms; to explain the differences between them requires consideration of a number of more complex factors, beginning with an overview of the geological history of the continent.

ELEVATION ZONES. Geologists refer the northern two-thirds of Africa as "low Africa." Most of the surface of this region is only about 650 feet (200 meters) in elevation. Some low elevations do occur in the southern third (particularly coastal regions), and mountain zones jut out of lower elevations in the northern two-thirds.

"High Africa," with typical elevations of about 300 feet (1,000 meters) or more, be-gins on the eastern side of the continent in the area of modern Kenya and Uganda and extends through most of the southern third of the continent. Geologists also refer to high Africa as the Southern African Superswell, a term that is linked to the tectonic origin of the continent. Tectonics considers the relative buoyancy of the African landmass and other continents as part of the plate system forming the crust of the earth.

NORTH AFRICA. North Africa is divided from the rest of the continent by the vast Sahara Desert. This division is further marked in the western half of North Africa by the east-west mountain complex of the Aures and Atlas ranges, running from western Tunisia to the Atlantic coast of Morocco. Mediterranean and Atlantic coastal plains in this region are relatively narrow.

*Sahara
Page 965*

Eastward from Tunisia to the Nile Delta in Egypt, there are some mountain out-croppings, mainly in the Jabal Akhdar of Cyrenaica, but the land generally extends southward to the interior at elevations near sea level. West of the Nile River is the extensive Qattara Depression, which descends to 440 feet (135 meters) below sea level. Because these lower regions are not far from either the Mediterranean or the Atlantic, winter rainfall is sufficient to sustain seasonal agriculture throughout most of the western half of coastal North Africa.

The most impressive mountain region of the High Atlas in Morocco reaches elevations that, at nearly 14,000 feet (4,267 meters), are only surpassed by eastern Af-

This view of southeastern Libyan desert, photographed from the space shuttle Columbia *in July, 1994, shows the volcanic peaks of Jebel Arkenu and Jebel Uweinat.* (Corbis)

rican peaks in Ethiopia and Kenya. Southeast of these mountains, and generally southward from points east of Tunisia, lies the desert expanse of the Sahara.

WEST AFRICA. On the western half of the continent south of the Sahara, major rivers originating in the Fouta Jallon highlands of Guinea (such as the Niger, the Senegal, and the Gambia) flow toward low coastal zones, saving much of West Africa from the harshness of the desert. The northern part of the vast West African region, comprising the modern countries of Senegal, Mali, Burkina Faso, and Niger, is the generally flat and bleaker half. Zones farther south (the coastal region of Guinea, Sierra Leone, and from Côte d'Ivoire to Nigeria) are more varied both topographically and in terms of vegetation.

EAST AFRICA. To the east, the complicated geology of the rift system creates a major division between the Sahara and the main zone of east Africa from the Horn of Africa in Somalia southward to the Zambezi River. Halfway between the northern mountain region of East Africa and the Zambezi River, Africa is cut through by the equator. Whereas the eastern equatorial zone inland from the Indian Ocean is mountainous—snowcapped Mount Kenya is on the equator—Central Africa at the equator is characterized by the lowlands of the great Congo River basin and the most extensive tropical rain forest on the continent.

SOUTHERN AFRICA. Beyond the Zambezi outlet to the Indian Ocean are the first mountains of Southern Africa and Africa's second-largest desert region, the Kalahari. The mountains of Southern Africa along the southeastern coast next to the Indian Ocean are generally not as high as the mountainous zones of northeastern and northwestern Africa. The Drakensberg Range, however, forms an extensive watershed for Southern Africa's major river, the Orange, which flows westward just south of the Kalahari Desert.

Beneath and above these easily observable features of the landscape are major physiographic factors that help explain why each broad region differs from the others. One factor includes geological phenomena; the second is rainfall, which is responsible for both varied vegetation zones and for the major rivers that crisscross Africa's surface.

TECTONIC FACTORS SHAPING AFRICA. Through studies of plate tectonics (the movement of different sections of the earth's crust "floating" over the molten core) scientists have been able to relate the geological origins of Africa to phenomena that created the other continents. Tectonic theory assumes that, in the most distant geological past, a huge single landmass, Gondwanaland, broke into segments in reaction to pressures rising to the earth's surface from the core. The gradual movement of these segments either in opposite directions (for example, the presumed separation of North and South America from the other continents) or pressing against one another and lifting (creating tectonic systems like the mountain masses of the Himalayas "pushed" by the Indian subcontinent or the Alps in Europe), can explain how Africa took the form it did.

Geologists have posited at least seven phases of major tectonic activity that shaped Africa. The earliest of these is dated to the early Permian period (between 280 and 222 million years ago), preceding the actual breakup of Gondwanaland. It is traceable in some early rock formations in Southern Africa, specifically the Karoo Basin. Another major tectonic period occurred in the late Triassic (225 to 190 million years ago) and early Jurassic periods, when northwest Africa broke free from North America. Still later, in the mid-Cretaceous period (135 to 65 million years ago), West Africa separated from South America. The early Cenozoic era (58 to 2 million years ago) saw the tectonic upheavals associated with the opening of the Red Sea and the East African Great Rift Valley.

EAST AFRICAN RIFT SYSTEM. Although technical explanations of African rift systems are still being debated, the observable features of rifting began to attract the attention of geologists as early as the 1830's. Generally speaking, rift systems are regions where extensive faults have caused a combination of upward movement of scarps, or cliffs, and downward movement of basins crushed between zones of uplifting. The East African system is one of the most easily recognized rift systems in the world. It is clearly connected with the formation of the narrow Red Sea separating Africa from the Arabian Peninsula, and extends southward through some of Africa's most spectacular ecological areas.

The northernmost section of the East African rift includes the Afar Depression, which is the product of rifting in the Cenozoic era. It appears that these northern segments of the Great African Rift are younger than areas stretching thousands of miles to the south.

The Afar Depression is a V-shaped depressed block that cuts into Ethiopia for 360 miles (600 km.) southward from the Red Sea. To its west and southeast rise major fault scarps leading toward the Ethiopian and Somalian plateaus; to the north, two uplifted blocks, the Danakil Block and the Aisha Block, separate the Afar Depression from the Red Sea and the Gulf of

THE SAHARA

The Sahara is the world's largest desert in the tropical latitudes. Eleven modern African countries, from Mauritania in the west to the Sudan in the east, fall within its boundaries. The Sahara covers more than 3.4 million square miles (8.8 million sq. km.), a good portion of which is totally uninhabited. Although geologists trace the initial stages of its desertification to the early Pliocene era about five million years ago, this vast zone has seen different periods ranging from extreme dry conditions to fairly substantial humidity. Pockets of mineral wealth, including iron, copper, zinc, magnesium, chromium, and even gold and silver, occur in restricted subregions of the vast desert.

Aden. Its lowest elevations (more than 60 feet/100 meters below sea level) are in the north, while its floor reaches 600 feet (1,000 meters) at its southernmost extension. The Ethiopian mountain mass alters the dominant rift pattern until it reappears prominently further south in modern Kenya.

The rest of the East African rift system contains a number of subsections that specialists study separately, such as the Gregory Rift, the Albert Rift, the Lake Tanganyika Rift, and the Lake Malawi Rift zone.

The broad lines of the Gregory Rift in Kenya include phenomenal rift scarps forming the western wall of the Kerio Valley. The highest elevation here is the Elgeyo escarpment, which rises 4,920 feet (1,500 meters) from the valley floor. The rift valley floor itself has high points and low points. At low points of about 1,640 feet (500 meters), basin-like structures gather water in lakes with high saline content, such as Lake Magadi. By contrast, Lake Naivasha is a freshwater lake at a much higher elevation (6,200 feet/1,890 meters).

The Albert Rift zone is due west of Lake Victoria in modern Uganda. It contains three of the best-known rift valley lakes: Albert, Edward, and Kivu, on the western borders of present-day Rwanda. Researchers have traced at least thirty-two basin structures in this area, all the product of extensive subsurface faulting. Perhaps the most spectacular area is northwest of Lake Albert. Here the Bunia scarp, considered to be a still-active fault system, juts up 4,265 feet (1,300 meters). South of the lake, the giant Ruwenzori Block rises to an elevation of 16,795 feet (5,119 meters). It also is situated in an area of recent seismic activity. By the time the rift system enters the area of Lake Edward on the boundary between Congo-Kinshasa and Uganda, an entire range of recently volcanic moun-

tains, the Virunga Range, dominates the horizon.

Although the next zone, the Tanganyika Rift, shares many of the characteristics of areas to its north, including ten separate basins and important scarps both to the west and east, there are no traces of magmetism. Volcanic activity does not reappear until the Rukwa Rift zone (a parallel segment of the Tanganyika Rift) enters the Rungwe volcanic province just north of Lake Malawi. From this point the Lake Malawi Rift zone, which includes the Livingston Fault scarp on the northeast side of the lake, proceeds another 370 miles (600 km.) southward.

Although signs of faulting beyond the Lake Malawi Rift zone appear in the Southern Mozambique Graben (thus, nearly to the Indian Ocean coast), these belong to a different geological era, and do not form part of the East African rift system.

LAKES. Five of Africa's major natural lakes are located in the East African rift system: Victoria, Turkana, Albert, Tanganyika, and Malawi. Lake Victoria is the only one of these lakes that contributes to the water runoff system that leads toward the Nile River. A less expansive lake, Tana, lies well to the east of the course of the Nile in Ethiopia. Tana is the most northerly of the rift-related lakes. Lake Chad, by contrast, is the result of long-distance drainage into lower elevations in the central Saharan region, and is relatively shallow from shore to shore. It is also the westernmost major lake on the African continent.

A number of different types of lakes are found in various regions of Africa. Lakes that have formed in depressions left by volcanic action include Kivu and Chala in Kenya. Soda lakes—those containing high concentrations of sodium bicarbonates that have dissolved out of the acidic basement-complex rocks beneath the lake bot-

Upper Nile Page 1164

toms—are found to the east and west of Lake Victoria. Another notable example is Lake Magadi in Kenya.

The rift valley system has the deepest lakes in Africa. Lake Tanganyika, the deepest of Africa's lakes in the Eastern Rift area, is nearly 900 feet (1,500 meters) deep, twice the average depth of Lake Malawi. Despite its huge size (25,637 square miles/ 66,400 sq. km., compared with Lake Tanganyika's 12,700 square miles/32,890 sq. km.), Lake Victoria is relatively shallow, averaging depths of about 300 feet (90 meters). This is partly because more than 80 percent of the water entering Lake Victoria comes from rain falling directly on its surface. Because of its vast surface area, much of Victoria's water is lost to evaporation.

SOILS OF AFRICA. The nature and quality of surface soils in different regions of Africa vary considerably. Technical experts use four major divisions to classify soils. Two of these make up most of the surface soil of Africa: pedalfers and pedocals.

Pedalfer soils constitute the largest group of soils in Africa. Within this group, ferralsols are probably the most common. They appear mainly in low topographical relief zones and span the continent in the central (but not coastal) equatorial and savanna belts. Their principal constituent elements are clay, aluminum oxides, hydroxides, and, as their name suggests, high levels of iron. The process called ferrallitization is typical of tropical regions, where long periods of high temperatures exist in combination with high levels of rainfall, creating extensive leaching. Chemically, ferralsols have a low base content, and require large additions of artificial fertilizers before they can sustain more than minor agriculture.

A second soil type in the pedalfer group, nitisols, are productive tropical soils. Nitisols tend to appear in small areas both west and east from the central ferralsol regions, for example, in the Cameroon highlands and southeastern Nigeria, or in the region west of Lake Victoria. The porous composition and relatively favorable chemical content of nitisols tend to promote growth of deep-rooted plants.

The third most common pedalfer in Africa is the acrisol group. These appear throughout the West African regions. They contain high levels of clays and low content of bases. These soils can maintain agriculture only if the thin surface layer, with its buildup of organic nutrients, is carefully maintained. If the protective natural covering of minor vegetation is removed, acrisol areas are very susceptible to erosion.

Pedocals are the second most common group of soils in Africa. Among five distinct soils in this category, calcisols and vertisols are most worthy of note. The calcisols dominate the northern third of Africa and also are found in the desert zone of Namibia in southwestern Africa. Vertisols are characteristic of the Sahel region south of the Sahara, but also appear in the East African rift zone and in pockets of the eastern edges of southern Africa.

All these soils are the product of chemical processes that, aided by relative levels of water brought by rainfall, break down constituent minerals on the surface. Thus, rainfall patterns in Africa help to explain a wide variety of organic and nonorganic features of each subregion.

RAINFALL AND DRAINAGE. Levels of annual precipitation vary greatly from region to region in Africa. Two extremes can be traced, from the lowest levels of the Saharan interior or in the Namibian desert—near zero—to high levels, near 394 inches (10,000 millimeters) around Mount Cameroon, or in Liberia in West Africa. More typical are annual rainfall lev-

Lake Tanganyika Page 1165

Lake Victoria Page 1167

Watershed map Page 972

*Flooding
Pages 971,
1100, 1101*

*Congo
River
Page 962*

els of 20-60 inches (500-1500 millimeters) in the savanna ecosystems immediately south of the Sahara and in large areas of South Africa.

Watershed patterns across Africa lend themselves to an extraordinary variety of tributary systems and, eventually, major rivers. One of the most widely known is the huge Congo watershed basin in the tropical zone, fed by high levels of rainfall. Another lesser-known, but physiographically important, watershed system creates the Niger River, which flows through one of Africa's driest surrounding environments. Each of the continent's other major rivers, including the Nile in the northeast, the Zambezi in the southeast, and the Orange in the southwest, is the product of different sources of drainage that are tied to land formations in the interior.

The total annual water flow from the interior of Africa to the oceans has been estimated to be 3,720 cubic kilometers, with 90 percent of this water flowing westward to the Atlantic, and only 10 percent into the Indian Ocean. Among Africa's major rivers, the Congo carries the largest annual runoff, amounting to 1,414 cubic kilometers, 38 percent of the total for the continent. The Niger and the Ogoué (in the equatorial zone of Gabon) contribute only 7.2 and 4 percent, respectively. From this point, runoff contributions of the next four major rivers drop off considerably, from 106 cubic kilometers for the Zambezi, through 73 cubic kilometers for the Nile, to 41 cubic kilometers for West Africa's Volta.

Despite its extraordinary length and the equatorial location of its main watershed, the volume emptied by the Nile is reduced by extensive loss to lateral swamps and high levels of evaporation along its course through desert areas.

Large volumes of river water moving from Africa's interior toward the sea (or in the case of Lake Chad, fed by the Chari River, into low elevation basins) can create flood conditions in certain seasons. Although the overall threat of major flooding is less notable in Africa than on other continents, the impact of high waters has consequences not only for the natural environment but also for human populations living along the rivers.

Egypt's very existence as an agricultural society, for example, has depended for millennia on the predictability of Nile flooding. In the case of the Nile and other river systems, the nature of sediments contained in runoff water has both upstream and downstream effects. Specific elements, such as calcium and magnesium, are taken from surface soils and either transferred to downstream ecosystems or deposited in the ocean. High-water seasons on these representative rivers occur in totally different periods of the year.

MOUNTAIN SYSTEMS. Africa cannot be considered a mountainous continent. Seen in broad profile, its main continental feature resembles a complex of high plateaus and broad river basins. Most mountains that emerged as a result of subsurface tectonic activity formed in the Mesozoic era. Some, especially in Southern Africa, are much older. If one looks at the several subzones in detail, however, almost all have some mountainous features, although these differ from region to region.

Northwest Africa's Atlas system (including the High Atlas, Middle Atlas, Saharan Atlas, and Rif mountains) are the product of the folding of basement rock along a rift fracture during the late Cretaceous period. This area and period of mountain formation were common to the Atlas and the European Alps on the other side of the Mediterranean trough.

The mountains of northeast Africa, and specifically those of Ethiopia, are among the most complex systems on the continent, running east-to-west in eastern Ethiopia and north-to-south on both sides of the Great Rift Valley that divides the country almost in two. The highest Ethiopian peaks—Ras Dashan, west of the rift near the Red Sea, and Mount Balu farther south, east of the rift—are more than or near 15,000 feet (4,570 meters).

The mountains of the East African interior owe their origin to volcanic activity. Unlike hot spot formations, however, great peaks like Mounts Elgon, Meru, Kenya, Kilimanjaro, and Uzungwa run along the fault system associated with the Rift Valley. By contrast, the Comoros Islands, halfway between northwestern Madagascar and the coast of East Africa, are considered to be part of the complex of mantle plumes, or hot spots, where volcanic activity remains latent. This apparently was not the case in neighboring Madagascar, where substantial mountain ranges on one side of the island reveal their origins in tectonic uplifting.

Several subzones of the Sahara are characterized by mountainous outcroppings, some very substantial, such as the Ahaggar and Tibesti (whose peaks are as high as 10,000 and 11,200 feet (3,050-3,415 meters), and the Jabal Marrah in the Darfur region of Sudan. The Ahaggar and Tibesti mountain zones are presumed to be the product of mantle plumes, where pressures coming from the hot mantle of the earth come relatively close to the surface. In such regions, the likelihood of continuing volcanic activity and the possible formation of mountains is greatest.

The Cameroon highlands in West Africa, just above the equator and spilling over into eastern Nigeria, have only a few

---

MOUNT KILIMANJARO

Located in northeastern Tanzania, the extinct volcano Mount Kilimanjaro is the highest mountain in Africa. Two peaks, linked by a saddle-like gap, crown its summit. Kibo, at 19,340 feet (5,895 meters), is the highest. Beside it is Mauenzi, which is 17,564 feet (5,354 meters) high. The slopes of Mount Kilimanjaro are covered with a rich volcanic soil that is ideal for cultivating two important crops, coffee and plantains. Despite its nearness to the equator, Kilimanjaro is topped with snow year-round. It takes part of its name from *kilima*, the Swahili word for mountain.

---

major peaks (notably Cameroon Mountain, at 13,350 feet/4,070 meters). Like the Tibesti and Ahaggar regions of the Sahara farther north, the Cameroon mountain region is the product of hot-spot volcanic thrusts upward from the earth's mantle. This extensive highlands complex provides a watershed source for several major rivers, the most important of which is the Benue, the last major tributary of the Niger before it flows into the Gulf of Guinea.

Something similar can be said about the Fouta Jallon and Nimba Mountains, which are at their highest (a little over 6,000 feet/ 1,830 meters) in modern Guinea. Ample rainfall in the West African mountain complex provides runoff waters that give birth to the Niger itself, as well as the westward flowing Senegal and Gambia Rivers.

The southern portion of Africa contains a wide variety of mountains. Older, less dominant complexes associated with what geologists call the Cape Fold Belt and the jutting peaks of the geologically more recent Drakensberg Mountains, running more or less parallel to the Indian Ocean coast, are the result of tectonic uplift and warping at the continent's edges.

Byron D. Cannon

Mt. Kilimanjaro Pages 965, 1162

Granite outcroppings Page 966

FOR FURTHER STUDY

Adams, W. M., A. S. Goudie, and A. R. Orme, eds. *The Physical Geography of Africa.* Oxford, England: Oxford University Press, 1996.

Aryeetey-Attoh, Samuel, ed. *The Geography of Sub-Saharan Africa.* Englewood Cliffs, N.J.: Prentice Hall, 1997.

Grove, A. T. *The Changing Geography of Africa.* 2d ed. Oxford, England: Oxford University Press, 1993.

_____. "Geomorphic Evolution of the Sahara and the Nile." In *The Sahara and the Nile,* edited by M. Williams and Hughes Faure. Rotterdam, Netherlands: Balkema, 1980.

Lewis, L. A., and L. Berry. *African Environments and Resources.* Boston: Unwin Hyman, 1988.

McConnell, R. L. "The East African Rift System." *Nature* 215 (1967): 578-581.

Peters, Sunday W. *Regional Geology of Africa.* Berlin: Springer-Verlag, 1991.

Summerfield, M. A. "Plate Tectonics and Landscape Development on the African Continent." In *Tectonic Geomorphology,* edited by M. Morisawa and J. T. Hack. Boston: Allen and Unwin, 1985.

CLIMATOLOGY

*Map
Page 967*

Africa's climates derive their characteristics from latitude, the elevation and orientation of the landforms, and ocean currents. No other landmass receives as much total sunshine as Africa, which is the only continent that lies mostly within the Tropics. The equator divides the continent almost equally in latitude, creating an arrangement of climatic belts mainly symmetrical on each side of the equator.

Because of the greater east-to-west extent of the continent in the north, large areas in the center of the Sahara are far away from the moderating influence of an ocean. This creates a continentality effect that increases temperature differences between summer and winter and decreases precipitation. The southern part of the continent is much narrower, which allows the maritime influence to extend further inland.

Africa lacks high mountain ranges that can act as a climatic barrier. Both the Himalayas in Asia and the Andes of South America greatly modify the climates of those continents. In Africa, the great size of the continent (about three times that of the United States) coupled with the uniformity of its altitude—ranging generally from 1,000 to 3,000 feet (300-915 meters)—creates large climate regions changing gradually from one climate to the next. The few higher mountains have climatic zones according to changes of elevation.

Finally, ocean currents modify temperature and precipitation regimes in Africa. Three ocean currents affect the climates of Africa: The Canary Current in the

north and Benguela Current in the south both carry cold water from the temperate zone into the Tropics; the warm Mozambique current brings warm water from the equatorial region of the Indian Ocean toward the east coast of Africa south of the equator and the east coast of Madagascar. Cold currents chill the winds that blow over them and reduce the amount of moisture that reaches the neighboring shores; warm currents increase rainfall.

CONTINENTALITY AND MARITIME EFFECTS. The northern part of Africa is much wider than the part south of the equator. Large areas in the north are more than 900 miles (1,500 km.) away from the oceans, unable to benefit from their moisture and their moderating effect on temperature. Dry land surfaces heat and cool relatively quickly because solar radiation cannot penetrate the solid surface of the earth to any meaningful extent. This property is called continentality or the continental effect; it results from the fact that precipitation decreases as distance from the oceans increases, and because the oceans have minimal influence on air temperatures located well inland. Water takes more time than land to heat up and cool down. Coastal areas benefit from the moderating influence of the ocean on air temperature because sea breezes cool down the air temperatures during the summer and warm up the air temperatures during the winter. This is the maritime effect on climate.

Seasons in the Southern Hemisphere are the reverse of those in the Northern Hemisphere. In the south, summer begins

*Benguela
Current
Page 969*

*Africa from
space
Page 970*

around December 22, fall around March 21, winter around June 21, and spring around September 23. In tropical climates, rainfall usually occurs when the Sun is high above the horizon (June 21 to September 22 in the Northern Hemisphere; December 2 to March 20 in the Southern Hemisphere). At the equator, the Sun's rays are perpendicular to the earth's surface around March 21 and September 23. These are the times of maximum precipitation. When precipitation is heavy, the ground temperature lowers.

TEMPERATURE. In a large area of high temperature, from 10 degrees south latitude to the tropic of Cancer, average monthly temperature does not reach below 64.4 degrees Fahrenheit (18 degrees Celsius) except on the East African plateaus and on the Abyssinian plateau, where elevations are much higher. In these high-elevation stations, all temperatures are lower than in stations situated in a lowland area at similar latitude. For example, Addis Ababa, the Ethiopian capital, is located at 7,620 feet (2,324 meters) above sea level; its yearly average temperature is 61.6 degrees Fahrenheit (16.4 degrees Celsius). Malakal, Sudan, at 1,272 feet (388 meters) above sea level, has a yearly average temperature of 80.2 degrees Fahrenheit (26.8 degrees Celsius). Beyond this area of high temperature, cooler temperatures are recorded during the winter, the low sun period.

The narrower southern half of the continent is cooler than the north because of the greater influence of the neighboring oceans. As one moves away from the equator seasonal temperature differences increase, but almost nowhere in Africa is the winter a truly cold season. The coldest monthly average recorded at sea level in northernmost Africa is greater than 50 degrees Fahrenheit (10 degrees Celsius); the coldest monthly average in southernmost

Temperature map Page 969

Africa is never lower than 57.2 degrees Fahrenheit (14 degrees Celsius). In equatorial Africa, where the sky is often overcast, the diurnal (day-to-night) range, although low, can be greater than the annual (seasonal) range; in arid regions, land temperatures drop rapidly at night as a result of radiation cooling, often many degrees within a few hours.

WINDS AND AIR MASSES. Africa is divided into two wind belts: the trade winds and the westerlies. The trade winds are created by the bands of high pressure that lie centered on latitudes thirty degrees north and south (subtropical anticyclone or subtropical highs). Because of the rotation of the earth, winds flowing from those high-pressure areas are deflected to their left in the Southern Hemisphere and to their right in the Northern Hemisphere. Therefore, the air moving toward the equator flows from east to west (the easterlies or trade winds), while the air moving toward the poles flows from west to east (the westerlies).

The trade wind zone usually is an area of sunshine and relatively little precipitation, largely because the air has subsided from upper levels of the troposphere and has been heated adiabatically. This explains why continental trade winds (those flowing from the north, over the broad expanse of northern Africa) bring meager precipitation, excessive aridity, and extreme evapotranspiration on the continent.

The air masses affected by the continental trade winds are continental tropical (cT), characterized as dry and warm. Trade winds from the south, blowing from the subtropical anticyclone located over the Indian Ocean, carry a greater amount of humidity. The amount of water vapor they bring to the east coast of the African continent depends on how long the air has moved over water since its descent from

To combat heat and humidity without using energy for cooling, many buildings in Africa are designed to allow breezes to pass through them continuously. This auditorium at the University of Dar es Salaam is essentially an open bowl loosely covered by another bowl so that breezes can pass through them. (R. Kent Rasmussen)

high in the troposphere. As the subtropical anticyclone is located in the middle of the Indian Ocean, this component of the trade winds bring heavy precipitation on the east coast of Africa between the two Tropics and the east coast of Madagascar. The total precipitation they deliver decreases westward.

Trade winds from subtropical oceanic highs of opposite hemispheres tend to converge along a line or a zone known as the intertropical convergence zone (ITCZ). Because subtropical anticyclones migrate north and south seasonally, this zone is located near the equator in March and September, during the equinoxes.

Ship captains in the trade wind zone during the days of sailing vessels knew these winds well, often detouring far from their course in order to benefit from those winds' steadiness. The trade winds were the winds that first blew Christopher Columbus and his flotilla to the Caribbean in 1492.

The ITCZ, also called the equatorial low (a low barometric pressure, generating convection and rainfall), accompanies the movement of the high sun from one hemisphere to the other. This migration of the equatorial low is more pronounced in the Northern Hemisphere. It reaches 25 degrees north latitude in July during the Northern Hemisphere summer. The displacement of the equatorial low into the Southern Hemisphere in January is much less important because of its more maritime character. The migration of the intertropical convergence zone across the equator creates a localized monsoon phenomenon. The monsoon is a seasonal wind that blows from the ocean during the summer and affects Western Africa particularly. Laden with moisture, these winds generate intense rainfall. In Conakry, the capital city of Guinea, precipitation in July is usually 44.5 inches (1,130 millimeters). This monthly average is greater than the average yearly precipitation in New York of 42.2 inches.

The westerlies flow out of the subtropical high but toward the cooler temperate zone. Westerlies dominate a zone of about thirty degrees of latitude in width in both hemispheres. They bring moist air from the west of the Mediterranean region during the local winter. The total precipitation they deliver decreases eastward. At times continental polar air masses, labeled cP on weather maps, reach the Mediterranean region and bring bitterly cold dry air. These occasional cold spells damage orange groves, orchards, and flower-produc-

ing farms. Maritime polar air masses (cold and moist) are associated with the winter precipitation that occurs over the Mediterranean climate belt.

PRECIPITATION. Generally, precipitation depends on barometric pressure, on air masses, and on the wind that flows over the continent and moves these air masses. Near the equator, the great number of sunny days, the presence of a low barometric pressure, and active convection—when the air, warmed at the contact of the earth's surface, rises—create the tropical wet climate. In this region, precipitation may reach 400 inches (10 meters) per year at the foot of the windward side of Mount Cameroon (13,340 feet/4,070 meters). Monrovia, the capital city of Liberia, gets more than 200 inches (5 meters) of rain. This represents about five times the yearly precipitation in New York or Philadelphia.

Precipitation in the center of Africa, on the equator, is greater than 80 inches (2,000 millimeters) and occurs all year. That kind of precipitation characterizes the tropical wet climate. There is no dry month in the tropical wet climate because areas with this climate are constantly covered by warm maritime air masses laden with moisture. Rainfall is heaviest in March and in September, when the Sun is perpendicular to the earth's surface and solar energy is concentrated.

In general, as one moves away from the equator, the amount of precipitation decreases toward the tropics of Cancer and Capricorn, then increases into the Mediterranean belt. The area between the tropical wet climate and the Tropics is bathed in wet, warm maritime tropical air masses (marked mT on weather maps) during the local summer, and in dry and warm continental tropical air masses (cT) during the local winter.

In addition to a decrease in yearly precipitation, a seasonal pattern of precipitation appears. A rainy season occurs during the local summer (June to September in the Northern Hemisphere, December to March in the Southern Hemisphere). A dry season exists during the local winter. This pattern characterizes the savanna climate, also named the tropical wet-and-dry climate. The yearly rainfall is proportional to the length of the rainy season.

Out of the 5.8 million square miles (15 million sq. km.) of tropical climates in Africa, about 3.9 million square miles (8 million sq. km.) receive more than 15 inches (400 millimeters) of rainfall. This is approximately the amount of precipitation that Salt Lake City, Utah, receives yearly. Since farming is possible without irrigation when rainfall exceeds 15 inches yearly, 53 percent of the tropical regions of Africa can be farmed without tapping the groundwater supply.

Across the tropic of Cancer and the tropic of Capricorn are subtropical deserts (Sahara in the north and Kalahari in the south) generated by a band of high pressure that prevents rainfall. A belt of drought and moisture called the tropical savanna climate surrounds these deserts. The local summer is rainy, and the local winter is dry. The narrow band of transitional precipitation regime between the savanna and the subtropical desert is called the semiarid steppe or Sahel.

In coastal areas, the summer rainy season of the savanna is sometimes exacerbated, creating the monsoon climate. Further away from the equator, both to the north and to the south, lies the Mediterranean climate, influenced by westerly winds that bring moisture during the local winter. Only the northernmost and southernmost tips of Africa are beyond the tropical climates' regions. The Mediterranean climate of these two extremities of Africa is characterized by precipitation

during the winter and drought during the summer.

Throughout Africa, coasts backed by mountainous highlands receive the highest rainfall. In the few areas where mountains exist, rainfall is higher on their windward side, and temperature decreases as elevation increases. This generates what is called a mountain climate.

REGIONAL CLIMATES. Thus, Africa has seven basic categories of climate: the tropical rain forest (or tropical wet), the tropical savanna (or tropical wet and dry), the monsoon climate, the Sahel climate (semiarid), the subtropical deserts (arid), the Mediterranean climate, and the mountain climate. Each climate has a significant impact on the life that exists there.

TROPICAL RAIN FOREST. The tropical rain forest (tropical wet) climate, located along the equator, is warm and rainy all year. The central part of Africa, located across the equator, has little variability in temperature; the range in temperatures increases away from the equator. Night is the "winter" of tropical Africa. Diurnal ranges of temperature are greater than the yearly temperature range. Temperatures are warm all year, unless cold currents or elevations bring cooling effects. Yearly mean temperatures increase away from the equator.

The natural vegetation associated with the tropical wet region is the tropical rain forest, a dense, lush, evergreen forest where gigantic trees can reach heights of 130-200 feet (40-60 meters), tall ferns can grow to 20 feet (6 meters), and orchids bloom in the upper reaches of the tall trees. As many as forty different species can be found in 2.5 acres (1 hectare). About 1 percent of the light that reaches the highest trees gets to the ground. Many insects, primates, and reptiles inhabit this climatic region.

Drought
Page 975

Sahara
Page 965

The tropical rain forest in Africa once covered much larger areas than it covers today. Deforestation is to blame for the loss of this precious ecosystem. True virgin rain forest, not yet lost to logging, can still be found in Congo-Kinshasa (formerly Zaire). Secondary rain forest, resulting from the regrowth of a forest after clearing the primary or virgin forest, exists along part of the coastal area that surrounds the Gulf of Guinea: Sierra Leone, Liberia, portions of Nigeria, Cameroon, and both Congos. Rivers that flow exclusively in the tropical wet climate are few and short. The longest rivers cross more than one climatic belt and have a complex structure, as does the Congo River or the Ubangi.

TROPICAL WET AND DRY OR SAVANNA.

Trees
Page 1026

A transitional belt of drought and moisture, called the tropical savanna, exists between the tropical rain forest climate and the Sahel climate. The rainy season occurs during the local summer, and the dry season during the local winter. Forests do not tolerate the dry season well. In general, the size of trees and the density of the natural vegetation is a function of the total precipitation of a region. This is why, as the total precipitation decreases away from the equator, the rain forest becomes shorter and less dense, and grassland extends.

Niger
Page 1163

Only along permanent rivers, on windward sides of mountains, and in the monsoon climate does the rain forest remain. It otherwise becomes a new vegetation formation called savanna, comprising grassland with scattered trees. The higher the precipitation, the higher the density of trees in the savanna. This region is home to large herbivores such as the elephant, gazelle, antelope, and giraffe, and carnivores such as the lion, lynx, and cheetah.

Giraffes
Page 1026

Rivers originating in this region flow most during the period of high sun and least during the period of low sun.

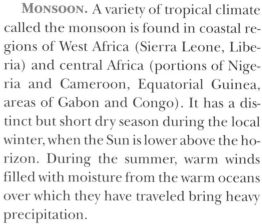

MONSOON.

A variety of tropical climate called the monsoon is found in coastal regions of West Africa (Sierra Leone, Liberia) and central Africa (portions of Nigeria and Cameroon, Equatorial Guinea, areas of Gabon and Congo). It has a distinct but short dry season during the local winter, when the Sun is lower above the horizon. During the summer, warm winds filled with moisture from the warm oceans over which they have traveled bring heavy precipitation.

Douala, the largest port of Cameroon, receives 150 inches (3,847 millimeters) of rainfall a year, about four times the precipitation of Washington, D.C. Rain forest grows in these very wet areas. It exhibits fewer plant species per unit area, the forest is lower and less dense, and more light reaches the ground, allowing more light-loving trees to grow.

THE SAHEL.

This region is a narrow zone of semiarid climate where yearly mean rainfall is between 10 and 25 inches (250 to 600 millimeters). The isohyet of 600 millimeters (the line connecting locations where the rainfall is 600 millimeters) runs eastward from Dakar. The northern part of Senegal, Mali, Burkina Faso, the southern part of Niger, Chad, and Sudan, and the western part of Ethiopia are part of this climatic region. The natural vegetation is grassland, also called a steppe. Acacias, an umbrella-like tree, grow intermittently.

Rainfall in the Sahel is highly variable from one year to the next. Farmers frequently have attempted to settle and farm areas where rainfall is below the 15 inches (400 millimeters) of rainfall needed for permanent, nonirrigated agriculture or for cattle ranching, but have suffered severe setbacks. In the late twentieth century, the Sahel suffered many episodes of famines; for example, famine struck in 1999 after the summer of 1998 did not bring enough rain to sustain local agriculture.

Like any other large animals, lions are most likely to be found near water. (PhotoDisc)

SUBTROPICAL DESERTS. North Africa covers about 7.3 million square miles (19 million sq. km.) north of 4 degrees north latitude. North Africa contains the largest, driest, and hottest desert in the world—the Sahara, where total precipitation is less than 4 inches (100 millimeters) per year.

About 42 percent of this area receives

Desert map
Page 968

Cape Town
Page 962

Namib
Page 969

Mt. Kili-
manjaro
Pages 965,
1162

Cashews
Page 1098

less than 4 inches of precipitation per year. In the Southern Hemisphere, the Kalahari Desert in Botswana, while not as dry or as hot as the Sahara, exists for the same reason the Sahara does. The subtropical high causes the air to descend from high in the troposphere. As the air descends, it warms up and dries up. Many of the plants in these deserts are ephemerals, germinating and completing their life cycle quickly after a rain. Perennial plants, such as cactus, remain dormant during much of the year. As soon as it rains, they begin to grow and store water in their stems.

The Namib Desert, in Namibia, is a coastal desert generated by the presence of the cold Benguela current and by its location in the vicinity of the tropic of Capricorn where a high pressure is located during the local winter (June to September). North of the Sahara and south of the Namib and Kalahari Deserts, there is slightly more precipitation—enough to change these areas into a semiarid steppe, similar to the Sahel in the north.

MEDITERRANEAN CLIMATE. The Mediterranean climate affects the northwest and southwest of the continent, north of the Sahara and south of the Namib and Kalahari Deserts. The Mediterranean climate is the only one in the world characterized by precipitation during the local winter (December 22 to March 20 in the Northern Hemisphere, June 21 to September 22 in the Southern Hemisphere) when the Sun is low above the horizon. This characteristic is explained by the movement of the ITCZ toward the Southern Hemisphere in December to accompany the high sun period. This migration allows the temperate zone low pressure to influence the Mediterranean region in the north and the southwest corner of South Africa. Westerlies take over and deliver maritime polar air masses (mP) to these regions during the local winter.

Average monthly temperatures seldom reach values less than 50 degrees Fahrenheit (10 degrees Celsius). The lowest temperature in Cape Town, South Africa, located at 38 58' south latitude, is 53 degrees Fahrenheit (11.9 degrees Celsius) in July. Algiers' coldest month is in January, with 51 degrees Fahrenheit (10.6 degrees Celsius). Farmers have adapted to this climate by planting mostly wheat, olive and orange groves, and vineyards. The natural vegetation is the Mediterranean scrub, which consists of widely spaced, hard-leaf evergreen shrub and deciduous trees such as pine and oak. In South Africa, this shrub is called *fynbos;* in the Maghreb, it is referred to as maquis.

MOUNTAIN CLIMATES. There are few high mountains in Africa: the mountains of Cameroon, the Ethiopian Highlands in the northern hemisphere, and the Kilimanjaro and Kenya peaks in East Africa. Windward sides of mountains receive higher precipitation. Temperatures decrease with an increase in elevation; this affects the savanna at the foot of these volcanic peaks. With the increased relative humidity at higher elevation, the savanna turns into open forests, then canopied evergreen forests, and finally to mountain meadows.

MADAGASCAR AND MOZAMBIQUE. The island of Madagascar and the mainland country of Mozambique lie within the belt of the southeast trade winds. Because of the location of the island, hurricanes (called cyclones in this area) frequently strike the populated shores. In 1994 Cyclone Daisy in January, then Cyclone Geralda in February, slammed into the island of Madagascar. Geralda was declared the "cyclone of the century" destroying 95 percent of the harbor of Toamasina. In March, Cyclone Nadia left almost 1.5 million people homeless in Mozambique and caused considerable damage to crops, including cashew trees, a major source of income for the nation. At the same time, heavy rains fell on most of the Sahel, resulting in the wettest growing season there in thirty years.

Denyse Lemaire

FOR FURTHER STUDY

Adams, W. M., A. S. Goudie, and A. R. Orme, eds. *The Physical Geography of Africa.* Oxford, England: Oxford University Press, 1996.

Aryeetey-Attoh, Samuel, ed. *The Geography of Sub-Saharan Africa.* Englewood Cliffs, N.J.: Prentice Hall, 1997.

Bramwell, Martyn. *Africa.* Minneapolis, Minn.: Lerner, 2000.

Griffiths, J. F., ed. *Climates of Africa.* New York: Elsevier, 1972.

Grove, A. T. *The Changing Geography of Africa.* 2d ed. Oxford, England: Oxford University Press, 1993.

James, Valentine Udoh. *Africa's Ecology: Sustaining the Biological and Environmental Diversity of a Continent.* Jefferson, N.C.: McFarland, 1993.

Suliman, Mohamed, ed. *Greenhouse Effect and Its Impact on Africa.* London: Institute for African Alternatives, 1990.

HYDROLOGY

Watershed map Page 972

The world's largest continent after Asia, Africa has several dominant physical features, including the Great Rift Valley of East Africa and Victoria Falls in Southern Africa, one of the largest waterfalls in the world. A significant feature that has a great impact on the continent's hydrology is the Sahara Desert—the world's largest—that stretches from the Atlantic Ocean in the west to the Red Sea in the east.

Sahara Page 965

A third of Africa is desert: The Sahara covers 3.5 million square miles (9 million sq. km.), the Kalahari 120,000 square miles (310,800 sq. km.), and the Namib 120,000 square miles (310,800 sq. km.). The Sahara, about the size of the United States, occupies much of North Africa; the Kalahari and Namib are found in Southern Africa.

Namib Page 969

The highest mountain in Africa, Kilimanjaro in Tanzania, at 19,340 feet (5,895 meters), along with Mount Kenya (17,058 feet/5,199 meters) and the Atlas Mountains (13,000 feet/3,960 meters) in northwest Africa, also influence the continent's hydrology. These mountains either act as obstacles to winds carrying moisture from the sea or ocean, causing a rain shadow effect, or serve as drainage boundaries for rivers or lakes.

With the world's largest desert, the world's longest river, and the lake with the the world's largest drainage basin, Africa is hydrologically an enigma. The continent has some of the wettest and driest places in the world. The extreme dryness and wetness cause severe drought and flood problems in several parts of Africa.

Drought Page 975

Despite Africa's size, its people make up only about 13 percent of the world's population. However, the continent has one of the fastest-growing populations in the world, and a large percentage of its people do not have access to a safe drinking water supply. The availability of water varies from country to country. The devastation brought by droughts in Africa during the 1980's was made public through pictures of starving and dying children in the Sahel region.

HUMAN SETTLEMENT. The largest concentrations of people on the continent are found in West Africa, the Great Lakes region of East Africa, the southeast of South Africa, the northwest of North Africa around the Mediterranean Sea, and along the Nile River. The distribution of people in Africa reflects the distribution of surface water, as in other parts of the world. More than 70 percent of Africa's people live within the equatorial and tropical zones and in the Nile Valley. The population is sparsest in the Sahara and Kalahari deserts.

More than 90 percent of Egypt's people live on 5 percent of the country's land area, making the Nile Valley one of the most populous areas in Africa. The Nile River is an example of peoples' dependence on water for survival. From ancient through modern times, the Nile has played a principal role in the life of Egypt.

SOURCES OF WATER. Factors that determine the availability of surface water include precipitation, soil type, the rock type beneath the surface, solar radiation, and geologic structure. Rivers, lakes, and rain water are the major sources of surface water.

The annual precipitation in Africa follows the lines of latitude. Places within 12 degrees north or south of the equator have an annual precipitation of more than 20 inches (50 centimeters). Annual precipitation of more than 79 inches (200 centimeters) is typical of Madagascar and the equatorial and tropical regions. Most places above 14 degrees north latitude are either arid or semiarid, with annual precipitation less than 10 inches (25 centimeters).

Parts of the East African Great Lakes region and southwestern Ethiopia have tropical climates. Rainfall occurs throughout these regions from April to October, and temperatures vary from 60 to 80 degrees Fahrenheit (15.6 to 26.7 degrees Celsius), with relative humidity around 80 percent. The southernmost part of Sudan has a semitropical climate, with 50 inches (1,270 millimeters) of rainfall during the rainy season.

As one moves northward, the rainfall decreases. For example, in the central region of Sudan, rainfall varies from 10 to 21 inches (254 to 533 millimeters) annually. North of Khartoum, the annual rainfall is 5 inches (127 millimeters). This area includes northern Sudan and the Egyptian desert. Precipitation is the source of rivers, lakes, and groundwater. More than 90 percent of Africa's surface water is concentrated around the equatorial and tropical regions, except the Nile River, which has a north-south trend.

Rain in a given area affects river flows and water levels in lakes. The lack of adequate precipitation can lead to drought, as has been constantly observed in the Sahel region (the southern fringe of the Sahara). Conversely, too much rainfall can cause severe flooding, as observed in the year 2000 in Mozambique. The heavy rainfall was the result of a tropical cyclone that also caused severe flooding in Madagascar. Flood waters in Mozambique and Madagascar left hundreds of thousands of people homeless and without adequate safe drinking water.

RIVERS. Sometimes called watersheds, drainage basins are areas that supply runoff water to rivers systems and lakes. For hydrological studies, Africa can be divided into five major drainage basins: the Nile River, Niger River, Congo River, Zambezi River, and Lake Chad. These basins cover about 75 percent of the surface area of the continent.

Most of Africa's rivers rise in the highlands and flow to the seas. The Nile flows northward from the plateaus of east central Africa to the Mediterranean. The Congo and Niger Rivers, Africa's second- and third-longest, drain the waters of west central Africa into the Atlantic Ocean. Most other important rivers in Africa also empty into the Atlantic, except the Limpopo and the Zambezi, which empty into the Indian Ocean.

Often called the Mother of Egypt, the Nile River represents Egypt's past civilizations, its present base, and its future. The Nile gave birth to the ancient civilization that continues to capture the imagination of modern people.

Flooding Page 971, 973, 1100, 1101

Boteti River Page 974

Congo River Page 962

VICTORIA FALLS

Discovered by the Scottish missionary-explorer David Livingstone in 1855, Victoria Falls on the Zambezi River marks part of the modern border between modern Zambia and Zimbabwe. These spectacular falls are 5,500 feet (1,676 meters) across, which is twice the width of Niagara Falls. They fall about 355 feet (108 meters), not into a basin, but into a rocky chasm, with sheer cliffs on both sides.

Nile River
Page 1164

The Nile is the longest river in the world, with a length of 4,181 miles (6,700 km.); in comparison, the Mississippi is 3,770 miles (6,065 km.) long. The source region of the Nile is in the equatorial lakes, and it empties into the Mediterranean Sea. The Nile's drainage basin consists of approximately 1.2 million square miles (2.9 million sq. km.), and includes parts of Burundi, Egypt, Eritrea, Ethiopia, Kenya, Rwanda, Sudan, Tanzania, Uganda, and Congo-Kinshasa. The annual water discharge of the Nile is 2.4 billion cubic feet (84 billion cubic meters) at Aswan Dam, with the Ethiopian subbasin supplying about 86 per cent of the total water flow.

The Nile is one of the few exotic rivers in the world. An exotic river is a perennial river that flows through arid or semiarid regions, similar to the Colorado River in the United States. Two sources of water exist for the Nile: Lake Victoria in East Africa is the source water for the White Nile and Lake Tana in Ethiopia is the source water for the Blue Nile.

The Congo River is the fourth-longest river (2,716 miles/4,373 km.) and has the second-largest drainage basin and discharge volume in the world. Rainfall affects the flows and water levels in rivers. However, where the drainage basin for a river system is large and within the same climatic setting, the weather pattern in an area of the basin may not significantly affect the water level in lakes. This is evident for the Congo River, whose entire drainage basin lies within the equatorial region, where a shortfall in precipitation amounts in one part of the basin has little effect on the flow of the river close to its discharge point.

The Congo River system comprises three distinct sections—the upper, middle, and lower Congo. The upper Congo contains confluences, lakes, waterfalls, and rapids.

Old-fashioned sailing craft on the Nile's upper reaches. (Corbis)

The Congo River has its beginnings in the Congo-Kinshasa, where several small rivers unite. Several tributaries of the Congo River include the Lualaba, Luvua, Ubangi, Sangha, and Kasai Rivers. The width of the Congo River varies from 3.5 miles (8 km.) up to 8 miles (12.8 km.) at the mouth of the Mongala River. The Congo discharges its water into the Atlantic Ocean.

The Niger River in West Africa is approximately 2,600 miles (4,186 km.) long with a drainage basin of 0.92 million square miles (2.3 million sq. km.). Its source region is the mountainous Fouta Jallon region in Guinea. The river flows northeast toward the Sahara with a middle delta (south of Timbuktu in the country of Mali) where a significant amount of water is lost to evaporation. It then flows southwest before flowing south, emptying into the Atlantic Ocean through the Niger Delta. The Niger River traverses Guinea, Mali, Niger, and Nigeria. The Benue River, a major tributary of the Niger, flows from Mount Cameroon to the west, joining the Niger at Lokoja, Nigeria.

Precipitation ranges from 160 inches (4,100 millimeters) per year close to the river mouth to almost nothing in the desert. Rainfall occurs during the annual monsoon period between July and September, which results in an annual flood that takes several months to propagate down through the river network. Because of climatic variations, the annual river flood occurs at different times in different parts of the basin. In the upper Niger, the high-water discharge occurs in June, and the low-water season is in December.

As the Nile is to Egypt, so is the Zambezi River to Southern Africa. The Zambezi is the eighth-largest river in terms of discharge in the world. It runs through Angola, Namibia, Zambia, Zimbabwe, and Mozambique. Spectacular features associated with this river include Victoria Falls,

Lake Kariba, and Mana Pools National Park. Concerns over the quality and quantity of the Zambezi River are growing due to tourism, irrigation, and damming for hydropower.

The Chari River in Central Africa is the major source of water for Lake Chad. The Chari and its major tributary, the Lagone River, supply approximately 85 percent of the water input to Lake Chad. The Chari/Lagone River system is unusual in that it takes the water approximately six months to get from its source in the Central African Republic to Lake Chad. Because the water arrives during the lake's dry season, Lake Chad's volume is highest during its dry season.

Other rivers in Africa include the Orange, Limpopo, Gambia, Senegal, Volta, Lagone, Ogowe, Sanaga, Cuanza, Jubba, Lugenda, Rovuma, and Shabeelle. Places north of 20 degrees north latitude lack perennial rivers, except for the Nile and small coastal rivers along the Atlantic Ocean. Climate influences the presence of rivers, as most of Africa's rivers are found in the equatorial and tropical regions. Rivers and lakes have a great influence on human settlements, as observed in the Nile Valley; on agriculture, as in the South Lake Chad Basin; and on industrialization, as in Zambezi River and the Great Lakes of East Africa.

LAKES. Lakes play a large part in Africa's hydrology. The large surface areas of some of the lakes provide water by evaporation, and they also act as reservoirs that can be used by people, plants, animals, and fish. Large African lakes are found south of the Sahara Desert, most of them in East Central Africa (the Great Rift Valley System).

Lake Chad is found south of the Sahara, in a region of Africa ranging from semiarid to arid. It has the largest drainage basin (936,821 square miles/2.4 million sq.

Victoria
Falls
Page 1166

km.) of any lake in the world and was once the sixth-largest lake in the world. The size of the lake has changed over time. In ancient times, it covered about 135,000 square miles (350,000 sq. km.), shrinking to 9,600 square miles (25,000 sq. km.) in the 1960's (about the size of Lake Erie), and to 772 square miles (2,000 sq. km.) by the end of the twentieth century. It is shallow (15 feet, approximately 5 meters), and the lakebed was dry at least once during the past millennium. The sand dunes that formed in the lakebed then are still visible in the lake. Satellite images acquired in 1963, 1973, 1987, and 1997 show the migrating shoreline nature of the lake due to changes in the climate.

Lake Chad is the main source of water in the region, both as surface water and groundwater. It is a closed-basin lake; that is, it has no direct outlet to the sea or other lakes. Unlike most old closed-basin lakes, such as the Great Salt Lake of Utah, its water is fresh, for three main reasons: the Chari/Lagone rivers put few dissolved solids (salts) into the lake, some dissolved solids precipitate or are absorbed by plants, and about 20 percent of the lake water seeps into the ground, carrying with it the dissolved solids.

People around Lake Chad use it for transportation, fishing, hunting, salt mining, farming, and drinking. Lake Chad also serves as a political boundary for the four nations that share it (Cameroon,

Nineteenth century engraving of Murchison Falls, through which the water of Lake Victoria begins its passage to the Nile River. (Samuel White Baker, *The Albert N'yanza*, 1866)

Chad, Niger, and Nigeria). When water levels are low, large portions of the lakebed become available for farming. The practice of farming the lakebed led to the displacement of more than 25,000 people after the heaviest rainfall in three decades occurred in Central Africa in December, 1999. Human activities such as damming and petroleum exploration may pose serious threats to the lake, its ecosystem, and underlying aquifers.

Lake Victoria is the largest lake in Africa and the second-largest freshwater lake in the world (after North America's Lake

Lake Victoria Page 1167

Superior). One of the two sources of the Nile River, it is located in Tanzania, Uganda, and Kenya, between the Eastern Rift Valleys and the Indian Ocean. Lake Victoria covers approximately 26,800 square miles (69,480 sq. km.) and is about 210 miles (337 km.) long and 150 miles (240 km.) wide, with more than 2,000 miles (3,220 km.) of coastlines. It is 3,720 feet (1,134 meters) above sea level and reaches a depth of 270 feet (82 meters).

Because of the abundant water supply and fish for food, several million people live within 50 miles (80 km.) of Lake Victoria, making it one of the most densely populated areas in Africa. Lake Victoria is shared by Uganda, Kenya, and Tanzania. The cities of Kampala, Entebbe, Kisumu, Jinja, Mwanza, Bukoba, and Shirati are built on or close to its coast. The lake is used for drinking water, transportation, fishing, tourism, and other industries.

GROUNDWATER. Potable water supply is found not only in the rivers and lakes in Africa, but also from groundwater. In some parts of Africa, groundwater is the only source of potable water. The use of groundwater is limited in some areas in Africa, because the groundwater is at a depth of approximately 328 feet (100 meters). Digging for water can be a labor-intensive activity, and without the right drilling equipment, groundwater may not be available. Some groundwater contains a high salt content, making it unfit for use; in urban areas, groundwater can become contaminated by sewage or refuse dumps. Another serious problem in those areas is the lack of scientific understanding of hydrology and hydrogeology.

Groundwater has become more important as surface water has become polluted with chemicals and disease-causing microbes. Satellite images and modern technologies are employed to locate groundwater resources. When rocks have breaks or cracks in them (referred to as fractures), they provide pathways for rain and other surface water to infiltrate into groundwater. These fracture zones and drainage patterns can help people find where to drill for groundwater.

The South Lake Chad drainage basin has underlying groundwater. Groundwater is found where the rocks, sand, or gravel have openings (pores or voids). Material that has interconnected openings, is filled with water, and yields enough water for use when a well is drilled into it is called an aquifer (which means "water bearing").

Three major aquifers exist in the southwest part of the Lake Chad Basin. The first and uppermost aquifer is shallow (less than 49 feet/15 meters). This aquifer generally can be used without drill equipment. The other two aquifers are deep (984 feet/300 meters) and drill equipment must be used. Water from the deep aquifers is hot (122 degrees Fahrenheit/ 50 degrees Celsius) and flows to the surface without pumping (artesian wells). The waters are left to flow freely and allowed to cool before being used by humans or animals. A large portion of this water is lost because of the high rate of evaporation. When water is extracted from the ground faster than it is replaced or recharged, groundwater depletion occurs. Groundwater depletion is occurring in North Africa, with Libya, for example, losing about 282 billion cubic feet (8 billion cubic meters) of water per year in the late 1990's.

Oases are also important to people in arid regions of Africa. Oases are groundwaters exposed because of wind erosion in the desert. Groundwater is abundant in most of the tropical and equatorial regions of Africa. However, groundwater's contribution to the total water supply is small in some parts of Africa. In South Africa, for example, groundwater accounts

Oasis
Page 973

for only 13 percent of the water supply. However, two-thirds of the South African population depends on groundwater, compared to 50 percent of the people in the United States. Groundwater resources need to be properly utilized, and care should be taken to protect this valuable resource as well as surface water.

Solomon A. Isiorho

FOR FURTHER STUDY

Adams, W. M., A. S. Goudie, and A. R. Orme, eds. *The Physical Geography of Africa.* Oxford, England: Oxford University Press, 1996.

Aryeetey-Attoh, Samuel, ed. *The Geography of Sub-Saharan Africa.* Englewood Cliffs, N.J.: Prentice-Hall, 1997.

Grove, A. T. *The Changing Geography of Africa.* 2d ed. Oxford, England: Oxford University Press, 1993.

Huang, P. M., and Iskandar Karam, eds. *Soils and Groundwater Pollution and Remediation: Asia, Africa, and Oceania.* Boca Baton, Fla.: Lewis, 2000.

James, Valentine Udoh. *Africa's Ecology: Sustaining the Biological and Environmental Diversity of a Continent.* Jefferson, N.C.: McFarland, 1993.

Sampat, Payal. "Groundwater Shock: The Polluting of the World's Major Freshwater Stores." *World Watch.* 13, no. 1 (January/February, 2000).

Suliman, Mohamed, ed. *Greenhouse Effect and Its Impact on Africa.* London: Institute for African Alternatives, 1990.

INFORMATION ON THE WORLD WIDE WEB

The International Lake Environment Committee Foundation (ILEC) hosts a Web site with information on lakes in Africa, and throughout the world. (www.ilec.org.jp/)

The African Water Page provides on-line information about water supply and sanitation in Africa. (www.africanwater.org)

Africa

Boats on the Congo River, one of Africa's three great rivers. (AP/Wide World Photos)

Cape Town, viewed from the north across Table Bay. Central Cape Town is nestled between the water and Table Mountain, which appears to be spewing the dramatic cloud formation. A fine natural harbor, Cape Town was settled by the Dutch in 1652 and became one of modern South Africa's major urban centers. (R. Kent Rasmussen)

Ring-tailed lemurs. No true monkey species are native to Madagascar, but that great island and its Comoro Island neighbors are unique in having the only true lemurs, small monkey-like, mainly nocturnal, mammals. (American Stock Photography)

Northern coast of Mahe island in the Seychelles. Tourists are drawn to the isolated Indian Ocean country for its beaches, diving, bird-watching, and the experience of being in a place more than 1,000 miles (1,600 km.) distant from its nearest neighbor. (AP/Wide World Photos)

PHYSICAL GEOGRAPHY OF AFRICA

Canary Islands

Atlas Mountains

Turis

Mediterranean Sea

Jabal
Akhdar

Qattara
Depression

Nile River

Tropic of Cancer

Lake Nasser

S a h a r a   D e s e r t

Nile River

Red Sea

Dakar

Senegal River

Gambia River

Niger River

Lake Chad

N'Djamena

Chari River

Khartoum

White Nile

Blue Nile

Afar
Depression
Lake
Tana

Gulf of Aden

Freetown

Volta River

Abidjan

Lagos

Benue River

Cameroon
Highlands

East African Rift

Ethiopian
Plateau

× Mount
Cameroon

Ubangi River

Lake
Turkana

Gulf of Guinea

Congo River

Lake
Albert

Mount
Kepya

Mogadishu

Equator

Libreville

Congo Basin

Lake
Edward

Lake
Victoria

Mount
Kilimanjaro ×

Indian
Ocean

Ogoué R.

Kasai River

Lake
Kivu

Zanzibar

Seychelles

Luanda

Lake
Mweru

Lake
Tanganyika

Dar es Salaam

Comoros

Lake
Malawi

Victoria
Falls

Zambezi River

Mascarenes

Atlantic

Ocean

Limpopo River

MADAGASCAR

Walvis Bay

Kalahari Desert

Johannesburg

Maputo

Tropic of Capricorn

Orange River

Drakensberg Range

Durban

The world's largest desert, the Sahara covers an area larger than the entire United States and it continues to grow. (PhotoDisc)

Africa's tallest mountain, Mountain Kilimanjaro rises to 19,340 feet (5,895 meters) on the higher of its two peaks. It is located along Tanzania's northeastern border with Kenya. Although it is close to the equator, it has a permanent snowcap. Its ancient lava flows have made its lower slopes one of the most fertile agricultural regions in Tanzania. (Corbis)

Domboshawa, Zimbabwe. Called "dombos" in Zimbabwe, immense, domed granite outcroppings are common in that Southern African country, which was one of the few regions with a precolonial tradition of building in stone. (R. Kent Rasmussen)

Sunset over the southern Atlantic Ocean, viewed from Cape Town. Africa's Atlantic coastline is one of the longest on a single ocean in the world, and the continent's history would have been vastly different if Europeans could have sailed to Asia without going around it. (R. Kent Rasmussen)

CLIMATE REGIONS OF AFRICA

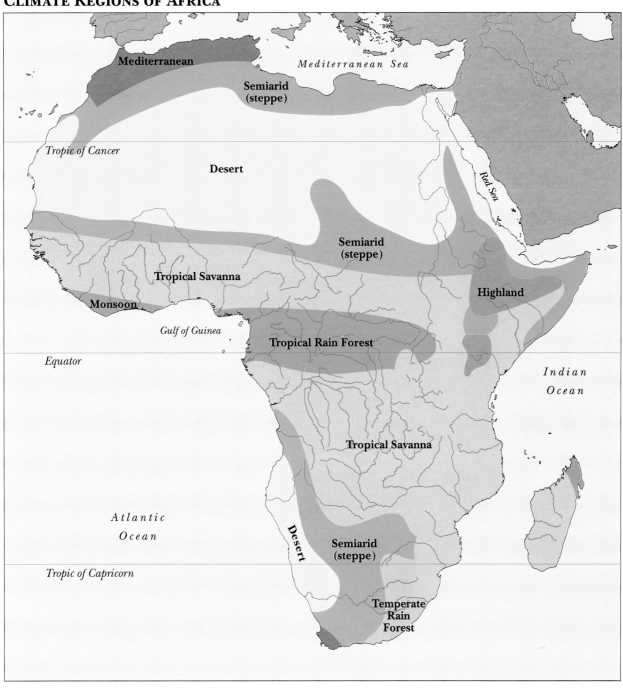

Mediterranean

Semiarid (steppe)

Mediterranean Sea

Tropic of Cancer

Desert

Red Sea

Semiarid (steppe)

Tropical Savanna

Highland

Monsoon

Gulf of Guinea

Tropical Rain Forest

Equator

Indian Ocean

Tropical Savanna

Atlantic Ocean

Desert

Semiarid (steppe)

Tropic of Capricorn

Temperate Rain Forest

INCREASING DESERTIFICATION OF AFRICA

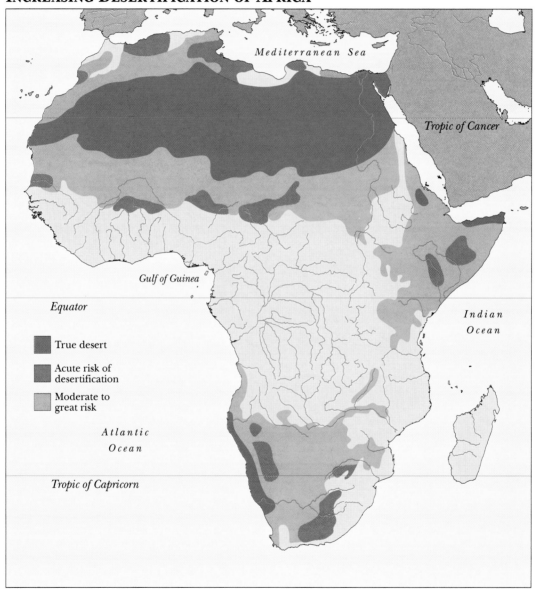

Mediterranean Sea

Tropic of Cancer

Gulf of Guinea

Equator

Indian
Ocean

True desert

Acute risk of
desertification

Moderate to
great risk

Atlantic
Ocean

Tropic of Capricorn

MEAN TEMPERATURES AND DISTANCE FROM EQUATOR

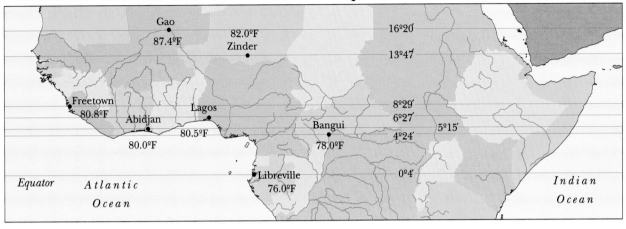

Gao
87.4°F

82.0°F
Zinder

16°20′

13°47′

Freetown
80.8°F

Abidjan

Lagos

8°29′

6°27′

5°15′

80.5°F

Bangui
78.0°F

4°24′

80.0°F

0°4′

Equator   *Atlantic
Ocean*

Libreville
76.0°F

*Indian
Ocean*

Southern Africa's Namib Desert, seen in this December, 1990, space shuttle photograph, is a coastal desert generated by the presence of the cold Benguela Current and by its location in the vicinity of the tropic of Capricorn where a high pressure is located during the Southern Hemisphere's winter. (Corbis)

Walvis Bay

Lüderitz

Most of Africa can be seen in this photograph taken from Apollo 17 during its return from the Moon in December, 1972. In general, the areas of low rainfall are lighter in color than the areas of high precipitation. (Corbis)

El Niño weather conditions similar to those that occur in the eastern Pacific Ocean also afflict East Africa periodically. Here a barefoot man wades through floodwaters on Kenya's Nairobi-Mombasa highway, while trucks make their way through the water, in early 1998. (AP/Wide World Photos)

Major Watersheds of Africa

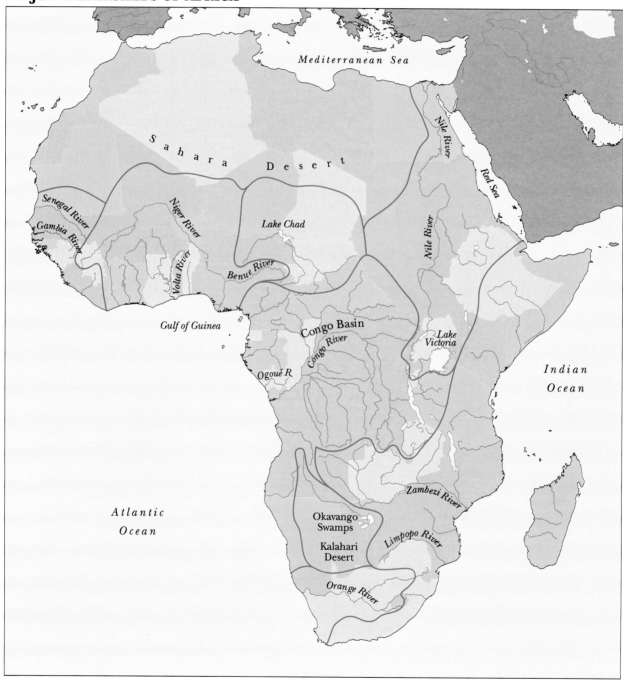

Mediterranean Sea

Red Sea

Nile River

Nile River

S a h a r a   D e s e r t

Senegal River

Gambia River

Niger River

Lake Chad

Volta River

Benue River

Gulf of Guinea

Congo Basin

Congo River

Ogoué R.

Lake Victoria

Indian Ocean

Atlantic Ocean

Zambezi River

Okavango Swamps

Limpopo River

Kalahari Desert

Orange River

Oasis at Tafraout in the Moroccan Saharan. Oases are important to people living in arid regions of Africa. Most oases are sections of groundwater exposed by wind erosion in the desert. (Corbis)

Somalis living near the Juba River, close to Somali's Kenya border fight floodwaters in late 1997. (AP/Wide World Photos)

Boteti River in Botswana. (Corbis)

Maasai boys water their cattle on a slope of Mount Kenya during the midst of a drought in East Africa in mid-2000. (AP/Wide World Photos)

The scarcity of water in North Africa makes water selling a remunerative occupation in Morocco. (Corbis)

RESOURCES OF AFRICA

Mediterranean Sea

Oil

Phosphates
Coal
Iron ore
Lead
Zinc
Cork
Mercury
Copper
Natural
Gas
Oil

Oil
Natural Gas

Gypsum
Phosphate

Phos-
phates
Iron
ore
Gold

Gold

Uranium

Niobium
Tin Tungsten
Oil

Oil
Natural Gas
Gold Chromite

Red Sea

Copper
Cobalt

Gold

Salt
Sodium
carbonate

Diamonds

Diamonds

Gold
Oil
Diamonds
Coal

Diamonds

Gold
Diamonds

Manganese
Mica Copper
Iron Ore
Coal
Natural Gas
Gold
Gypsum
Manganese
Platinum

Bauxite
Gold

Oil

Copper

Tin
Tungsten
Nickel
Sodium
carbonate

Gulf of Guinea

Natural Gas
Oil
Zinc
Lead
Niobium

Coal

Gold
Diamonds

Indian
Ocean

Diamonds
Gold
Iron Ore

Copper
Cobalt

Oil
Phosphates
Salt

Coal

Natural Gas

Oil
Chrome
Graphite

Atlantic
Ocean

Copper
Lead
Diamonds
Zinc

Diamonds

Soda-Ash
Coal

Gold
Timber

Chrome
Platinum

Gold
Uranium
Vanadium
Diamonds
Manganese
Andalusite

BIOGEOGRAPHY
AND
NATURAL
RESOURCES

NATURAL RESOURCES

*Map
Page 976*

Africa is one of the largest and least tapped sources of natural resources, including minerals, in the world. Much of Africa's great natural wealth has not been developed, although some development has occurred on the North African coast and in Southern Africa. Development typically has been of oil resources and such relatively rare minerals or metals as diamonds, gold, and chromium. Few African nations have the economic resources needed to develop their natural and mineral wealth. Such efforts generally have been financed from outside of Africa. Political instability and the lingering presence of former colonial powers has discouraged outside sources of development funds. The infrastructure—such as good roads and a rail system to transport supplies, raw materials, and finished products—did not exist.

MINERAL RESOURCES. Africa's known mineral wealth places it among the world's richest continents. Its mineral resources include coal, petroleum, natural gas, uranium, radium, low-cost thorium, iron ores, chromium, cobalt, copper, lead, zinc, tin, bauxite, titanium, antimony, gold, platinum, tantalum, germanium, lithium, phosphates, and diamonds. The only significantly valuable mineral the continent seems not to have in abundance is silver.

Major deposits of coal exist in four coal basins—in Southern Africa, North Africa, Congo-Kinshasa, and Nigeria. Proven petroleum reserves in North Africa occur in Libya, Algeria, Egypt, and Tunisia. Exploration has been concentrated north of the Ahaggar Mountains in southern Algeria. There may also be major Saharan reserves

to the south. The other major oil reserves are in the West African coastal basin—mainly in Nigeria and also in Cameroon, Gabon, and Congo-Brazzaville—and in Angola. Africa's natural gas reserves are concentrated in basins of North Africa and coastal central Africa.

Southern Africa is one of the world's seven major uranium provinces. In South Africa, the joint occurrence of uranium with gold has increased awareness of the presence of uranium and decreased the cost of production. Other countries with significant uranium deposits are Niger, Gabon, Congo-Kinshasa, and Namibia.

Most of Africa's copper is contained in the Central African Copperbelt. This stretches across Zambia and into the Katanga (Shaba) area of Congo-Kinshasa. Other minerals are present in the layer, with cobalt the most common. Africa has about half the world's reserves of bauxite, the chief aluminum ore. Virtually all of this occurs in a major belt of tropical laterite stretching some 1,200 miles (1,930 km.) from Guinea to Togo. The largest reserves are in Guinea.

NORTHERN REGION. This region comprises Morocco, Algeria, Tunisia, Libya, and Egypt. Morocco, Tunisia, and especially Algeria and Libya have great natural wealth in the form of oil and natural gas. Morocco has natural gas reserves and both light oil and heavy oil deposits. (Light oil has shorter molecules than heavy oil.) These resources are still largely unexplored and await development. Algeria is one of the major producers of oil and gas in Africa, and its full potential in this area

*Oil drilling
Page 1025*

AFRICAN GOLD AND THE EUROPEAN RENAISSANCE

The portion of western Mali known as the Bambuk has long been a gold-producing region of Africa. In medieval times, traders came to Mali from Morocco and Algeria to trade salt for gold. The gold eventually went to Europe and was used for trade and commerce, enabling Europe to emerge economically from the Dark Ages into the Renaissance. The word "guinea," used in Great Britain for some gold coins, may have originated from the city Djenne, in southeastern Mali.

has yet to be established. In 1994 more oil was discovered in Algeria than in the rest of the oil-producing countries in the world—a total of 1.13 billion barrels (a barrel is about 208 liters or 55 gallons).

Libya is North Africa's biggest oil producer and Europe's biggest North African oil supplier. Current reserves are estimated to be 50 billion barrels of crude oil and 43 trillion cubic feet of natural gas. Despite United Nations and United States oil sanctions in the 1990's, the oil industry in Libya remained active. In 1994 Libya produced 49.2 million tons of crude oil.

Tunisia's oil reserves and production are relatively modest for North Africa. At the end of the twentieth century, its reserves were believed to be 1.7 billion barrels of crude oil and 810 billion cubic feet of natural gas. Crude oil production in 1994 was 4,364 tons. In 1993 Tunisia became a net importer of crude oil, but new exploration may change that.

Morocco is the world's largest exporter of both phosphate rock and phosphoric acid. Phosphate reserves are estimated to be close to 60 billion tons. Algeria has major deposits of phosphates and iron ore, as well as smaller deposits of coal, lead, and zinc. Some mercury and copper are also mined.

A bonanza of high-grade gold has been found in the Ahaggar Desert hills of southern Algeria. Five vast geological provinces, each about 400 miles (600 km.) long, have been identified. Exploratory drilling at two deposits produced yields graded at 0.89 ounce (25.1 grams) of gold per ton of ore and 0.58 ounce (16.49 grams) per ton of ore.

In South Africa's declining gold industry, 0.23 ounce (6.4 grams) per ton is considered a good yield. Egypt has modest mineral reserves that include iron ore, petroleum, natural gas, gypsum, phosphate rock, manganese, coal, limestone, salt silica, kaolin, fluorspar, uranium, chromium, ilmenite (an oxide of iron and titanium), tantalum, molybdenum, and some gold.

SUDANO-SAHELIAN REGION. This region comprises Mauritania, the Western Sahara, Senegal, Mali, Burkina Faso, Niger, Chad, and the Sudan. Since 1992, Mali has become Africa's third-largest gold producer after Ghana and South Africa. Large deposits of diamonds are being uncovered.

The Western Sahara has vast reserves of phosphates, which remain largely undeveloped because of political uncertainties. At the end of the twentieth century, it was still to be decided if the Western Sahara, a former Spanish possession, would be an independent nation or part of Morocco.

Mauritania has become the major African supplier of iron ore to European steelmakers, providing 8 percent of 1994 European imports. A mine near Akjoujit was scheduled to open in late 1999 and expected to produce 366,000 tons of copper, 802,000 ounces (22,700 kilograms) of gold, and 2,100 tons of cobalt in its lifetime. There are also deposits of diamonds, chromium, sulfur, and yttrium.

Senegal has phosphate mining and deposits of iron ore and gold. Burkina Faso produces two tons of gold per year, mines nickel and manganese, and has deposits of copper, iron, phosphate, and tin. Niger is the world's second-largest producer of uranium, producing 3,000 tons per year. Salt and sodium carbonate are mined, and there are deposits of copper, iron ore, phosphate, and tin. Some companies are prospecting for gold.

Chad has oil reserves estimated to be 650 million barrels of crude. Production from the Kome, Miandoum, Bolobo, and Sedigui fields is expected to yield 150,000 barrels per day. Chad has deposits of sodium carbonate and alluvial diamonds, both of which are mined, along with marble and uranium. The area around the Tibesti Mountains in northern Chad has deposits of niobium, tantalum, tin, and tungsten. Deposits of iron ore have been found at several locations, and there are bauxite deposits at Koro in the south. The Sudan's oil reserves are estimated at 300 million barrels, and its gas reserves have been estimated at 774 billion cubic feet. Gold, chromite, manganese, and mica are mined. There are also deposits of copper and iron ore.

GULF OF GUINEA. This region comprises Guinea-Bissau, Cape Verde, Gambia, Guinea, Liberia, Sierra Leone, Côte d'Ivoire (Ivory Coast), Togo, Ghana, Benin, and Nigeria. Guinea-Bissau has some offshore tracts to be explored for possible crude oil reserves, but exploration has been blocked by

a border dispute with neighboring Senegal.

Benin is believed to have 100 million barrels of crude oil; production in 1994 was 275,000 tons. Benin has deposits of iron, gold, phosphate, chromium, diamonds, limestone, and titanium. Côte d'Ivoire's (Ivory Coast) oil reserves have been estimated at 25 million barrels and recoverable gas reserves at 812 billion cubic feet or more. Its offshore Espoir and Pelier oil fields began production in the late 1970's and peaked at 28,000 barrels of oil per day in 1986. Production from these fields has tapered off to less than 4,000 barrels per day. Côte d'Ivoire also produces gold and about 15,000 carets of diamonds per year. It has reserves of iron ore, bauxite, manganese, copper, cobalt, and nickel. Ore containing cobalt and nickel together has begun to be mined.

Liberia has iron ore, gold, and diamond mining that became largely inactive

African ironworkers in mid-nineteenth century Ethiopia. (Samuel White Baker, *The Albert N'yanza,* 1866)

after a civil war began in 1989. The country's iron ore reserves are in the billions of tons. It also has deposits of bauxite, ilmenite, zircon, thorium, and the rare-earth element mineral monazite. Guinea has nearly half of the world's bauxite reserves, iron ore reserves in excess of 3 billion tons, and gold reserves of 1,000 tons of metal. Guinea also has deposits of copper, manganese, and uranium. Ghana is Africa's second-largest gold producer, and the world's eleventh-largest. Gold accounted for 45 percent of Ghana's export earnings in 1994.

Diamond miners Page 1097

Diamonds were first discovered in Sierra Leone in 1930. Its diamonds continue to attract foreign investment because of their outstanding size and beauty. Sierra Leone produced 2.5 million carats of diamonds a year prior to the outbreak of civil war in 1992. It was the world's second-largest producer of titanium dioxide ore (rutile), mining 144,000 tons of the ore in 1994. There are also bauxite mines, but their activities have been hampered by war. Togo is the world's fifth-ranking producer of phosphate, mining more than two million tons in 1996. Cape Verde and Gambia have little in the way of natural resources.

CENTRAL REGION. This region comprises Congo-Kinshasa, Cameroon, Gabon, Equatorial Guinea, São Tomé and Príncipe, Rwanda, and Burundi. The Congo has great reserves of copper and cobalt—half of the world's reserves of cobalt can be found there. It also has reserves of zinc and lead (which often occur together), gold, tantalum, beryllium, germanium, and lithium. Congo-Brazzaville has estimated current oil reserves of 1.29 billion barrels and was producing 215,000 barrels per day in the 1990's. There are

The discovery of diamonds in South Africa in 1871 changed the history of the country and Kimberley became famous for its deep open-pit diamond mines. (Arkent Archive)

large reserves of natural gas associated with the oil reserves. The Congo also is known to have small reserves of copper, gold, iron ore, lead, and potash rock (potassium carbonate).

Cameroon produces 6.24 million tons of crude oil per year, which is 2 percent of Africa's oil production. The country also has untapped gas reserves, estimated at 3.9 trillion cubic feet. There are also deposits of bauxite, rutile, and gold. The Central African Republic produces more than 500,000 carats of diamonds per year. Gold is also mined, and deposits of copper, iron ore, tin, uranium, and zinc have been found.

Burundi has deposits of nickel, gold, vanadium, and phosphate, which have not been developed because of internal strife. Gabon produces 350,000 barrels of crude oil per day. Manganese is produced from the Mouana deposits near Moanda and uranium from the Okla mine. There are also phosphate, niobium, and iron ore. Gabon will soon produce 15 percent of the world's supply of niobium, and also has deposits of gold, lead, and silver.

São Tomé and Príncipe has few or no natural resources. In 1994 Equatorial Guinea produced 6,000 barrels per day of crude oil and 27 million cubic feet of natural gas. Its current oil reserves are estimated at 44 million tons.

EASTERN REGION. This region comprises Eritrea, Djibouti, Ethiopia, Somalia, Kenya, Tanzania, and Uganda. With the exception of Uganda, the Eastern region is mineral-poor. Kenya produces 350,000 tons of sodium carbonate per year. Fluorspar (calcium fluoride) and small quantities of gold, iron ore, garnets, and limestone are produced also, and there are deposits of rutile and zirconium. Eritrea mines diamonds and has deposits of gold and potash. Ethiopia has reserves of coal, and natural gas reserves estimated

to be 216 million cubic feet. Gold, manganese, and platinum are mined, and there are deposits of potash. Somalia has one of the largest known deposits of gypsum. Djibouti has little in the way of natural resources.

Gold and diamonds are mined in Tanzania, which also has deposits of nickel, coal, salt, and uranium, and rich seams of lead and tin. Uganda has mines of copper, tin, tungsten, columbine-tantalite, beryl, bismuth, phosphate, limestone, and glass-sand. Mining declined in the mid-1970's as a result of the country's poor political climate and its economic policies. In 1997 Uganda issued new exploration and mining licenses covering a large part of its territory. Part of this exploration included an airborne electromagnetic survey by a Canadian company. Gold exports from Uganda, which were 15,000 pounds (6,800 kilograms) in 1997, have been increasing steadily from a base of zero in 1990.

INDIAN OCEAN ISLANDS. These islands are Madagascar (the Malagasy Republic), Mauritius, Comoros, and the Seychelles. Madagascar may have promising reserves of heavy crude oil. In the 1990's, the island nation produced a modest 37,000 tons of crude oil and 2,500 tons of natural gas per year. It is the world's tenth-largest producer of chrome and also produces graphite. Small-scale gold mining produces 100,000 ounces (2,830 kilograms) per year. There are also deposits of bauxite (aluminum), iron, coal, nickel, titanium, and zirconium. Madagascar has the world's largest-known accumulation of flake graphite deposits. The Comoros, Mauritius, and the Seychelles have little in the way of natural resources.

SOUTHERN REGION. This region comprises Angola, Zambia, Zimbabwe, Mozambique, Malawi, Botswana, Namibia, Lesotho, Swaziland, and South Africa. South Africa has 45 percent of the world's vana-

*Scrap metal
Page 1025*

dium reserves, 90 percent of the platinum-group metal reserves, 68 percent of the chrome ore reserves, 81 percent of the manganese, around 40 percent of the gold reserves, and 37 percent of the world's reserves of andalusite (a form of aluminum ore).

South Africa also has substantial reserves of other industrially important metals and minerals, including antimony, asbestos, diamonds, coal, fluorspar, phosphates, iron ore, lead, zinc, uranium, vermiculite, and zirconium. It is the world's largest producer of gold, platinum-group metals, vanadium, and alumino-silicates, and one of the world's top producers of antimony, chromite, diamonds, ferrochrome, ferromanganese, fluorspar, manganese titanium, vermiculite, and zirconium. The country is also a major producer and exporter of bituminous coal, cobalt, nickel and granite.

Zambia is the world's fourth-largest copper-producing nation and the largest producer of cobalt, producing 20 percent of the world's total. It also has deposits of gold, emeralds, limestone, gypsum, feldspar, lead, coal, and tin. Gold, coal, and emeralds are being mined. Zimbabwe is Africa's fourth-largest gold producer after South Africa, Ghana, and Mali. Other principal metals and minerals produced there are coal, diamonds, ferroalloys, nickel, asbestos, iron and steel, copper, tin, and graphite.

Angola is one of the major oil-producing countries of Africa. After Nigeria, it is the most significant oil producer in sub-Saharan Africa, producing 650,000 barrels per day. The country's known recoverable reserves are estimated to total almost 4 billion barrels. In Angola, 70,000 cubic feet of gas is flared off per day, but the government is studying ways to use that gas as liquefied natural gas or methanol. It produces 400,000 barrels of oil per day

offshore from its enclave of Cabinda, with the remainder of its 650,000 barrels per day coming from onshore and offshore sites.

Angola has substantial deposits of diamonds, gold, iron ore, phosphates, manganese, copper, lead, quartz, gypsum, marble, black granite, beryl, zinc, and numerous base and strategic metals such as chromium. Mining in Angola has been limited to diamond mining in the Lunda Norte Province, ornamental stones in the Huila and Namibe areas, and salt.

Namibia is the site of the richest alluvial diamond deposits in the world. It has become one of the world's leading gem-quality diamond producers, contributing 30 percent of the world's output. About 98 percent of the diamonds mined in Namibia are of gem quality. Since mining started near Luderitz in 1908, more than 100 million carats have been mined. In 1996 diamond production was 1,486 million carats, mostly gem quality. Onshore diamond deposits are becoming exhausted, but offshore diamond mining in Namibia soared during the 1990's, growing from 29,000 carats in 1990 to 650,00 carats in 1997. The potential for gem diamonds off Namibia's shores has been estimated at 1.5 billion to 3 billion carats, of which 95 percent are expected to be gem quality.

Namibia has considerable reserves of uranium, copper, lead, and zinc. The world's largest uranium mine, located at Rossing near Swakopmund, produces low-grade uranium oxide. Production is close to its full capacity of 4,000 tons per year. The Haib copper mine, situated just north of the South African border near the town of Noordoewer, is expected to become the seventh-largest producer of copper in the world, producing 85,000 tons a year. The same mine is expected to produce 7,000 ounces (200 kilograms) of gold and

One of Africa's major mineral exports, asbestos is a flame-resistant and flexible mineral fiber that was widely used to make fire-retardant products until it was discovered that inhalation of microscopic asbestos fibers can cause cancer. (U.S. Geological Survey)

800,000 pounds (363,000 kilograms) of molybdenum concentrate also. Namibia's known reserves of zinc and lead are in the vicinity of 6.5 million tons.

Botswana is Africa's third-largest mining producer, after South Africa and the Democratic Republic of Congo. Diamonds, copper-nickel, soda ash, coal, and gold are mined. Botswana is Africa's largest and the world's third-largest producer of diamonds and second-largest producer of gem diamonds. Other known mineral deposits include asbestos, chromite, feldspar, graphite, gypsum, iron, kaolin, talc, and uranium.

Malawi has several million tons of coal reserves, which are beginning to be exploited. Mozambique has considerable natural gas reserves, for which develop-

ment was halted by internal strife and civil war. Some gold, bauxite, graphite, and marble have been mined, and it has major deposits of gold, tantalite, beryl, iron ore, and salt, and smaller reserves of diamonds and asbestos. Swaziland has 200 million tons of coal reserves, asbestos, and diamonds. All three are being mined. Lesotho has some diamonds.

WATER RESOURCES. Although the surface area of Africa is about one-fifth of the earth's land surface, the combined annual flow of African rivers is only about 7 percent of the world's river flow reaching the oceans. North Africa's few rivers originate in the mountains of Algeria and Morocco, and their water is used extensively for irrigation.

From the relatively well-watered areas of the Gulf of Guinea and Central Africa, the Senegal, Niger, Logone-Chari, and Nile Rivers flow through the drier inland zones. The Niger River, which originates in the highlands of Guinea, forms a vast floodplain south of Timbuktu in Mali. The Logone-Chari River feeds Lake Chad. The Nile River, the world's longest, receives more than 60 percent of its water from Ethiopia; however, it originates farther south in the mountains of Burundi.

Several rivers flowing in a more-or-less southerly direction into the Atlantic Ocean drain the southern part of Western Africa. Many flow rapidly over bedrock before entering the coastal plains, draining into the systems of lagoons and creeks along the coast. During the dry season, the upper reaches of these rivers are without water. In Guinea, Sierra Leone, and Liberia, the dry season is short and the rivers flow throughout the year. In the

Water sellers Page 975

*Congo
River
Page 962*

*Niger
Page 1163*

well-watered western part of equatorial Africa, the total average annual flow of the Congo River is enormous: 44 trillion cubic feet (1.25 trillion cubic meters).

Groundwater reserves are important for wells. Large inland depressions in Africa's basement rock sometimes form important groundwater reservoirs. These are in Niger, the central Sahara region of Algeria, the Libyan Desert, Chad, the Congo basin, the Karoo area of South Africa, and the Kalahari Desert. The East African plateaus usually contain little or no groundwater, and aquifers (geologic formations containing water) are found only in humid areas where the crystalline rock is weathered or fractured. The chalky shales and dolomitic limestones, which sporadically cover the basement rock of Africa, can contain important aquifers, as in Zambia and South Africa. In the coastal areas of Senegal, Côte d'Ivoire (Ivory Coast), Ghana, Togo, Benin, Nigeria, Cameroon, Gabon, Congo-Brazzaville, Angola, Mozambique, the East African countries, and Madagascar, aquifers are found in sandstone, limestone, and sand and gravel.

Large-scale irrigation has long been practiced mainly in the Northern region, the Sudan, South Africa, Mali, Zimbabwe, and Mozambique. Medium-scale irrigation projects have been operated in Madagascar, Senegal, Somalia, and Ethiopia. In Côte d'Ivoire (Ivory Coast), Burkina Faso, Kenya, Nigeria, Ghana, and Zambia, small-scale and medium-sized projects have been constructed.

FORESTS. The role of forests as a natural source of timber in Africa is limited by their small original extent and deforestation. The bulk of North Africa's forestry production is for local firewood, charcoal, and industrial timber. Cork is produced for export from the large areas of cork oak trees that grow near the Mediterranean Sea, especially in the west. In East Africa,

exports of natural hardwoods are limited. Black wattle, introduced from Australia, is widely grown for firewood. Its spread has been greatly encouraged by its being grown as a crop for tannin bark.

The eucalyptus is the most widely introduced tree from Australia and grows rapidly under eastern African conditions. Grown for firewood and poles, eucalyptus trees are a part of the landscape, especially in upland Ethiopia. Forest reserves cover 3.8 million acres of Uganda. High tropical forests cover about 1.8 million acres, savanna forests 1.9 million acres, and plantation forests 49,000 acres. There are about 7.8 million cubic feet (220,000 cubic meters) of saw logs available per year. Zimbabwe's timber industry is one of the most important in Africa. It is based on natural forests of teak and other native hardwoods and large-scale plantations of pine, eucalyptus, and wattle.

POWER. Spectacular growth in the use of electric energy took place in the second half of the twentieth century. It resulted from the growth of the petroleum industry and the establishment of large hydroelectric and thermoelectric plants. A number of steam power stations are located in ports and cities near the coasts. The largest installations of this kind operate in Tunis, Tunisia; Casablanca and Oujda, Morocco; Dakar, Senegal; Abidjan, Côte d'Ivoire (Ivory Coast); and Lagos, Nigeria. Steam power stations using coal are the most common, especially in South Africa. Electric energy consumption in large urban centers has increased considerably. Some countries have extended electrical transmission networks to the rural areas or have increased the numbers of isolated, low-powered stations and independent networks. Nevertheless, progress in rural electrification has not been especially noteworthy.

Dana P. McDermott

FOR FURTHER STUDY

Grove, A. T. *The Changing Geography of Africa.* 2d ed. Oxford, England: Oxford University Press, 1993.

Huang, P. M., and Iskandar Karam, eds. *Soils and Groundwater Pollution and Remediation: Asia, Africa, and Oceania.* Boca Baton, Fla.: Lewis, 2000.

James, Valentine Udoh. *Africa's Ecology: Sustaining the Biological and Environmental Diversity of a Continent.* Jefferson, N.C.: McFarland, 1993.

Karekezi, Stephen, and Timothy Ranja. *Renewable Energy Technologies in Africa.* New York: St. Martin's Press, 1997.

Kesse, G. C. *Mineral and Rock Resources of Ghana.* Brookfield, Vt.: Ashgate, 1985.

Lawry, Steven W. *Tenure Policy and Natural Resource Management in Sahelian West Africa.* Madison: University of Wisconsin-Madison, Land Tenure Center, 1989.

United Nations. *Natural Resources Development in the Sahel: The Role of the United Nations Systems.* New York: United Nations, 1986.

INFORMATION ON THE WORLD WIDE WEB

Mbendi, a Web site devoted to African business opportunities, features current news articles on African resources. (www.mbendi.co.za)
New Africa.com, a site that leans towards agriculture in Eastern Africa, also has information on African forests and fisheries. (www.newafrica.com)

FLORA

More than any other continent, Africa is tropical. With few exceptions, its vegetation is tropical or subtropical. This is primarily because none of the African continent extends far from the equator, and there are only a few high-elevation regions that support more temperate plants. Listed in order of decreasing land area, the three main biomes of Africa are tropical savanna, subtropical desert, and tropical forest. The vast size and uniqueness of each of these areas has made them familiar to most people. The flora in southern Africa has been most studied; the flora of central and northern Africa is less well known.

The subtropical desert biome is the driest of the biomes in Africa and includes some of the driest locations on Earth. The largest desert region is the Sahara in northern Africa. It extends from near the West Coast of Africa to the Arabian Peninsula, and is part of the largest desert system in the world, which extends into south central Asia. A smaller desert region in Southern Africa includes the Namib Desert, located along the western half of Southern Africa, especially near the coast, and the Kalihari Desert, which is primarily inland and east of the Namib Desert.

Namib
Page 969

Where more moisture is available, grasslands predominate, and as rainfall increases, grasslands gradually become tropical savanna. The difference between a grassland and a savanna is subjective. How many trees does it take for a grassland to be considered a savanna? The grassland/tropical savanna biome forms a broad swath across much of central Africa and dominates much of eastern and southern Africa.

Tropical forests cover a much smaller area of Africa than the other two biomes. They are most abundant in the portions of central Africa not dominated by the grassland/tropical savanna biome and are not far from the coast of central West Africa. Scattered tropical forest regions also occur along major river systems of West Africa, from the equator almost to Southern Africa.

SUBTROPICAL DESERT. The subtropical deserts of Africa seem, at first, to be nearly devoid of plants. While this is true for some parts of the Sahara and Namib Deserts that are dominated by sand dunes or bare, rocky outcrops, much of the desert biome has a noticeable amount of plant cover. Even in the driest, most inhospitable locations, plants are present. The Sahara is characterized by widely distributed species of plants that are found in similar habitats. The deserts of Southern Africa have a more distinctive flora, with many species endemic to specific local areas.

To survive the harsh desert climate, desert plants use several adaptations: Some, typically called succulents, store water in their leaves and/or stems; others grow near a permanent or semipermanent water source such as a spring, an intermittent stream, or an underground source; others are ephemerals, that is, annuals whose seeds germinate when moisture becomes available, quickly mature, set seed, and die. Each of these adaptations is well represented in African plants.

SUCCULENTS OF THE SUBTROPICAL DESERT. Many succulents are able to retain such large amounts of water because they use a specialized type of photosynthesis. Most plants open their stomata (small openings in the leaves) during the day to get carbon dioxide from the surrounding air, but this leads to high amounts of water loss in a desert environment. Succulents open their stomata at night and, through a special biochemical process, store carbon dioxide until the next day, when it is released inside the plant so photosynthesis can occur without opening the stomata. *Mesembryanthemum*—iceplants and sea figs—is a widespread genus, with species occurring in all of Africa's deserts. It typically has thick, succulent leaves and colorful flowers with numerous parts.

As a further adaptation to prevent water loss, many succulents have no leaves. *Anabasis articulata*, which is widespread in the Sahara desert, is a leafless succulent with jointed stems. Cacti are only found in North and South America, but a visitor to the Sahara would probably be fooled by certain species in the spurge family that bear a surprising resemblance to cacti. For example, *Euphorbia echinus*, another Saharan plant, has succulent, ridged stems with spines. The most extreme adaptation in succulents is found in the living stones of Southern Africa. Their plant body is reduced to two plump, rounded leaves that are very succulent. They hug the ground, sometimes being partially buried, and have camouflaged coloration so that they blend in with the surrounding rocks and sand, thus avoiding being eaten by grazing animals. Other succulents, such as the quiver tree, attain the size and appearance of trees.

WATER-DEPENDENT PLANTS OF THE SUBTROPICAL DESERT. Water-dependent plants are confined to areas near a permanent water source. The most familiar of these plants is the date palm, which is a common sight at desert oases. Date palms have been cultivated for thousands of years for food, but interest in date farming has waned and many date palms are in danger. When not properly cared for, they can become water-stressed and often fall prey to a fungus disease called bayoud. Tamarind and acacia are also common where water is available. A variety of differ-

---

WELWITSCHIA: AFRICA'S STRANGEST PLANT

There are many unusual plants in Africa, but one of the most unusual is the Welwitschia, a resident of the Namib Desert. It has a short, swollen stem only about four inches (ten centimeters) high, which terminates in a disc-like structure. Coming off the top of the stem are two strap-like leaves. These two leaves last for the lifetime of the plant and continue to grow very slowly. As they grow, they twist and become shredded, so that an individual plant appears to have many leaves. The reproductive structures rise from the center of the stem, and, instead of flowers, Welwitschia has small cones.

Welwitschia is such a successful survivor of the Namib that it easily lives for hundreds of years. Some specimens have been dated to about two thousand years old. Older plants can reach tremendous sizes, with the top of the stem sometimes reaching 5 feet (1.5 meters) in diameter. Specimens of Welwitschia are extremely difficult to grow in cultivation, requiring special desert conditions and room for the deep taproot.

As in other parts of the tropical world, coconut palms can be found throughout Africa. (PhotoDisc)

ent sedges and rushes occur wherever there is abundant permanent freshwater, the most famous of these being the papyrus or bulrush.

EPHEMERALS OF THE SUBTROPICAL DESERT. Desert ephemerals account for a significant portion of the African desert flora. A majority of the ephemerals are grasses. Ephemerals are entirely dependent on seasonal or sporadic rains. A few days after a significant rain, the desert turns bright green, and after several more days flowers, often in profusion, appear. Some ephemerals germinate with amazing speed, such as the pillow cushion plant, which germinates and produces actively photosynthesizing seed leaves only ten hours after being wetted. Reproductive rates for ephemerals, and even for perennial plants, are rapid. Species of morning glory can complete an entire life cycle in three to six weeks.

TROPICAL SAVANNA. Tropical savanna ranges from savanna grassland, which is dominated by tall grasses lacking trees or shrubs, to thicket and scrub communities, which are composed primarily of trees and shrubs of a fairly uniform size. The most common type of savanna in Africa is the savanna woodland, which is composed of tall, moisture-loving grasses and tall deciduous or semideciduous trees that are unevenly distributed and generally well spaced. The type of savanna familiar to viewers of African wildlife documentaries is the savanna parkland, which is primarily tall grass with widely spaced trees.

GRASSES AND HERBS OF THE AFRICAN SAVANNA. Grasses represent the majority of plant cover beneath and between the trees. In some types of savanna, the grass can be more than 6 feet (1.8 meters) high, giving rise to such names as elephant grass. Although it has been much debated, two factors seem to perpetuate the dominance of grasses: seasonal moisture with a long intervening dry spell and periodic fires. Given excess moisture and lack of fire, savannas seem inevitably to become forests. Other activities by humans, such as grazing cattle or cutting trees for firewood, also perpetuate, or possibly promote, grass dominance.

A variety of herbs exist in the savanna, but they are easily overlooked, except during flowering periods. Many of them also do best just after a fire, when they are better exposed to the Sun and to potential pollinators. Some, like types of hibiscus and coleus, are familiar garden and house plants popular the world over. Vines related to the sweet potato are also common. Many species from the legume or pea and sunflower families are present. Wild ginger often displays its showy blossoms after a fire.

TREES AND SHRUBS OF THE SAVANNA. Trees of the African savanna often have relatively wide-spreading branches that all terminate at about the same height, giving the trees a flat-topped appearance. Many are from the legume family, most notably species of *Acacia*, *Brachystegia*, *Julbernardia*, and *Isoberlinia*, which, with the exception of *Acacia*, are not well known outside of Africa. There is an especially large number of *Acacia* species ranging from shrubs to trees, many with spines. A few also have a symbiotic relationship with ants that protect them from herbivores. The hashab tree, a type of acacia that grows in more arid regions, is the source of gum arabic.

Although not as prominent, the baobab tree is renowned for its large size and odd appearance and occurs in many savanna regions. It has an extremely thick trunk with smooth, gray bark and can live for up to 2,000 years. Another odd tree is the sausage tree, which gets its name from the large, oblong, sausage-like fruits that dangle from its branches. Many savanna trees also have showy flowers, like the flame tree and the African tulip tree. Both trees are pollinated by sunbirds.

TROPICAL FOREST. The primary characteristics of African tropical forests are their extremely lush growth, high species diversity, and complex structure. The diversity is often so great that a single tree species cannot be identified as dominant

*Trees
Pages
1026, 1027*

Baobab trees. (Digital Stock)

in an area. Relatively large trees predominate, and they grow so close together that their crowns overlap, limiting the amount of light that reaches beneath them. A few larger trees, called emergent trees, break out above the thick canopy of trees and may grow to almost twice as high as the average height of the canopy below.

Another layer of smaller trees live beneath the main canopy. A few smaller shrubs and herbs grow near the ground level, but the majority of the herbs and other perennials are epiphytes, that is, plants that grow on other plants. On almost every available space on the trunks and branches of the canopy trees there are epiphytes that support an entire, unique community. All this dense plant growth is supported by a monsoon climate in which 60 inches (150 centimeters) or more of rain often falls annually, most of it in the summer.

The most notable feature of trees in the African tropical forest is their great diversity. Although some species are widespread and relatively common, many are rare and endemic to extremely small areas. Many of the trees belong to families that are found only in the Tropics. Larger trees often have extensive buttresses, which are extremely large, flared bases. Buttresses appear to give tropical trees greater stability. A similar adaptation is stilt roots, roots that arise from buds lower down on certain trees and radiate out and down to the soil.

Among the tallest of the forest trees is the silk cotton tree, one of the sources of kapok (traditionally used to fill life preservers), which can exceed 150 feet (45 meters) in height. Many of the taller trees are valuable as timber. *Ochroma* is the source of the uniquely light balsa wood. Ironwood, a member of the legume family, forms dominant stands in many areas. Ironwood is named for its extremely dense wood, which is resistant to decay and termites, in addi-

tion to being difficult to cut. Its wood also has alternating color patterns of light and dark wood, referred to as zebra wood. Because of its strength, it traditionally has been used for heavy duty flooring and in shipbuilding. Some of the more valuable timber trees include iroko and sapele.

LIANAS AND EPIPHYTES OF THE TROPICAL FOREST. Lianas are large, woody vines that cling to trees, many of them hanging down near to the ground, and were made famous by Tarzan movies. Many lianas belong to families with well-known temperate vine species, such as the grape family, morning glory family, and cucumber family. Many other related plants are simply climbers and either never become as sturdy as lianas, or remain intimately connected to the trunks of trees. One of these, the strangler fig, is a strong climber that begins life in the canopy.

The fruits are eaten by birds or monkeys, and the seeds are deposited in their feces on branches high in the canopy. The seeds germinate and send a stem downward to the ground. Once the stem reaches the ground, it roots; additional stems then develop and grow upward along the trunk of the tree. After many years, a strangler fig can so thoroughly surround a tree that it prevents water and nutrients from flowing up the trunk. Eventually, the host tree dies and rots away, leaving a hollow tube composed essentially of the strangler fig itself. Other climbers include members of the Araceae family, the most familiar being the ornamental philodendron.

The most common epiphytes are bryophytes, lower plants related to mosses, and lichens, a symbiotic combination of algae and fungus. The most abundant higher plants are ferns and orchids. As these plants colonize the branches of trees, they gradually trap dust and decaying materials, eventually leading to a thin soil layer that other plants can also use. Accumulations of epiphytes can be so great in some cases that branches break from the weight. Epiphytes are not parasites (although there are some parasitic plants that grow on tree branches) but simply use the host tree for support. They also provide a habitat for a variety of animals, including amphibians, birds, reptiles, and insects. Orchids, of which there are thousands of species, are especially noted for their interactions with insects. Some orchid flowers actually mimic their own pollinators, small species of wasps, and entice males to mate with them. The wasps' attempts at mating result in pollen transfer for the orchid. The epiphyte plant community is probably the least well understood plant community in the tropical rain forest because of its inaccessibility.

TROPICAL FOREST FLOOR PLANTS. Many of the herbs of the forest floor are small and inconspicuous. Grasses are almost entirely absent, and those that occur there have much broader leaves than usual. Some forest-floor herbs are able to grow in the deep shade beneath the canopy, occasionally being so thoroughly adapted to the low available light that they can be damaged if exposed to full sunlight. Some of the most popular house plants have come from among these plants, because they do not need direct sunlight to survive. Still, the greatest numbers of plants occur beneath breaks in the canopy, where more light is available.

Some of the larger herbs are in the ginger and arrowroot families. Species of *Costus* have particularly showy flowers and have often been cultivated in greenhouses. Prayer plants are grown for their beautiful foliage. Members of the pepper family also occur here, some of them shrubs and small climbers. Leaves of *Piper betle* are wrapped around betel nuts and chewed by many of the indigenous peoples of Africa. The leaves cause excessive production of saliva, and the betel nuts produce a red juice that stains the teeth of habitual chewers. There is some evidence that betel nut stains on the teeth may help prevent tooth decay.

OTHER PLANT ASSOCIATIONS. In addition to the three major biomes, several smaller areas in Africa that have some distinctive plant associations. Southern Africa is especially rich in plant life and contains some of the most unusual plant associations on the continent, if not the world.

THE FYNBOS BIOME. The fynbos biome is located in the extreme southwestern and southern parts of Southern Africa. Climatically, the western part is a Mediterranean-type ecosystem with winter rains and summer drought. Moving more to the east, the rains become less seasonal. The literal meaning of the term "fynbos" is "fine-leaved bush," which refers to the dominant vegetation type in this biome. The fynbos is primarily a fire-prone, evergreen shrub land. Many of the shrubs are from the heath or protea families. The grasses are typically evergreen and very wiry. Although the fynbos covers only a relatively small area geographically, it has about seventy-three hundred species of plants, 80 percent of them endemic.

THE NAMA-KAROO BIOME. This biome is also found in Southern Africa and occupies a little more than 22 percent of the region. The nama-karoo is a desert-type biome receiving, in its wetter parts, less than 16 inches (410 millimeters) of rain per year, with some areas receiving less than 3 inches (80 millimeters) of rain yearly. As a consequence, the plants display typical desert adaptations. Dwarf shrubs, some of them succulent, dominate much of the landscape. Some areas are dominated by grasses.

Many of the plants belong to such familiar plant families as the sunflower, lily, and foxglove. Many of the species from the

CENTRAL AFRICAN TROPICAL RAIN FORESTS IN PERIL

Although the rain forests of central Africa are at lower risk of deforestation than are tropical forests in some other parts of the world, they are still in great danger. First, they contain many valuable timber trees that are being exploited actively. Second, these forested areas are in demand for other uses. In some areas, excessive timber harvesting and clearing to make way for oil palm and rubber plantations leaves little untouched forest. Some of the worst damage has occurred in Liberia and the Ivory Coast, where populations are on the rise. Much research is being done to develop sustainable and regenerative ways to harvest trees. In many areas, certain parts of the forest are considered sacred and are jealously guarded from all encroachment by local tribes. Medicinal plants are obtained from these areas, and they also are used as burial grounds that shelter the tribes' ancestral spirits.

lily family in this biome are highly prized by gardeners the world over. The mesembryanthemum family is also prominent here, and a number of species have been introduced to other parts of the world. One of these, commonly called the iceplant, was introduced to various parts of California to stabilize sand and soil in freeway medians. Since its introduction, it has escaped extensively and has permanently altered some natural sand dune communities, endangering native plants.

THE SUCCULENT KAROO BIOME. This biome is another desert-like biome, but it receives slightly more rainfall than the nama-karoo. As its name implies, most of the species are succulent, with a preponderance of succulent-leaved shrubs from the mesembryanthemum and stonecrop families. There are also succulent monocots, such as aloes, and some cactus-like members of the spurge family. This biome also has the highest species richness for any semiarid biome, with more than five thousand species, 50 percent of them endemic. Also found there are species of living stones discussed under the subtropical desert section.

Other types of low-growing succulents, like living stones, blend in with their surroundings by resembling soil, stones, or animal dung. Some of the shrubs belong to families generally thought of as herbaceous, such as the milkweed, asparagus, and nightshade families. Even the genus *Aloe*, best known to many people by the small succulent, aloe vera, is represented by many shrubs, some of them resembling small trees. Spines are a relatively common feature of many of the succulent herbs and shrubs as well, making them seem superficially like cacti.

THE MEDITERRANEAN ECOSYSTEM. Only a few places in the world have the combination of climate factors commonly called Mediterranean climate, which is characterized by warm, dry summers and cool, wet winters. Two regions in Africa have this type of climate. The first was discussed in the section on the nama-karoo biome. The second area is the part of northern Africa that borders the Mediterranean Sea.

Two vegetation associations predominate. Mixed evergreen woodlands composed of holm oak, Aleppo pine, and Aleppo fir thrive in moister areas. At higher elevations, the two conifers are replaced by cedar, although cedars have disappeared from much of the area after centuries of overexploitation. Olive and mastic trees also occur here, although they are less common than in the past. Shrubs in the Mediterranean ecosystem are primarily evergreen with leathery, drought-tolerant leaves. Some of these shrubs, like holly, also have spines on their leaves. The climate in North Africa has become gradually warmer and drier, making it harder for many Mediterranean species to persist. Human-caused damage to the vegetation has compounded the problem, with the result that more desertlike species have become established and grassland is all that remains in some areas.

Bryan Ness

FOR FURTHER STUDY

Alpert, Peter. "Integrated Conservation and Development Projects." *Bioscience* 46, no. 11 (December, 1996): 845-856.

Becker, Hank. "Floral Gems." *Agricultural Research* 45, no. 9 (September, 1997): 8-13.

Blundell, M. *Wild Flowers of East Africa.* New York: HarperCollins, 1994.

Boroughs, Don. "Battle for a Wild Garden." *International Wildlife* 29 (May/June, 1999): 12-21.

Ghazanfar, Shahina A. *Savanna Plants of Africa: An Illustrated Guide.* New York: Macmillan, 1990.

Morrissey, Brian. "The Making of a Rainforest." *Natural History* 107 (June, 1998): 56-61.

Pooley, Elsa, and Vincent Carruthers. *Flowers, Grasses, Ferns and Fungi (Southern African Green Guide).* Menasha, Wisc.: Menasha Ridge Press, 1999.

Steentoft, Margaret. *Flowering Plants in West Africa.* New York: Cambridge University Press, 1988.

FAUNA

*Map
Page 1028*

*Animals
Pages 1029-
1032*

Known for the enormous diversity and richness of its wildlife, Africa has a greater variety of large ungulates, or hoofed mammals (some ninety species), and freshwater fish (two thousand species) than any other continent. However, probably no group of animals is more identified with Africa than its flesh-eating carnivore mammals, of which there are more than sixty species. In addition to the better-known big, or "roaring," cats, such as lions, leopards, and cheetahs, there are wild dogs, hyenas, servals (long-limbed cats), wildcats, jackals, foxes, weasels, civets, and mongoose.

There are many theories as to why Africa has such an abundance of wildlife, and large wildlife at that. While early North American human societies drove mammoths, giant beaver, and saber-tooth tigers to extinction, early Europeans wiped out lions and rhinos, and Asians domesticated their landscapes, Africans lived in relative accord with creatures that were no less grand or ferocious. Some African folklore places animals on the same footing with people.

Another theory is that the tsetse fly, by spreading the sleeping sickness, made much of tropical Africa uninhabitable by humans and protected the wilderness and wildlife from human depredation. Still another possibility may have been the constancy and small size of the African population in comparison with European and Asian numbers—too few people to either overhunt large mammals or exhaust their habitat. One more possibility is that the savannas of Africa—grassy plains with scattered tree cover—provide good habitat for so many ungulates. Humans cannot hunt ungulates easily under these conditions because the humans can be seen and

Zebras inhabit Africa's savannas and some mountain areas in eastern, central, and southern Africa. Although they are close relatives of horses, they have never been successfully domesticated. (PhotoDisc)

outrun easily. At the same time, a large population of ungulates supports an appreciable population of predators such as lions and scavengers such as hyenas.

ORIGIN OF AFRICAN FAUNA. At one time, most African fauna was believed to have originated in the Palearctic regions, that is, Europe, northwest Africa, and much of Asia. There is no doubt that as recently as fifteen thousand years ago, a milder Saharan climate allowed typically Ethiopian forms, such as clariid catfish, to reach the river systems of North Africa. Similarly, northern animal life and vegetation seem to have extended far south into the Sahara. The white rhinoceros evidently coexisted with elklike deer.

The spread of forests during the wetter epochs created separate northern and southern wooded grasslands. This led to the evolution of such closely related northern and southern species of antelope as the kob and puku, the Nile and common lechwe, and the northern and southern forms of white rhinoceros. In earlier periods, the animal life was even more remarkable than in modern times. Fossil deposits have revealed sheep as big as present-day buffalo, huge hippopotamuses, giant baboons, and other types similar to existing species. These "megafauna" probably lived in wetter periods and died out as the climate became drier.

EFFECTS OF HUMAN POPULATIONS. The fine conditions for Africa's fauna in the mid-to-late nineteenth century started to come to an end when European settlers arrived in many parts of Africa. Technologies, in the form of Western medicine and sanitation, sparked a demographic revolution. In places like Rhodesia (now Zimbabwe), the human population exploded

ENDANGERED CHIMPANZEES THE SOURCE OF HIV?

A type of chimpanzee that is feared to be headed for extinction by the year 2010 carries a unique genetic blend of human immunodeficiency virus (HIV) and simian immunodeficiency virus (SIV). Scientists have stated that, in the genetic family tree of all known HIVs and SIVs, this virus appears to be the strain that could be the source of all HIVs. Once the strain known as SIVcpz made its way into the human species, probably in the 1950's, it mutated into the existing human strain, adapting naturally to its new host.

The chimpanzees are being driven from their homes by loggers in the rain forests of the Congo River basin. They also are being slaughtered for their meat. However, scientists consider it is crucial that this species of chimpanzee remain in existence so they may study them for critical HIV research.

twenty-fold during the ninety-year reign of white settlers.

Since 1940 the combined pressures of hunting and habitat destruction have cut wildlife numbers greatly. The antelope known as the Zambian black lechwe, believed to have numbered one million in 1900, had been reduced to less than eight thousand by the late twentieth century. The population of African elephants declined from two million in the early 1970's to 600,000 by 1990, largely because of poaching for the ivory trade.

Elephants Pages 1029, 1032

Since the 1960's, poaching has caused a 95 percent decline in the world's black rhino population to fewer than 2,600 in 1997. The African white rhinoceros reached the verge of extinction in 1980. In West Africa, the continual southward advance of the Sahara Desert has amplified the twin pressures of habitat destruction and human population. The larger fauna that lived there, caught between the desert and the burgeoning population, are largely gone now.

Rhinoceros Page 1030

In Kenya, farmers have long since cleared most of the central part of the

One of nineteenth century Africa's most renowned hunters was Frederick Courteney Selous, whose career was nearly ended by an elephant in 1878. (Frederick Courteney Selous)

country that was once a densely forested region inhabited by wild animals. Some people have invaded national parks for commercial purposes such as logging and cattle grazing, thus forcing wildlife out of their preserved habitats. Some animals have had no alternative but to fight with humans for food and water. Along the Kenyan coast, many people have been attacked and killed by charging hippopotamuses and crocodiles in search of food and space. Similar cases have been common in the highlands, where Kenyans have lost their lives to charging elephants or to leopards and buffalo.

In recent years, human-elephant conflicts in Cameroon have become a major issue. Such conflicts are more acute in the savanna ecosystem, due to the loss of the elephant's range and habitat following the conversion of natural vegetation to farmland and the logging of large tracts of forests. Cameroon still has a relatively large herd of elephants, estimated at about twenty thousand in 1997. Approximately 75 percent of these elephants live in the dense equatorial forest.

ENDANGERED MAMMALS OF AFRICA

Common Name	Scientific Name	Range
Aye-Aye	*Daubentonia madagascariensis*	Madagascar
Cat, black-footed	*Felis nigripes*	Southern Africa
Cheetah	*Acinonyx jubatus*	Africa to India
Chimpanzee	*Pan troglodytes*	Africa
Eland, western giant	*Taurotragus derbianus*	Senegal to Ivory Coast
Gazelle, mountain	*Gazella cuvieri*	Morocco, Algeria, Tunisia
Gorilla	*Gorilla*	Central and western Africa
Hyena, brown	*Parahyaena brunnea*	Southern Africa
Impala, black-faced	*Aepyceros melampus petersi*	Namibia, Angola
Lemurs	*Lemuridae*	Madagascar
Mandrill	*Mandrillus sphinx*	Equatorial West Africa
Rhinoceros, black	*Diceros bicornis*	Sub-Saharan Africa

Source: U.S. Fish and Wildlife Service, U.S. Department of the Interior.

Another issue in Cameroon in 1999 was a 652-mile (1,050-kilometer) pipeline proposed to traverse tropical rain forests and link oil fields in landlocked Chad to an export facility in Kribi, Cameroon. The original route of the pipeline was changed to go through two less-fragile ecosystems, but the new route was still designed to cut through tropical areas and provide easier access to endangered species such as gorillas, chimpanzees, and elephants.

MAMMALS. The main group of herbivores is the African antelope, which belong to four subfamilies of the ox family. The first subfamily is further subdivided into the African buffalo and the twist-horned antelope, including the eland (the largest of all antelopes), kudu, nyala, and bushbuck. The second subfamily is

the duiker, a small primitive antelope that lives in the thickets, bush, and forests. Other well-known large African herbivores include the zebra, giraffe, hippopotamus, rhinoceros, and African elephant.

Africa's large number of endemic or native mammal species is second only to that of South America. These include several families of the ungulate order *Artiodactyla* (mammals with an even number of toes), such as the giraffe and hippopotamus. Some carnivores—such as civets, their smaller relations, the genets, and hyenas—are chiefly African. The rodent family of jumping hares is endemic, and one order, the aardvark, is exclusively African. The Malagasy Republic (Madagascar) has a remarkable insect-eating family. These are the tenrecs, animals with long,

Giraffes
Page 1026

Giraffes in Namibia's Etosha National Park. (Corbis)

Baboon family in Botswana's Chobe National Park. (Corbis)

Lemurs
Page 963

pointed snouts. Some tenrecs are spiny and tailless.

PRIMATES. The primates include about forty-five species of Old World monkeys and two of the world's great apes: the chimpanzee and the world's largest ape, the gorilla. The gorilla is present in two subspecies: the lowland gorilla of Central and West Africa and the mountain gorilla of East Africa. The rare mountain gorillas live only in the upland forest on the borders of Uganda, Rwanda, and Congo-Kinshasa (Zaire). There are two populations of roughly equal size. One is in Uganda's Bwindi Impenetrable Forest National Park, where a 1998 census counted 292 gorillas. The second is in the Virunga Mountains, on the borders of the three countries. The last census there, completed in 1989, estimated 324 gorillas in the Virungas, but war has prevented a recount.

Presimian primates include pottos or African lemurs and galagos, bush babies, or small arboreal lemurs. These and other African lemurs tend to be small and nocturnal. In the Malagasy Republic, where there are no true monkeys, the lemurs have occupied all ecological niches, both diurnal and nocturnal, that the monkeys would have taken. Accordingly, the world's most diverse collection of presimian lemurs survives in Madagascar.

REPTILES AND AMPHIBIANS. Most African reptiles have their origins elsewhere—mainly in Asia. These include lizards of the agamid family, skinks, crocodiles, and tortoises. Endemic reptiles include girdle-tailed and plated lizards. Large vipers are common and diverse. Certain species have extremely toxic venom, but they are rarely encountered. One of the most noted is the black mamba. Amphibians also belong mainly to Old World groups. Salamanders and toothed tree frogs are confined to the Palearctic northwest Africa. Abundant and more common frogs and toads include such oddities as the so-called hairy frog of Cameroon, whose hairs are auxiliary respiratory organs.

BIRDS. The birdlife south of the Sahara includes almost fifteen hundred resident species. An additional 275 species either reside in northwestern Africa or are winter migrants from Europe. Once there may have been as many as two billion individual migrants, but their numbers have been reduced considerably by severe droughts and by human land use and predation. The few endemic bird species include the ostrich, shoebill, hammerkop, and secretary bird. The many predators of land mammals include eagles, hawks, and owls. Many more, such as storks, waders, and a few species of kingfishers, prey on fish. Even more feed on insects.

INSECTS. Insects include large butterflies, stick insects, mantises, grasshoppers, safari ants, termites, and dung beetles. Spiders abound throughout the continent, and scorpions and locusts can be plentiful locally. Huge swarms of locusts periodically spread over wide areas, causing enormous destruction to vegetation. Mosquitoes that carry malaria are present wherever there is a body of water. Female blackflies transmit the nematode *onchocera volvulus*, a parasitic filarial or threadlike worm. This organism eventually collects in many parts of the body, including the head near the eye. Nematode clusters around the eyes cause a blindness known as "river blindness." This disease has prevented any significant human habitation in many of Africa's river valleys.

Tsetse flies carry the parasite that causes African sleeping sickness in humans and nagana in livestock. These flies are found in all tropical portions of sub-Saharan Africa. The controversial chemical pesticide, DDT, which is banned in the West, is being used in Zimbabwe and other countries to eliminate the tsetse fly. DDT has adversely affected birds and fish there and has even been found in nursing mothers' breast milk.

CONSERVATION EFFORTS. If people can benefit from wildlife, their attitudes and actions toward wildlife will improve. Starting

Ostriches Page 1030

TSETSE FLY: WINGED GUARDIAN OF WILDERNESS

The tsetse fly acts as a carrier for trypanosomiasis, a parasite that causes the sleeping sickness, which is a wasting disease. When the sleeping sickness is acute, the symptoms are high temperature, anemia, fitful appetite, and swollen limbs. The victim eventually sinks into an irritable haze, then slips into a coma and dies.

The sleeping sickness has had a long history in Africa. One subspecies of the trypanosomiasis parasite lives amicably in the bloodstream of wild animals such as antelopes. However, when it gets into a cow, it makes the animal waste away and die. As a consequence, raising livestock has been difficult or impossible in much of sub-Saharan Africa. More than 3 million square miles (8 million sq. km.) of that region are off-limits to cattle, and in places where they are raised, three million cows die of the disease each year. The tsetse fly is cheered by conservationists because it makes so much of Africa largely uninhabitable for humans and cattle, thus preserving wildlife. However, it is estimated that the sleeping sickness spread by the tsetse fly threatens fifty million Africans.

Wildebeest in South Africa's Rooipoort Game Reserve. (Corbis)

in Namibia in 1967 and extending to Zimbabwe in 1975, lawmakers put the idea into action. Large landowners were allotted ownership rights to wildlife, an idea totally alien to the European and the United States' tradition of exclusive state ownership. Landowners, for the first time since the imposition of colonial rule, were free to make economically informed—and, as it turned out, ecologically desirable—market decisions on how best to use their land. By 1990, 75 percent of Zimbabwean ranchers in areas too dry to support crop production had shifted partly or entirely to wildlife ranching. That change was due to the nearly quadruple net profit per acre advantage held by wildlife over cattle.

Rinderpest, a highly contagious bovine plague that has killed millions of Africa's cattle, buffalo, and wildlife in the past century, is finally being brought under control. The disease has been eradicated in West and Central Africa, and is contained in most of East Africa. Rinderpest, caused

by morbillivirus, attacks ungulates such as cows, sheep, buffalo, and giraffe and is almost always fatal. It is easily transmitted through direct contact and by drinking water contaminated with the dung of sick animals. It is believed to persist in the Sudan and possibly Somalia, and about four other places in the world.

In Swaziland, pastoralists known as Shewula are breaking with tradition by giving more than 7,400 acres (3,000 hectares) of land used for grazing cattle to a large new game reserve. It will be part of a new transnational reserve with neighboring South Africa and Mozambique. In return, donors have provided funds to build tourism facilities on the land and to train the community in conservation, management, and marketing skills. The goal is to develop the reserve's tourism potential to benefit the rural villagers who have chosen wildlife over cattle.

Similar arrangements have been made between an international hotel chain and a village community outside Tanzania's Serengeti National Park. The agreement involved more than 25,000 acres (10,000 hectares) of land in the Loliondo buffer zone between the Serengeti and the Masai Mara of neighboring Kenya. The Loliondo corridor is used by thousands of stampeding wildebeest during their famed migrations between the Serengeti and the Mara.

Progress has been made in efforts to increase the elephant population. In East Africa, the numbers of elephants are slowly increasing after the poaching rampages of the 1980's. The areas around Tsavo National Park in Kenya and in neighboring Tanzania have reported a count of eighty-one hundred elephants, as opposed to about six thousand elephants in the late 1980's. In 1972, however, there were about twenty-five thousand elephants in the greater Tsavo area. The elephant conservation record of Namibia, Botswana, and Zimbabwe has been impressive. As of the summer of 1999, they had an estimated 200,000 elephants.

Dana P. McDermott

FOR FURTHER STUDY

Chadwick, Douglas H. "Elephants—Out of Time, Out of Space." *National Geographic* (May, 1991): 2-49.

Conniff, Richard. "Cheetahs: Ghosts of the Grasslands." *National Geographic* (December, 1999): 2-31.

_____. "Africa's Wild Dogs." *National Geographic* (May, 1999): 36-63.

Disilvestro, Roger L., ed. *The African Elephant: Twilight in Eden.* New York: John Wiley & Sons, 1991.

Estes, Richard Despard. *The Behavior Guide to African Mammals: Including Hoofed Mammals, Carnivores, Primates.* Berkeley: University of California Press, 1991.

Halliburton, Warren J. *African Wildlife.* Columbus, Ohio: Silver Burdett Press, 1992.

Linden, Eugene. "Bonobos, Chimpanzees With A Difference." *National Geographic* (March, 1992): 46-53.

Lyons, Maryinez. *The Colonial Disease: A Social History of Sleeping Sickness in Northern Zaire, 1900-1940.* New York: Cambridge University Press, 1992.

Masai Mara Page 1162

INFORMATION ON THE WORLD WIDE WEB

The African Wildlife Foundation's Web site features information on the wild animals of the African continent and efforts to preserve animal habitats (www.awf.org)

HUMAN GEOGRAPHY

PEOPLE

The study of how humans and their prehuman predecessors came to increase in number and eventually spread across the African continent is one of the most dramatic and fascinating stories in history. Using such modern scientific fields of study as archaeology and physical anthropology, fossil remains, tools, and artifacts have been examined. From these, researchers have been able to discover what prehumans and humans were like millions of years ago.

Additional scientific fields of study, such as genetics, botany, zoology, linguistics, and cultural anthropology, have provided information on where humans came from, where they went, and when they began to increase in numbers and migrate across thousands of miles of rivers, deserts, grasslands, and forests. Combining all these tools with history and geography has provided the basis for determining how much cultures changed after humans traveled over so vast a space and over so long a period of time.

Over an incredible expanse of time, humans rose from the Great Rift Valley in Africa and followed the Sun across the grasslands of the Sahel (the semiarid belt south of the Sahara) in search of game and dependable sources of water. As they discovered how to make and use stone tools, they increased in number and began to fill the continent. Then, the Sahara cooled and shared its bounty during a brief wet phase. Humans slowly moved in and learned to domesticate both animals and plants.

These skills became the building blocks of an Egyptian culture in North Africa.

With the coming of the Iron Age, the last barrier to human expansion was overcome. People relentlessly expanded across the breadth of sub-Saharan Africa, eventually establishing a cultural environment that remained much the same until the expansion of Islam and European colonialism.

ORIGINS OF HUMAN POPULATION. For many years, people believed that humans came out of a Garden of Eden in the Middle East or the Far East. The naturalist Charles Darwin, writing in the nineteenth century, suggested that humans must have come from another place. He reasoned that humans were tropical animals and that they must be related to monkeys, since those were the animals most like humans. He subsequently concluded that humans must have originated in Africa, the place that combined the largest tropical landmass with the site of the most varieties of primates.

A number of scientific discoveries in the twentieth century supported Darwin's theory. Robert Broom and Raymond Dart found archaeological evidence of australopithecines in southern Africa. These were a type of manlike prehuman ancestor, called hominids. The australopithecines were an important evolutionary step toward *Homo sapiens*, or modern humans. They were only about four feet, six inches tall, and they stood upright when they walked. More important, their hands were enough like ours to allow them to make simple tools from bone or stone.

Beginning in the 1960's, Louis B. Leakey and Mary Douglas Leakey made several additional discoveries in East Africa that helped to place the origin of humans in Africa. They uncovered numerous fossils and artifacts of australopithecines at Olduvai Gorge, in the Great Rift Valley. Many of these were from the Lower and Middle Pleistocene geological epochs, between one and a half and two million years ago.

By examining these remains within the context of where they were found and what that area was like at that time, the Leakeys determined that small bands of these manlike ancestors had lived along the edges of small ponds, subsisting largely on plants and small animals. After reviewing information on the most recent finds across Africa, the Leakeys decided that three important steps in human evolution had taken place in Africa. First, the original ancestors of all apes had arisen in the Nile region at some point during the Oligocene epoch, between thirty million and forty million years ago.

Second, the branch of apes from which humans had emerged must have broken away from the others during the late Miocene or early Pliocene epochs, about twelve million years ago. Third, approximately two million years ago, toward the end of the Pliocene epoch, "true man," who had eventually become *Homo sapiens*, had separated from "near man," or the australopithecines in East Africa. Many scientists came to agree with the Leakeys' conclusion that humans had came out of Africa.

HISTORICAL MIGRATION PATTERNS. The australopithecines began to use simple stone tools about three million years ago, during the Stone Age. Over an immense length of time, these tools became heavier and more sophisticated. One of their greatest advantages was that they gave their users the ability to become better hunters. Although they were only able to kill small or medium-sized animals

in the beginning, humans could now kill them more frequently and process them more efficiently. Meat was an important addition to the human diet, because it allowed them to increase their nutrients and caloric intake. As their diet improved, people began to live longer and have more children. The population was slowly increasing.

Sometimes, families grew rather large. Anthropologists call clans extended families of grandparents, children, and grandchildren. When game became too scarce in a particular area, clans typically would divide into smaller groups and move to new areas. This process of growth, division, and migration is similar to what bees do when their hives become too crowded or when food becomes too scarce. This process of "hiving" began to accelerate among the hominids about a million years ago, when the quantity and quality of stone tools vastly improved.

Many scientists now suggest that the various human species arose in Africa about 200,000 years ago during the Middle Pleistocene epoch. Then, about 50,000 years ago, during the Upper Pleistocene epoch, those human populations began to increase rapidly. This was largely because humans' distant relatives, *Homo neanderthalensis* and *Homo rhodesiensis*, and direct relatives *Homo sapiens*, had learned how to make fire, live in caves, and carry burdens. These skills enabled them to protect and feed larger groups in relative comfort, settle in one area longer, and travel greater distances. Slowly migrating westward from the Great Rift Valley to the Congo basin, along the grasslands north of the Niger and Benue Rivers, and then into the Sahel, humans had covered most of sub-Saharan Africa by some time between fifty and sixty thousand years ago.

Scientists have learned a great deal about what Africa was like fifty thousand years ago. They have determined that many of the outward physical variations that make people from different regions appear different had already occurred. They also have learned that more than half of the humans living on earth during this period were living in sub-Saharan Africa. One of the means they have used to determine this is the study of genetics—the science of heredity and the variation of organisms from generation to generation.

Through genetic research, scientists have determined that populations living in sub-Saharan Africa have a higher degree of in-group diversity than people living in any other part of the world. They did this by studying particular components and attributes of the deoxyribonucleic acid (DNA) of numerous subjects from sub-Saharan Africa, East Asia, and Europe. The high degree of genetic diversity within the African test group led to the conclusion that the human population in sub-Saharan Africa fifty thousand years ago had been larger than the human populations of Asia and Europe combined. It was also evidence that the human population there had grown more rapidly than anywhere else. One reason that humans in Africa increased in number was that they had found new and better ways to feed themselves. As their numbers increased, they sought new ways to obtain food and new places to live.

The Pleistocene epoch was beginning to come to a close during the Middle Stone Age, about 35,000 B.C.E. During this period, *Homo sapiens* began to replace other types of humans across Africa. About 10,000 B.C.E., as the Middle Stone Age was ending, a climatic change took place in Africa that profoundly affected the future of nearly all humans in Africa.

The Sahara Desert slowly grew cooler during this period, and rain occasionally fell. In time, grass began to grow and small

rivers began to appear in what had been an inhospitable desert. Humans inevitably followed wild animals into the Sahara. As humans living along the Mediterranean Sea to the north moved down into the Sahara, they began to mingle with those who were moving up from the Sahel to the south.

In time, the people who inhabited the Sahara began to domesticate animals and then plants, which heralded the agricultural revolution. This was a significant advantage, because now they could increase the number of calories they could obtain from the areas they occupied. As their diets improved, their numbers began to increase once again, and they began to migrate even farther across the continent. Archaeologists have discovered that people were managing herds of wild cattle in Egypt's western desert as early as 7,500 B.C.E., and that Barbary sheep were being managed in Libya at about the same time. As they began to domesticate animals, the way people lived began to change.

Cattle
Page 1033

At Nabta Playa in Egypt's Western Desert, huge uncarved stones dating back to about 4,500 B.C.E., have been discovered. These megaliths are interesting for two reasons: They were aligned with the heavenly bodies, and ceremonial cattle burials from the same period were found nearby, beneath artificial mounds of rocks called "tumuli." This archaeological find indicates a higher level of social organization and religious ritual among humans than had been found before in Africa. It is unlikely that this is an isolated phenomenon, since the domestication of animals had spread across the Sahara by the sixth millennium B.C.E.

The regular cultivation of edible plants and grains was another important step in human progress. Botanists have discovered that people were experimenting with both sorghum and millet in Nabta Playa about 7,000 B.C.E. Grinding stones and storage pits for processing wild grains were discovered at Foum el-Alba in Mali and date back to 4,500 B.C.E. The abundance of wild grains along the small lakes and rivers of the Sahara made it unnecessary to rely heavily on plant cultivation. The Sahara is interesting, because it appears that people had domesticated animals there thousands of years before they domesticated plants. This is the exact opposite of the pattern of civilization in the Middle East. Nevertheless, people in the Sahara were already exhibiting all of the traits of sedentarism—living in one place year-round—long before they were growing regular crops.

*Sahara
Page 965*

CHANGING SPATIAL DISTRIBUTIONS.

After people were living in clusters of permanent settlements and producing more food than they needed for their own use, they had the opportunity to develop special skills. Some, for example, became metalworkers or potters, while others began to travel long distances trading the surplus goods from their own areas with those from other areas. These special skills permitted people to enjoy a better lifestyle, because people could exchange the product of their own labor for items that they could not manufacture. For example, although one might not be a good potter, one could still possess an excellent figurine by means of exchange.

Between 5,500 and 2,500 B.C.E., it began to rain more often in the Sahara. Its wide rivers teemed with fish, and trees covered its hillsides. People were now raising large herds of cattle, as well as millet, sorghum, and other crops. The people of the Sahara were quietly laying the foundation for the Egyptian culture of the Nile Valley.

*Sorghum
Page 1033*

The Nile River Valley only became widely habitable between 8,000 and 5,000 B.C.E. During this period, the rich soil from the Upper Nile was slowly deposited over the gravel and silt of the Lower Nile. By about 5,200 B.C.E., the people along the Nile River were finally cultivating regular crops. The seasonal floods of the Nile Valley continually brought more rich soil down from the north and provided a wonderful environment for agriculture. As the art of cultivating plants improved, people began to have continually greater surpluses of food available than ever before. Permanent settlements became larger and closer together than anywhere else in Africa. Eventually, all the different people from north to south along the Nile Valley became unified in the ancient civilization of Egypt.

NATURAL BARRIERS TO MOVEMENT. As early as 2,000 B.C.E., the people of the central Benue River valley in Nigeria were cultivating plants. Unfortunately, the deep equatorial rain forest of the Congo River Basin lay to the south, effectively blocking further movement in that direction. In time, however, the advent of the Iron Age and the technology of iron making would overcome that barrier and forever change their culture.

At Taruga in Nigeria, iron furnaces have been discovered that date from the eighth century B.C.E. Furnaces found to the north, at Termit in Niger, may date from as early as 1,300 B.C.E. In fact, this new technology seems to have emerged independently over a wide span of years and at far-flung sites across sub-Saharan Africa. It appears that iron had come into general use in the Nile Valley, Kush, and Axum by 500 B.C.E., and the fabrication of iron may have become a major handicraft industry in Meroë by 200 B.C.E. Archaeologists have also discovered that true steel was being produced in Tanzania in the middle of the first millennium B.C.E., and on the other side of the continent at Jenne-Jeno in Mali by 250 B.C.E. Africa was rapidly changing.

While iron making may have come to

the people of the central Benue River Valley much earlier than generally has been supposed, it traditionally has been accepted that it arrived there about two thousand years ago. With the appearance of iron tools and weapons, the Nok culture arose along the central Benue River. At long last, the great trees could be felled to clear the land for cultivation, timber could be used to shore the walls of an increasing number of mines, and wood could be burned to make charcoal with which to smelt an increasing quantity of iron ore. With iron implements, a small band of people could accomplish more work and feed more people than ever before. They also could defeat a larger army with stone or even bronze weapons. Once again, populations increased dramatically in number, and vast numbers of people began to seek new lands to call home. This time, they would make a new path: to the east through the forests and across the coastal plain to the Indian Ocean, and to the southeast across the Congo, Zambezi, and Limpopo Rivers to the Kei River in South Africa.

TRACING MIGRATION THROUGH LINGUISTICS. One of the ways that modern scientists have been able to approximate the beginning and the direction of this great migration of people has been through linguistics, the study of languages. Perhaps the leading expert on African languages is Joseph Greenberg of Stanford University. Greenberg was able to organize all of the languages of Africa into four families: Nilo-Saharan, Niger-Congo, Khoisan, and Afro-Asiatic. One of the eight branches of the Niger-Congo family is Benue-Niger, which includes Bantu.

The Bantu branch seems to have arisen no more than two thousand years ago in east central Nigeria, along the Benue and Niger Rivers. By comparing the similarities and differences among languages, lin-

RACES AND CULTURES IN ANCIENT EGYPT

Although much controversy exists over the racial makeup of ancient Egypt, the important fact is that ancient Egypt thrived because of its diversity. For thousands of years, black Africans from south of the Sahara commingled with the Afro-Asiatic people who lived along the Mediterranean Sea to the north. A similar process took place along the Nile Valley, as the people from the Upper Nile commingled with those living along the Lower Nile. This process was often fraught with conflict, however, which continued for many years.

The growth of Egyptian civilization was driven not only by Asian immigrants from the Near East, as had previously been supposed, but also by a much larger number of immigrants from the west and south-

west. As the climate of the Sahara became drier after 2500 B.C.E., the desert began to slowly reclaim its forests, grasslands, rivers, and lakes, and the people living there began to disperse to its periphery. Many of them moved to the north and west to form a vibrant Berber culture that learned to survive in the harsh dry climate, but most seem to have moved eastward to Egypt. It seems clear that ancient Egyptian culture was not solely a foreign invention imported from the Near East, but an African innovation built upon the experiences and efforts of people of many races and cultures. When the Greek historian Herodotus traveled through Egypt after 450 B.C.E., he saw clearly that Egypt's cultural roots lay in Africa.

guists have been able to trace which languages are related to Bantu. With this knowledge, they determined that the ancestors of the Bantu-speakers had begun to move eastward and southeastward through the equatorial rain forest as early as 3,000 B.C.E. To be sure, they asked other scientists for their help.

It seemed that another good clue would be to examine evidence of the types of plants and animals the Bantu-speakers had domesticated and taken with them on their journey across Africa. It is known that they grew plants that were suited to the warm and wet climate of West Africa—African yams, oil palm, kola nut, bananas, and taro—and that their most numerous domesticated animals were cattle. All their plants were successful as they moved deeper into the forest, but nearly all their cattle soon died because of the tsetse fly. As they pushed into the forests, they began to displace the Pygmies of the Congo rain forest. Without crops or domesticated animals and possessing only stone tools and weapons, the Pygmies were unable to compete with the Bantu speakers.

As the Bantu-speaking people continued southward, they encountered the Khoisan people. When they met Khoi herders, who had domesticated sheep centuries before, they often bypassed them in search of wetter climates suitable for their crops. It was only years later, after having increased dramatically in number, that they returned to overwhelm the areas they had earlier left behind. When they met the San hunter-gatherers, the results were very much the same as with the Pygmies. Without crops or iron implements, the San were defenseless against the Bantu-speakers. Only a small remnant of the San people now remains in the harsh Namib Desert.

The story was different as the Bantu-speakers entered the western Cape region of South Africa. They seemed to have ev-

San paintings Page 1038

ery advantage: They greatly outnumbered the indigenous Khoi herders, they had far better tools and weapons, and they possessed domesticated plants and animals, but they could not adapt to the Mediterranean climate of the western Cape. Their plants grew best with wet summers, and the rains only fell during the winter in the western Cape. The Bantu-speakers were stopped at the Kei River.

Those Bantu-speaking people who had journeyed east from the Benue and Niger Rivers experienced much the same success as those who had traveled to the south. Increasing in number, they came forth from the east edge of the forest some time after 1,000 B.C.E. Passing the great lakes and the Great Rift Valley, they continued east to settle in the wet forests, which were better suited to their crops. In time, they adopted sorghum and millet, which were better suited to the dry plains. Thereafter, they supplanted the remaining Khoi herders. By the end of the last century B.C.E., they had occupied most of East Africa south of Ethiopia.

COLONIALISM IN AFRICA. Although the colonial era spanned less than a century, it dramatically changed the spatial structure of the African countries. The modernizing influence of Europe disrupted traditional ways of production and traditional African ways of life. Most of Africa was marginalized from the global economy, and Africa struggles to achieve social, political, economic, cultural, and spatial development.

Hari P. Garbharran

FOR FURTHER STUDY

Aryeetey-Attoh, Samuel, ed. *The Geography of Sub-Saharan Africa.* Englewood Cliffs, N.J.: Prentice-Hall, 1997.

Beckwith, Carol, and Angela Fisher. "The Eloquent Surma of Ethiopia." *National Geographic* (February, 1991): 77-102.

Davidson, Basil. *Africa in History.* New York: Touchstone, 1991.

Grove, A. T. *The Changing Geography of Africa.* 2d ed. Oxford, England: Oxford University Press, 1993.

Murdock, G. P. *Africa: Its People and Their Culture History.* New York: McGraw Hill, 1959.

Reader, John. *Africa: A Biography of the Continent.* New York: Alfred A. Knopf, 1997.

POPULATION DISTRIBUTION

Map
Page 1035

One of earth's largest continents, Africa is the most sparsely populated of any except Australia. The common division between North Africa and sub-Saharan Africa reflects racial and cultural contrasts. Most North Africans have light skins and European physical characteristics, while most Africans south of the Sahara have dark skins and other features that set them apart from North Africans. North Africa has an almost uniformly Islamic culture, and Islam also dominates the countries that border the Sahara. Farther south, the influence of Islam fades rapidly. In the past, traditional ethnic religions associated with only one ethnic group dominated Africa south of the Sahara. Africa is mainly populated by native Africans, interspersed with Asian and European populations that are minorities in most areas they inhabit.

Although precise data are not available, it is estimated that Africa's population in 1900 was between 115 million and 155 million. Around that time, the population declined in the continent, especially in equatorial Africa. Population growth resumed around the 1930's through a combination of factors, including changes in colonial policy and the diffusion of medical and health programs. Growth rates increased to between 2 and 3 percent by midcentury. Some countries experienced higher growth rates: Kenya's growth rate was as high as 4 percent until the late 1980's, at which time it began to decrease.

Pesticide
spraying
Page 1036

MODERN DISTRIBUTION OF PEOPLE. Many modern scholars identify the countries of North Africa—Egypt, Libya, Tunisia, Algeria, Morocco, and Western Sahara—with the Arabic-speaking nations of the Middle East. In 1999 North Africa was dominated by an Arab-Islamic culture, and its population totaled 141 million. The population of sub-Saharan Africa was approximately 630 million, which can be further subdivided as follows: Western Africa, 223 million, Eastern Africa, 264 million, Middle Africa, 94 million, and Southern Africa, 49 million.

The percentage of natural increase for the world's population in 1996 was 1.5 percent. The Population Reference Bureau in Washington, D.C., published statistics in 1996 listing the twenty-nine countries worldwide with the highest rates of natural increase (3 percent and above). Twenty-one of these countries were in Africa: There was a 3.7 percent increase in Libya; 3.6 percent in Togo and Comoros; 3.5 percent in Côte d'Ivoire; 3.4 percent in Niger; 3.3 percent in Uganda; 3.2 percent in Congo-Kinshasa, Madagascar, Somalia, and Swaziland; 3.1 percent in Nigeria, Ethiopia, Mali, Benin, and Liberia; and 3 percent in Tanzania, Sudan, Ghana, Malawi, Zambia, and Burundi. Not a single African nation was among the countries with the lowest rates of natural increase, less than 0.1 percent.

DIFFUSION OF POPULATION. The populations of countries in North Africa differ greatly. For example, Western Sahara has a population of 0.2 million, Libya 5 million, Tunisia 9.5 million, Morocco 28.2 million, Algeria 30.8 million, and Egypt 67 million. Most of these countries are sprawling nations, but much of the region is engulfed by the Sahara desert.

Additionally, the Atlas Mountains of Morocco, Algeria, and Tunisia are located in northwestern Africa, between the Mediterranean Sea and the Sahara Desert. In this harsh setting, people generally gravitate toward coastal locations along the Mediterranean Sea or the Atlantic Ocean, or settle along rivers. Except in Egypt, more than 90 percent of the populations of North African countries live within two hundred miles of the Mediterranean Sea or the Atlantic Ocean.

The ancient land of Egypt, situated at Africa's northeastern corner between the Mediterranean and Red Seas, is almost totally dependent on a single river. The Greek historian and geographer Herodotus aptly referred to Egypt as "an acquired country—the gift of the Nile." The Nile River has defined a meandering greenbelt for thousands of miles across the desert and provides a home for approximately 95 percent of Egypt's people, who live within twelve miles of its banks.

Population densities, generally, are low in sub-Saharan Africa. Less densely populated areas are scattered irregularly throughout the desert and semidesert areas of sub-Saharan Africa and across the grassy and forested areas of tropical bush that encompass most of Africa.

Most of the region's people live in a small number of densely populated areas that together cover only a small part of the region's total area. The most densely pop-

Late nineteenth century Arab market at Tébessa, an inland Algerian town. (Arkent Archive)

ulated areas generally are along the coast and in the highlands. These include five core areas south of the Sahara: the coastal belt along the Gulf of Guinea, stretching from southern Nigeria westward to southern Ghana; the savanna grasslands in northern Nigeria; the highland regions surrounding Lake Victoria in Rwanda, Burundi, Tanzania, Kenya, and Uganda; the highlands of Ethiopia; and the eastern coast and parts of the high veld of South Africa.

FERTILITY RATES. Total fertility rate (TFR) refers to the average number of children women have during their childbearing years, which typically are defined as ages fifteen to forty-nine. Fertility is generally high throughout tropical Africa, with many countries recording TFRs between six and eight. However, national statistics obscure some remarkable variations within countries, where in some areas TFRs are between two and five.

Zanzibar
Page 1168

Research has revealed a belt of low rates from southwestern Sudan, through the Central African Republic, and into Congo-Kinshasa. Low-fertility areas also include parts of Cameroon and Gabon, isolated locations in the savanna zone of West Africa, parts of Namibia and Botswana inhabited by San peoples, parts of the East African coast, parts of Ethiopia inhabited by nomadic pastoralists, and the Lake Victoria area. Research shows that in each of these cases there is a close relationship between a low TFR and a particular ethnic group.

Mombasa
Page 1165

Four reasons were noted for relative low rates of fertility in these areas: cultural variations in the length of time a baby is breast-fed; impact of diseases such as gonorrhea and syphilis; poor nutrition; and cultural aspects related to marriage. Among African women, the age at first marriage is consistently in the mid-teens, but exceptions to the rule clearly cause reduced fertility. For example, among the

Rendille of northern Kenya, cultural practices result in one-third of the women not marrying until their mid-thirties. Among nomadic pastoralists, spousal separation for long periods of time may reduce fertility.

URBAN AND RURAL COMPARISONS. The urban landscapes of Africa south of the Sahara reflect the political, economic, and cultural changes that have affected the region. Towns have become increasingly important as people migrate to them in search of higher wages, improved health and educational facilities, and safer, better formal and informal job opportunities. Urban areas are growing rapidly and adding extensive tracts of new housing, shantytowns, and industrial and commercial landscapes related to urban functions.

The oldest urban landscapes are found in East and West Africa and are less common from Congo-Kinshasa southward. In East Africa, the old Arab-Swahili ports extend from the Red Sea to Mozambique, including Zanzibar, Mombasa, and Malindi, and are characterized by stone buildings reflecting the pre-European era. Addis Ababa in Ethiopia, Kampala in Uganda, and Kumasi in Ghana are some of the cities that have pre-European buildings, including places of worship and palaces. In West Africa, old urban centers include the trading centers of Kano in Nigeria and Timbuktu in Mali, at the southern end of trade routes across the Sahara. They are still dominated by craft workshops.

European settlement and colonization brought new types of urban centers into Africa. Many were ports to link the new colony to the home country. In the interior, major inland towns developed and were linked to the coast by railroad. Brazzaville, the capital of the Republic of the Congo, and Kinshasa, the capital of the Democratic Republic of the Congo, provide a contrast on opposite banks of the Congo River, reflecting their different French and Belgian colonial heritages.

Other new towns developed as mining settlements, such as Enugu in Nigeria and Johannesburg in South Africa. In the southern region of the Congo-Kinshasa and northern Zambia, a series of towns developed around the copper mines. Nairobi in Kenya started as a center where railroad workshops were established along the route from the port of Mombasa to Lake Victoria.

RURAL COMMUNITIES. Most African people live in rural areas. Rural landscapes include cultivated plots, areas where little natural vegetation has been disturbed, mining areas, and human settlements in villages and small towns. In individual countries of sub-Saharan Africa,

the estimated percentage of the population living in rural areas ranges from approximately 65 percent to a high of 95 percent in Rwanda and Burundi. Other predominantly rural populations are found in Ethiopia (86 percent), Uganda and Burkina Faso (85 percent), Nigeria and Lesotho (84 percent), and Niger (83 percent).

Villages and small towns are a growing feature in rural areas of Africa. Most people live in villages, although dispersed homes on individual farms are prevalent in some areas. The typical rural home is a small hut made of sticks and mud, with a thatched roof, no electricity or plumbing, and a dirt floor. Recent trends have seen small homes built of concrete blocks and roofed with corrugated iron. Some villages have evolved into small service cen-

The construction of a railway linking Uganda to the coast around the turn of the twentieth century spurred the development of what became Kenya, whose capital city, Nairobi, arose as a railway stop about midway along the new line. (Arkent Archive)

Tanzanian thatched-roof house, made of sticks and mud. (R. Kent Rasmussen)

ters with shops and market stalls, where food and consumer goods are sold. The governments of Tanzania and Zimbabwe have policies to develop small rural towns as service centers to ease population pressure on the largest cities.

ECONOMICS AND POPULATION DISTRIBUTION PATTERNS. Sub-Saharan Africa has the highest fertility and mortality rates in the world, as well as the highest proportion of young dependents. However, there is both considerable subregional variation in these trends and a gradual decline in these trends. Although rapidly growing populations are evident in the region, about 47 percent of the forty-eight sub-Saharan countries have populations under five million and 73 percent have populations under ten million. Only seven countries have populations of twenty-five million; listed in descending order of population, they

are Nigeria, Ethiopia, Zaire, South Africa, Tanzania, Kenya, and Sudan.

These population figures are estimates or indirect measures of actual, observable data sets. Sub-Saharan Africa has had several population enumeration and survey problems, especially before 1974. Additionally, some countries had not conducted comprehensive surveys during the last two decades of the twentieth century.

The spatial distributions of population in sub-Saharan Africa coincide with a number of environmental factors—soil, topography, vegetation, and climate; developmental issues—agricultural development, levels of urbanization, and degree of industrialization; and sociopolitical characteristics, such as ethnic disputes, oppressive regimes, and resettlement schemes. The West African coastal strip, for example, is dominated by most of the region's economic, urban, and political centers. Other economic centers—such as the diamond and gold mining centers of South Africa's Witwatersrand region, the Copperbelt of Congo-Kinshasa and Zambia, and the tourist centers of the Lake Victoria borderlands—attract large population clusters.

DUAL ECONOMIES. Similar to other developing nations, African countries typically have dual economies. Economic activities ranging from mineral extraction, production of tropical crops, or energy development are focused on primate cities of each country. These economic activities and the primate cities, except for those in Southern Africa, are externally oriented. The national economies of African countries are under-industrialized and overly dependent on the export of a few primary products, particularly minerals and cash crops. Africa's place in the commercial world is mainly that of a producer of foods and raw materials for sale to the outside world. Economic benefits from these activities and cities only marginally impact the majority of African populations.

Most Africans are engaged in agriculture, the other segment of the African economy. Agricultural workers range from nomadic herdsmen, to subsistence-level sedentary cultivators who produce crops primarily for their own use, to farmers producing commercial crops such as coffee, cacao, cotton, peanuts, and oil palm for export. Subsistence agriculture is the main occupation in nearly all countries. Generally, African farmers south of the Sahara operate on a subsistence basis and have little cash income. Women do a large share of the farm work and produce 80 to 90 percent of Africa's food, in addition to doing household chores and bearing children.

Almost all African countries are heavily in debt to foreign lenders. During the postcolonial era (especially during the late 1970's), many billions of dollars in outside grants and loans have failed to eliminate poverty in the region. At the end of the twentieth century, many African governments were in debt to international lenders such as the International Monetary Fund, the World Bank, and private banks. Many countries have had difficulty in meeting just the interest payments on these debts. Additionally, the amount of economic and humanitarian assistance to the region has slowed considerably since the end of the Cold War.

REFUGEE MOVEMENTS. Refugee movements that involve people forced to migrate, usually for political reasons, have become a growing problem in Africa. Of the approximately fifteen million refugees across the globe in the late 1990's, about seven million (47 percent) were in Africa. In Central Africa, for example, the last half of the twentieth century witnessed a series of brutal conflicts that resulted in mass movement of refugees. Push and pull factors, such as the war in Rwanda-Burundi and peaceful episodes in Tanzania and Congo-Kinshasa, have resulted in migration.

Continuing refugee problems are experienced in the Horn of Africa, comprising Ethiopia, Djibouti, and Somalia. The Horn, along with neighboring Sudan, is a land of refugees. The refugee crisis in this region has resulted from a combination of human and physical geographic factors. War broke out between Somalia and Ethiopia in 1977-1978 when the region was plagued with drought. Local political conflicts were further complicated by subsequent U.S. and Soviet involvement.

FUTURE PROJECTIONS. Sub-Saharan Africa's population doubled in just twenty-five years to 630 million. It is projected to double again in the first third of the twenty-first century, even after accounting

Zimbabwe farmers Page 1034

Horn of Africa Page 1161

for declining birth rates and rising deaths from AIDS. For more than two decades, annual population growth rates between 2.6 and 3 percent have outpaced economic gains and food production increases. As a result, people in sub-Saharan Africa were, on average, 22 percent poorer in the late 1990's than they were in 1975. Just to meet the region's basic food needs in the year 2050, agricultural production would have to increase fivefold. If current trends continue, it is projected that by 2025, six out of ten Africans will lack basic services such as potable water and food.

Sub-Saharan countries have begun to change their previous lukewarm attitude toward family planning. This change has resulted partly from the three World Population Conferences held in Bucharest (1974), Mexico (1984), and Cairo, Egypt (1994). The Bucharest conference laid the foundation of the World Population Plan of Action, a framework that provides guidance and serves as the standard reference on population issues.

At the Third African Population Conference at Dakar, Senegal (1992), African leaders addressed most of the issues covered in the plan of action and pledged to improve the quality of lives of Africans. One goal was to reduce the regional natural growth rate from 3 percent to 2.5 percent by the year 2000, and to 2 percent by the year 2010. Declining fertility rates are already seen in Zimbabwe, Botswana, and Kenya.

Hari P. Garbharran

FOR FURTHER STUDY

Caputo, Robert. "Tragedy Stalks the Horn of Africa." *National Geographic* (August, 1993): 88-122.

Grove, A. T. *The Changing Geography of Africa.* 2d ed. Oxford, England: Oxford University Press, 1993.

James, Valentine Udoh. *Africa's Ecology: Sustaining the Biological and Environmental Diversity of a Continent.* Jefferson, N.C.: McFarland, 1993.

Millennium Supplement. "Population." *National Geographic* (October, 1998): 2-75.

Murdock, G. P. *Africa: Its People and Their Culture History.* New York: McGraw Hill, 1959.

Ramsay, Jeffress, ed. *Africa.* 8th ed. New York: McGraw Hill, 1999.

Reader, John. *Africa: A Biography of the Continent.* New York: Alfred A. Knopf, 1997.

Salter, C., J. Hobbs, J. Wheeler, and J. Kostbade. *Essentials of World Regional Geography.* 3d ed. Orlando, Fla.: Saunders College, 2000.

CULTURE REGIONS

The African continent has remarkable cultural diversity, with many ethnic, language, and religious differences. Africa exceeds all other continents in the number of distinct peoples and cultures, a major reason for the numerous ethnic conflicts and repeated political unrest. With only about one-seventh the area of the inhabited world and a population constituting less than one-tenth of all humankind, Africa contains one-third of the world's languages. More than fifteen hundred distinct languages are spoken in Africa, and forty of them have one million or more speakers. The varieties of indigenous religions are even more numerous. Before the arrival and subsequent domination of Christianity and Islam, each traditional society had developed its own system of faith and ritual intimately related to its distinctive culture.

Dividing this complex cultural mosaic into fifty-two different states (forty-six south of the Sahara) made it inevitable that some culture groups would be divided by political boundaries. Nation-states—states with only one culture group—are rare in Africa. Multination states—states with multiple culture groups—and multistate nations—culture groups split by political boundaries—are the norm. Thus, identifying culture regions in Africa, broad areas with similar culture characteristics, is no easy task. Nevertheless, eight major cultural regions can be identified in the continent. Below, a brief general description of each region is presented, followed by a spotlight on one or two cultures that characterize the region. The goal is to identify the similarities and differences be-

Nigerian bronze. Southern Nigeria is noted for its traditional of bronze sculpture, which goes back at least seven centuries. (Leo Frobenius, *The Voice of Africa*, 1913)

Wherever water is scarce in North Africa, camels are valued as carriers. (PhotoDisc)

tween culture regions and facilitate comparison.

NORTH AFRICA (MAGHREB). Extending from the North African coast to the upper reaches of the Niger River, North Africa has strong cultural and ethnic ties with the Arabic Middle East and in many ways is more a part of that world than of Africa south of the Sahara. North Africa demonstrates the strong relationship between environment and culture. Life in the desert breeds a nomadic existence: grasslands, water scarcities, and sparse populations encourage continuous movement. This affects social organization, such as inheritance laws, and economic and political organization. Perhaps due to the difficult environment, crop production is not as popular as raising animals.

North Africa is the home of the camel, an animal valued for its ability to go long periods without water and to subsist on sparse vegetation, a major asset for trans-

port and swift communication. Other animals are kept in the larger oases or on the fringe of the Nile. Islam is the dominant religion, but indigenous religions persist.

The veil is a common article of clothing for men. Wrapped around the face and head leaving only slits for the eyes, it not only protects the nose and mouth against the wind and sand of the desert, but also indicates the status and propriety of the wearer. Traveling in caravans for trade across the desert and encountering the dangers inherent therein make skill in warfare, physical prowess, and valor highly coveted values.

The people of North Africa are a mixture of Arab stock, including the Tuaregs and Berbers. The Tuaregs are predominantly Sunni Muslims, monogamous, and a matriarchal society with a strong hierarchy of various classes: nobility, vassals, freed slaves, and slaves. Social status is determined through matrilineal descent,

Caravan
Page 1038

Tuaregs
Page 1033

and matrilineal inheritance is the norm. While women retain title to their property after marriage, their husbands must make extensive gifts to their wives' families and assume the costs of the wedding ceremony. The initial residence of the family after marriage is matrilocal—close to the wife's kin. Men begin wearing the veil, which is never removed even in front of family members, at the age of twenty-five. Most people are Muslim, but believe in the continuous presence of various spirits, and divination using the Koran is common. Tuaregs are a multistate nation scattered over Algeria, Libya, Mali, Niger, and Burkina Fasso. The bulk of the population lives in Niger and Mali.

Similarly, Berbers are a multistate nation spread across Morocco (more than 10 million), Algeria (more than 5 million), Mauritania (about 400,000), Tunisia (250,000), and Libya (about 200,000). Although predominantly Muslim, Berbers are less orthodox and include many elements of pre-Islamic and traditional religious rituals. Traditional Berber occupations are raising sheep and cattle, but increasing numbers raise crops. Other economic activities include flour-milling, wood-carving, quarrying of millstones, and production of domestic utensils, agricultural implements, pottery, jewelry, and leather goods. Much Berber art is in the form of jewelry, leather, and finely woven carpets.

THE NORTHEASTERN HORN. Comprising Ethiopia, Somalia, Djibouti, Eritrea, and Eastern Kenya, the northeastern Horn of Africa is occupied by three

*Berbers
Page 1096*

*Horn of
Africa
Page 1161*

Moroccan horsemen who escorted trans-Saharan caravans in the 1890's. (Arkent Archive)

groups of people—the Galla of south-western Somalia and eastern Kenya, the Somali, and the Afar who live along the southern slopes of the Red Sea. Cereal agriculture and animal rearing—sheep, horses, and donkeys—predominate, but hunting plays an important subsidiary role. Inheritance of property is patrilineal; marriage is usually monogamous and may be effected by the mock or actual capture of a bride after which a bride price (gift of cattle) is paid to the wife's family.

Unique to this area are age-grade organizations for men that govern the performance of particular social functions and patterns of behavior. Men of approximately the same age constitute an age grade, and each of the five grades—Dabelle, Folle, Qondala, Luba, and Yuba—require eight years to advance. Thus, a son enters each grade exactly forty years after his father did. As members of each grade grow into the next age grade, the functions of the group change and its members acquire more power and responsibility in their communities. Common membership of age grades helps to reduce the friction between communities and unites them to defend against external threats. Islam is a major unifying factor in this region.

THE UPPER NILE. This culture region extends from the upper reaches of the Nile River westward to Lake Chad and covers modern Sudan. Primarily pastoral in economy, most people survive on a diet of milk, butter, and fresh blood drawn from cattle (especially the Maasai), supplemented with millet and maize grown for subsistence. While polygamy is permitted it is rare, because no man can take a second wife until other men his age have been married. Inheritance is patrilineal

Maasai cattle herder. (Corbis)

*Maasai
Pages 975,
1037*

and domestic residence, patrilocal. Marriage entails the payment of a substantial bride price (forty head of cattle), which can sometimes be reduced by bridal services—labors for the wife's parents or an appropriate relative.

The Maasai are the southernmost Nilotic speakers and are linguistically most directly related to the Turkana and Kalenjin, who live near Lake Turkana in west central Kenya. Maasai are pastoralist and have resisted the urging of the Tanzanian and Kenyan governments to adopt a more sedentary lifestyle. Demanding grazing rights to many of the national parks in both countries, they routinely ignore international boundaries while moving their great cattle herds across the open savanna with the changing of the seasons.

Continued on page 1041

Algerian oil drilling operation in the Sahara. Egypt. Morocco, Tunisia, Algeria, and Libya have great natural wealth in the form of oil and natural gas. (American Stock Photography)

Abandoned truck in Tanzania. Although iron is always needed, few African countries can generate enough commercial demand to make recycling of scrap iron an economic undertaking. (R. Kent Rasmussen)

The flat-topped acacia is perhaps the most characteristic tree of the African savanna regions. (Digital Stock)

Giraffes foraging in typical African savanna land. (PhotoDisc)

Renowned for its large size and odd, almost upside-down, appearance, the baobab tree grows in many of Africa's savanna regions. It has an exceptionally thick trunk with smooth, gray bark and can live as long as 2,000 years. (Corbis)

HABITATS AND SELECTED VERTEBRATES OF AFRICA

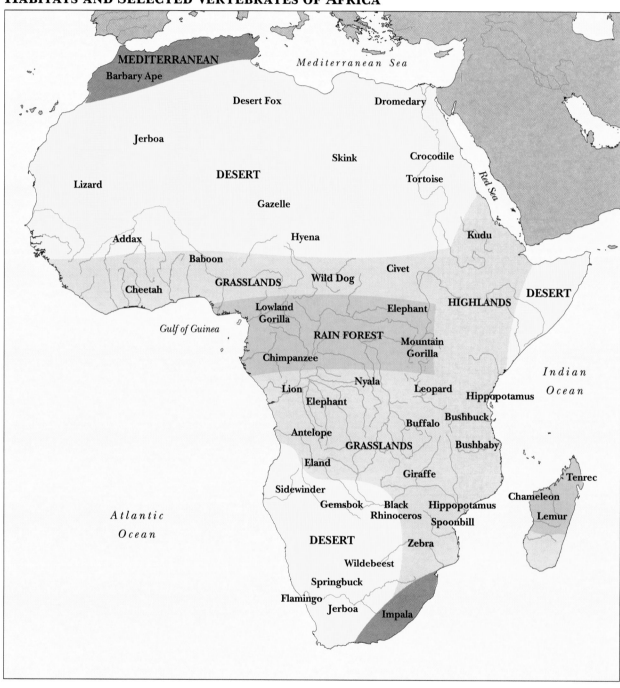

Africa's elephants have not fared well in their competition with humans for space. Expanding human settlements have reduced the amount of land on which elephants can forage for food, and poachers—who hunt elephants for the ivory in their tusks—have intensified the pressure. Between the early 1970's and 1990 alone, the population of African elephants is estimated to have declined from two million to 600,000. (PhotoDisc)

Rhinoceroses in South Africa's Kruger National Park. Hunted to near-extinction for the supposed aphrodisiatic powers of their horns, African rhinos appeared to be making a comeback at the beginning of the twenty-first century. (Corbis)

Ostriches are found throughout Africa's savanna regions. They are the largest living variety of bird; some stand as tall as ten feet (three meters) and weigh more 300 pounds (135 kilograms). They are flightless but can run at speeds greater than thirty miles (50 km.) per hour. (PhotoDisc)

Second only to the elephant in size, the hippopotamus is a largely aquatic mammal that ranges throughout Africa, from the Upper Nile to South Africa. It takes its name from the Greek word for "river horse." (PhotoDisc)

Water buffalo in Botswana. The water buffalo is one of the most widespread and dangerous animals in Africa. (Corbis)

Africa's most famous large predators, lions, are found throughout the continent, particularly in savanna regions. (PhotoDisc)

Classified as monkeys, baboons are one of the most widespread large animals in Africa. Their speed, intelligence, and strength permit them to survive easily near human communities. (PhotoDisc)

Tourism plays a major role in the economies of many African nations, particularly in eastern and southern Africa, where tourists are drawn by large game preserves and comparatively mild weather. (Corbis)

A drought-resistant crop that has a short-growing season, sorghum is an ideal grain crop in Africa's many semiarid regions. Archaeological evidence shows that West Africans were experimenting with sorghum cultivation more than six thousand years ago. (PhotoDisc)

Tuareg cattle herders in northern Mali carry on an African tradition that goes back thousands of years. Much of the early history of Africa was driven by quests for grazing land for cattle and other animals. (AP/Wide World Photos)

In 2000, twenty years after Zimbabwe became independent under majority rule, the inequitable distribution of land that was a heritage of colonial rule, remained a major issue. Many Africans simply moved onto white-owned farms and sowed their own crops. (AP/Wide World Photos)

During a mid-2000 trip, U.S. president Bill Clinton meets school children in a village of Nigeria, which is home to one of every five people in Africa. Nigeria's size and comparative wealth make it a focus of U.S. foreign policy in Africa. (AP/Wide World Photos)

POPULATION DENSITIES OF AFRICAN COUNTRIES
(BASED ON MID-1999 ESTIMATES)

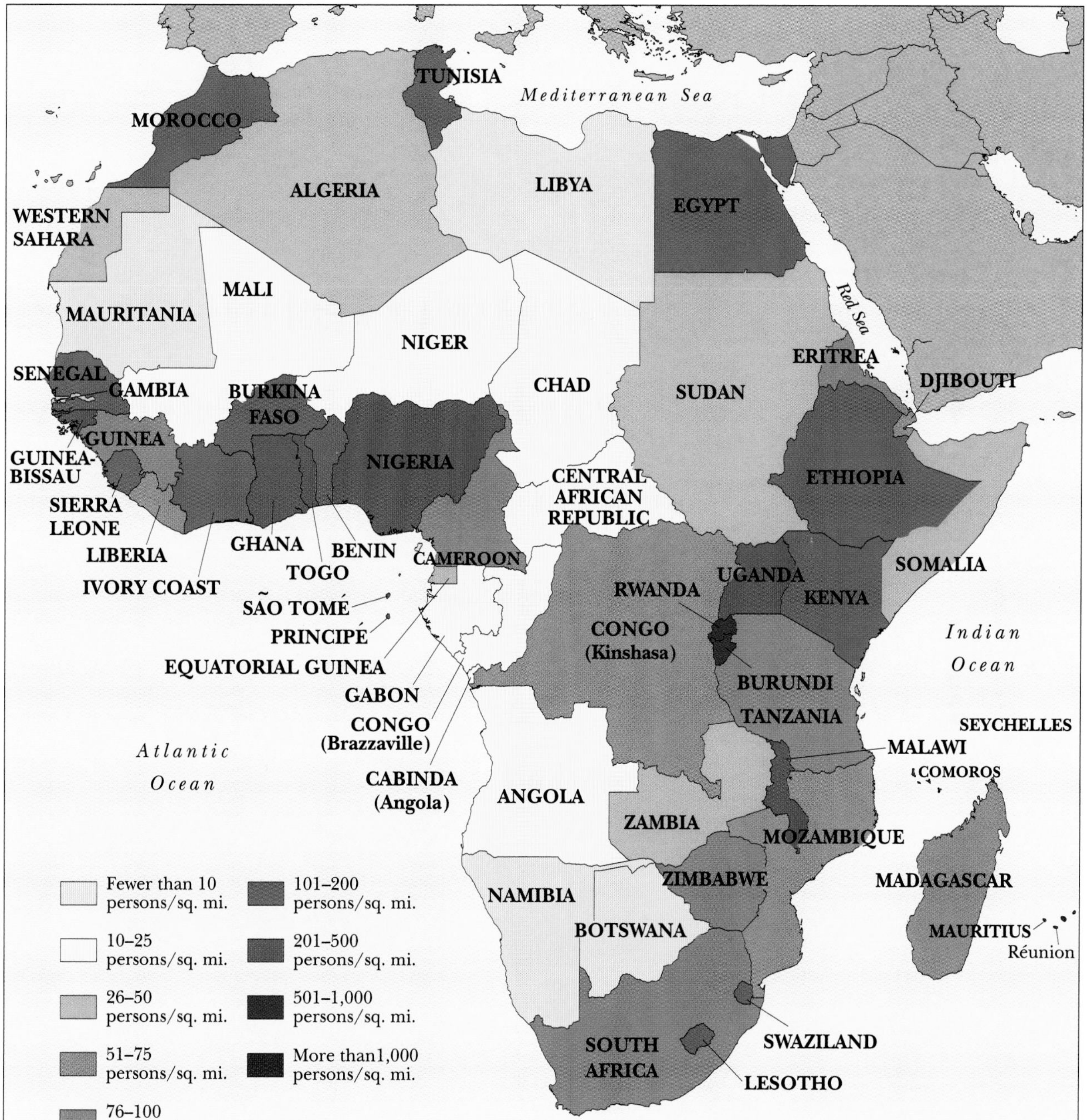

TUNISIA

MOROCCO

Mediterranean Sea

ALGERIA

LIBYA

EGYPT

WESTERN
SAHARA

MALI

Red Sea

MAURITANIA

NIGER

ERITREA

DJIBOUTI

SENEGAL

GAMBIA

BURKINA
FASO

CHAD

SUDAN

GUINEA

NIGERIA

ETHIOPIA

GUINEA-
BISSAU

CENTRAL
AFRICAN
REPUBLIC

SIERRA
LEONE

GHANA

BENIN

CAMEROON

SOMALIA

LIBERIA

TOGO

RWANDA

UGANDA

KENYA

IVORY COAST

SÃO TOMÉ

CONGO
(Kinshasa)

*Indian
Ocean*

PRINCIPÉ

BURUNDI

EQUATORIAL GUINEA

TANZANIA

GABON

SEYCHELLES

CONGO
(Brazzaville)

MALAWI

COMOROS

*Atlantic
Ocean*

CABINDA
(Angola)

ANGOLA

ZAMBIA

MOZAMBIQUE

MADAGASCAR

ZIMBABWE

NAMIBIA

BOTSWANA

MAURITIUS

Réunion

SOUTH
AFRICA

SWAZILAND

LESOTHO

Fewer than 10
persons/sq. mi.

101–200
persons/sq. mi.

10–25
persons/sq. mi.

201–500
persons/sq. mi.

26–50
persons/sq. mi.

501–1,000
persons/sq. mi.

51–75
persons/sq. mi.

More than 1,000
persons/sq. mi.

76–100
persons/sq. mi.

1035

A helicopter sprays poison into a Côte d'Ivoire River to kill the larvae of a type of fly that transmits the worm causing river blindness—a disease that once afflicted many millions of West Africans. The hot, humid countries of West Africa have some of the worst health problems on the continent. (AP/Wide World Photos)

The Ndebele people of central South Africa (no relation to the Ndebele of Zimbabwe) are famous for their colorful houses and dress. (American Stock Photography)

Maasai dancers in Tanzania. Throughout Africa, dance is one of the most important forms of artistic expression. (Corbis)

Rock paintings in Zimbabwe. Valuable visual evidence of Africa's deeper past can be found in the rock paintings scattered throughout Southern Africa. The San (Bushman) people were still painting as late as the nineteenth century.
(Corbis)

Modern Tuaregs from Mali carry on the ancient tradition of trans-Saharan salt caravans on camelback.
(AP/Wide World Photos)

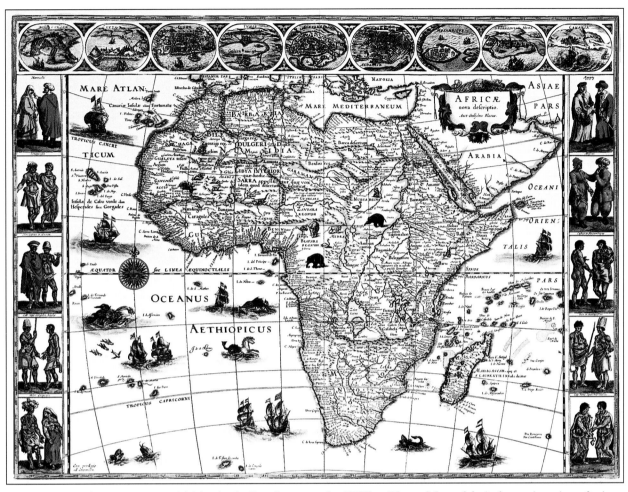

Mid-seventeenth century map of Africa by the Dutch geographer Willem Blaeu. Most of the information given for interior regions was completely fanciful. (Corbis)

This amphitheater in Alexandria, Egypt, is one of many tangible reminders of early Roman rule in North Africa. (Corbis)

Kuruman, the South African mission station of Robert Moffat, the father-in-law of famed missionary/explorer David Livingstone, and a significant explorer in his own right. (Robert Moffat, *Missionary Labours and Scenes in Southern Africa,* 1842.)

A cannon points out from a parapet in a fort built by Europeans to hold slaves on the coast of Ghana in the sixteenth century. European slave traders rarely penetrated West Africa's coastlines, where they conducted most of their business with African middlemen. (AP/Wide World Photos)

Cattle are central to Maasai life, providing their food (milk, blood, and meat), their materials (skin for clothes and dung to seal their houses), and their only recognized form of wealth. Rarely killed, cattle are accumulated as a sign of wealth and traded or sold to settle debts. Young men tend the herds and often live in small camps, moving frequently in the constant search for water and good grazing lands. They live in small clusters of huts (kraals or bomas) made of sticks sealed together with cow dung. Kraals also provide enclosures for the cattle. Maasai also sell their beadwork to the tourists with whom they share their grazing land.

Maasai community politics are embedded in age-grade systems that separate young men and prepubescent girls from the elder men and their wives and children. Marriages are often arranged, and polygamy is practiced. All children, whether legitimate are not, are recognized as the property of the woman's husband and his family.

Maasai diviners (*laibon*) are consulted whenever misfortune arises. They also serve as healers, dispensing their herbal remedies to treat physical ailments and ritual treatments to absolve social and moral transgressions. Respected as the best healers in Tanzania, Maasai *laibon* peddle their knowledge and herbs in the urban centers of Tanzania and Kenya. Maasai are best known for their beautiful beadwork, used primarily for ornamentation of the body. Beading patterns are determined by each age-set and identify social grades.

THE SUDAN. Between the tropical forests of West Africa, the Nile Valley, and the Sahara Desert lies the Sudan culture region. Cereal agriculture, sorghum and millet, some hunting, and raising animals—donkeys, sheep, pigs, chickens, guinea fowl, and cattle (the most prestigious)—are the mainstays of the economy.

Frequently, cattle are kept mainly as prestige and a form of invested capital, and are slaughtered for food only on rare occasions.

The division of labor follows sex and age structure. Those who are too old to work guard the home and take care of younger children. Men clear and prepare the fields for planting; women cultivate the fields, perform all household chores, and also market the surplus from their farms; children gather firewood and assist parents with chores. Marriage is polygamous and patrilocal, and inheritance is patrilineal. Land is owned by the lineage (family land), belongs to the living, the dead, and the yet unborn, and rights of cultivation are determined by patrilineage. The extended family emphasizes community and mutual support of family members. Islam is the dominant religion—about 93 percent of Senegal's population is Muslim.

The Hausa, numbering about 15 million people, characterize this culture region. The Hausa language, which belongs to the Chad branch of the Afro-Asiatic language family, is an important lingua franca in West Africa. Hausa culture manifests more specialization and diversification than most of the surrounding peoples.

Subsistence agriculture is the predominant occupation, but tanning, weaving, dyeing, and metalworking are also widespread. Hausas are famous as long-distance itinerant traders and wealthy merchants. Agriculture, scheduled around the May-to-October rainy season, focuses on millet, maize, Guinea corn, and rice to supply the bulk of the diet. Peanuts, cowpeas, sweet potatoes, cotton, sugarcane, bamboo, tobacco, cassava, and other root crops are grown both for household consumption and as cash crops. Livestock raising (mainly horses, donkeys, goats, sheep, and poultry) is an important economic activity.

Social organization is stratified, based on occupation, wealth, birth, and patron-client ties. Occupational specialties are ranked but tend to be hereditary, and the first son is expected to follow his father's occupation. Patrilineal inheritance and patrilocality is the norm. Polygamy is common, especially among Muslims. In the household division of labor, men are responsible for agriculture, collecting activities, marketing, sewing, laundry, building repairs, and transport. Women cook, clean house, take care of children, pursue their craft specialties, and sometimes engage in trade. Traditional Hausa religion centers on a variety of spirits, both good and bad, and rituals include sacrifices to the spirits and spirit possession.

WEST AFRICA'S GUINEA COAST. This culture region extends along the Guinea Coast from Liberia to Southern Nigeria. It supports the cultivation of yams, cassava, plantain, bananas, oil palm, and cocoa, the latter two mainly for export. Pigs and chickens are the principal domestic animals; some sheep and donkeys are found in the northern margins. Fishing occurs in the rivers and lakes and along the coastal regions. Periodic (usually weekly) markets provide for the exchange of livestock and cotton products from the north for fish and kola nuts.

Matrilineal inheritance is the norm, which makes the mother's brother, rather than the father, more influential. All members of the matrilineage share responsibility for the debts and legal offenses of its individual members and assume collective responsibility for funeral expenses. Reverence for the dead is very important and is demonstrated by periodic sacrifices offered at various shrines to invoke the blessings of the ancestors.

The Asante (also known as Ashanti) combine ancestor worship with the worship of Onyame, the supreme being, and

several lesser deities, including the spirits of trees, plants, and animals. Libations of palm wine, liquor, and the blood of sacrificial animals are regular tenets of ancestor veneration and worship.

The Yoruba people of southwestern Nigeria are primarily farmers, growing cocoa and yams as cash crops. Other crops included in their three-year rotational system include cassava, maize, peanuts, cotton, and beans. Their homeland, known as Yorubaland, is characterized by numerous densely populated urban centers with surrounding fields for farming. The Yoruba claim 401 deities known as orisha, and the high god is Olorun. No organized priesthoods or shrines exist in honor of Olorun, but his spirit is invoked to ask for blessings and to confer thanks.

The Yoruba believe that dead ancestors still have influence on the earth, and lineage heads honor all deceased members

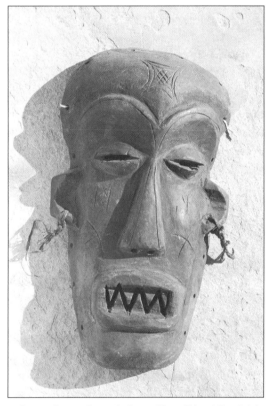

Carved wood mask from Namibia. (Corbis)

of the lineage through a yearly sacrifice. Maskers (*egungun*) appear at funerals and are believed to embody the spirit of the deceased person. The arts of the Yoruba are as numerous as their deities, and many objects are placed on shrines to honor the gods and the ancestors. Beautiful sculpture abounds in wood, brass, and the occasional terra cotta. Varied masking traditions have produced a great diversity of mask forms. Other important arts are pottery, weaving, beadwork, and metalsmithing.

THE CONGO BASIN. This culture region comprises the tropical rain forest area from the Atlantic Ocean to Lake Tanganyika south of the Sudan, spanning the area drained by the Congo River and its tributaries. Economic activity ranges from hunting and fishing among the Pygmies to cultivation of manioc, bananas, maize, yams, taro, and sweet potatoes. Principal domestic animals include goats, chickens, and dogs. While men tend livestock and clear the fields for planting, women do all agricultural work.

Metalworking is important here; prominent objects include arrowheads, spear and axe blades, copper rings, bracelets, and bells. Patrilineal inheritance is the norm for inheritance and succession, but because the bride price received by her kinsmen is usually used to obtain a bride for her brother, the sister acquires certain rights over her brother's wife and her children. These rights may include the sister's children claiming the property of her brother, a claim that supersedes the rights of his own children. Religion is based on a supernatural Supreme Being, and music and dance are major channels of expression.

The Bamileke represent this region quite well. The Bamileke are part of a larger cultural area known collectively as the Cameroon Grasslands. Within the Bamileke complex there are numerous smaller groups who are loosely affiliated and share many similarities while retaining separate identities. Primarily farmers, growing maize, yams, and peanuts as staple crops, they also raise some livestock, including chickens and goats, which play an important role in daily sustenance. Women, who are believed to make the soil more fruitful, are responsible for planting and harvesting the crops. Men usually help with the clearing of the land and practice some hunting.

Authority among the Bamileke, as is the case in most of the western grasslands, is invested in an elected village chief, the Fon, who is supported by a council of elders. Beside his role as dispenser of supreme justice, the Fon is also the de facto owner of all the land that belongs to a given village. He holds it in trust on behalf of the people.

While recognizing a supreme god, the Bamileke pay homage to ancestral spirits embodied in the skulls of deceased ancestors. These skulls are carefully protected and preserved. When a family decides to relocate, a dwelling, which first must be purified by a diviner, is built to house the skulls in the new location. Most Bamileke art centers on the Fon and includes statues and carved masks that represent him as well as associated beadwork.

EASTERN AFRICA. This region comprises the peoples of southern Uganda, Rwanda, Burundi, northwestern Tanzania, the Kikuyu of Kenya, the Chagga of the southern slopes of Mount Kilimanjaro, the Swahili on the island of Zanzibar, and the Nyakusa at the northern end of Lake Nyasa. While the northern parts are mostly patrilineal and cattle-based, the southern parts are predominantly matrilineal and almost without cattle. For example, the peoples of Malawi are predominantly matrilineal. Polygamy and divorce are widespread and common. Ancestral worship, the worship of local deities and the supreme god, and witchcraft are all part of the religion. Fertility of the land and the health of the community are all due to the benevolence of the local deities. Because cattle provide a measurement of relative wealth, cattle exchanges between individuals and groups reinforce their interdependence and mutual interests.

The Kikuyu are a Bantu-speaking people of northern Kenya, live in the highlands northeast of Nairobi, and make up the largest culture group in Kenya. Traditionally an agricultural people, the Kikuyu long resided in separate family homesteads raising crops of millet, beans, peas, and sweet potatoes. Some groups also raised animals to supplement their diet, with little or no hunting or fishing. In these family homesteads, the basic social unit consists of a patrilineal group of polygamous men and their wives and children. The Kikuyu have a reputation for being careful with money, making good accountants, traders, and shopkeepers. Kikuyu families own many stalls in the Nairobi tourist market.

SOUTHERN AFRICA. Botswana, Lesotho, Namibia, Zimbabwe, Swaziland, South Africa, and the southern portions of Angola, Mozambique, and Zambia comprise the last culture region. The region's large groups include the Shona, Swazi, Tswana, and Zulu. Pastoral economy predominates. Arranged marriages are common: Girls are betrothed between two and six years of age to adolescent boys and begin living with them from the age of nine, although sexual relations are not initiated until puberty. Instead of a bride price, the groom usually renders bride services for the parents of the bride. Inheritance and descent are bilateral, and patrilocality and matrilocality exist side by side. Some po-

lygamy exists, but not as widely as in other parts of Africa. Polygamous men prefer marrying sisters because they tend to be cooperative and less quarrelsome. Shona and Zulu characterize this culture region.

The Shona of Zimbabwe are best known for their beautifully adorned wooden headrests. Most of the art associated with Shona is either personal or utilitarian. Although they produce no figurative sculpture, they do have a rich tradition of metalworking and woodcarving. Shona are primarily agricultural. Their main crops include maize, millet, sorghum, rice, beans, manioc, peanuts, pumpkins, and sweet potatoes. They raise some cattle, sheep, and chickens, and women usually supplement their income by selling pottery and handwoven baskets that are primarily utilitarian objects. Cows, usually used to pay the bride price, are considered taboo for women, so men must do all of the milking and herding. Men also do some hunting and fishing, and some even work as blacksmiths or carvers by commission.

Men and women both participate in farming. Traditionally, Shona peoples lived in dispersed settlements, usually consisting of one or more elder men and their extended families. Shona peoples believe in two types of spirits—bad spirits that are associated with witchcraft, and good spirits that induce individual talents associated with healing, music, or artistic ability. When illness or problems arise in a Shona family, they consult a traditional healer, *n'anga*, who prescribes medicines, charms, and herbs. If these fail to work, the problem is in the realm of the ancestors and appropriate sacrifices and divination is applied.

The Zulu of South Africa are best known for their beadwork and basketry. Rural Zulu raise cattle and farm corn and vegetables for subsistence purposes. Men

*Art
Pages
1037, 1038*

are primarily responsible for the cows, which are grazed in the open country, while the women do most, if not all, of the planting and harvesting. Women also own the family house and have considerable economic clout within the family. Zulu religion includes belief in a creator god who does not intervene in day-to-day human affairs. Appealing to the spirit world is through divination and invoking the ancestors. Thus, the diviner, who is almost always a woman, plays an important part in the daily lives of the Zulu. Zulus attribute all bad things, including death, to evil sorcery or offended spirits. No misfortune is ever seen as the result of natural causes.

MODERNIZATION AND AFRICAN CULTURE. Traditional African cultures now face many pressures. Traditional values of community support and care, especially for the elderly and children, are crumbling under the weight of an ever-increasing population of poor elders and AIDS orphans. Urban residence and difficult economic crises are slowly weakening extended family and kinship ties and producing nuclear families. Rapid population growth is changing land tenure, and traditional support mechanisms are dying.

By the 1990's, different culture groups were increasingly mixing in cities and even rural areas. Intermarriage among different groups and increased mobility are slowly erasing differences between regions. Previously, people living in a particular region usually had work and life-styles in common, but differences now abound. Standards of living and employment options vary not only according to where people live but also according to the opportunities they have had for education

and training. Thus, people now identify with many different groups, not just their culture groups or geographic roots. People in large cities share a way of life and culture similar to those of urban people in other parts of the world. No part of the world seems immune to the spread of global culture, spearheaded by modern technologies, particularly television. How Africa's cultures respond to these challenges now will determine the future of Africa's culture regions.

Joseph R. Oppong

FOR FURTHER STUDY

Barakat, H. *The Arab World: Society, Culture and State.* Berkeley: University of California Press, 1993.

Berg, M. *Contemporary Africa: Development, Culture and the State.* White Plains, N.Y.: Longman, 1986.

Blakely, T. D., W. E. A. van Beek, and D. L. Thomson, eds. *Religion in Africa: Experience and Expression.* London: James Currey and Heinemann, 1994.

Chapman, G. P., and K. M. Baker, eds. *The Changing Geography of Africa and the Middle East.* London: Routledge, 1992.

Oppong, J. R. "Culture, Conflict and Change in Sub-Saharan Africa." In *The Geography of Sub-Saharan Africa,* edited by Samuel Aryeetey-Attoh. Englewood Cliffs, N.J.: Prentice-Hall, 1997.

Mazrui, Ali A. *The Africans: A Triple Heritage.* Boston: Little, Brown and Company, 1986.

Reader, John. *Africa: A Biography of the Continent.* New York: Alfred A. Knopf, 1997.

Ungar, Sanford J. *Africa: The People and Politics of an Emerging Continent.* New York: Simon & Schuster, 1986.

EXPLORATION

Map
Page 1039

In the Western world, Africa has often been depicted as a Dark Continent. Until recently, scholars downplayed the importance of indigenous contributions in African history and viewed the continent as a backward land populated by primitive human beings who lived in virtual isolation from one another. Thus, many early studies concluded that African exploration did not begin until the arrival of European explorers in the late fifteenth century. Modern research, however, has dismantled those myths.

Both the northern and eastern shores of Africa had been open to commerce and conquest centuries before Europeans appeared. While Africa may have been virtually unknown and uncharted to the Western world before the coming of Portuguese navigators, a considerable amount of geographical exploration had already taken place. Many African societies had organized expeditions and migrated throughout the continent prior to 1500; consequently, much of the geographic foundation that facilitated European exploration was the result of earlier exploration.

EGYPT. Archaeological and literary evidence indicates that several Egyptian pharaohs conducted southern expeditions along the Nile River region. Lacking sufficient timber supplies to build seafaring vessels, the Egyptians constructed boats of papyrus reeds and traveled to Nubia in search of vital natural resources. Ancient tombs reveal that during Egypt's Old Kingdom period, approximately 2340 B.C.E., the pharaohs Mernere and Pepi II sent the explorer Harkhuf on four expeditions into the Nile Valley. From his base at Elephantine, Harkhuf journeyed into the Sudan and obtained ample supplies of livestock, gold, ivory, ebony, and laborers, and provided the Egyptians with security on their southern frontier. Harkhuf left behind a series of brief descriptions detailing the earliest geographical discoveries of Africa, and his actions initiated the exploration of Africa.

After trade routes were established with the Mediterranean world, the Egyptians were able to acquire timber, which enabled them to build ships that could navigate the open seas. When Queen Hatshepsut assumed control of the dynasty during the fifteenth century B.C.E., she initiated several public works projects and an aggressive trade policy. She sent five large ships to explore the African coastline of the Red Sea and secure relations with the fabled land of Punt along the coast of Somalia. Her tomb, discovered in the late nineteenth century at Deir el Bahri, across the river from Thebes, reveals that she established prosperous ties with the region and was able to procure much-needed natural resources, including gum, myrrh trees, and animal hides.

Pictorial records list ships, inventories, and slaves, and provide considerable insight into living conditions in Punt. By the time of Hatshepsut's death, the Egyptians had gathered an impressive body of knowledge about Africa's geography that would readily benefit subsequent conquerors. Hatshepsut's activities indicate that the Egyptians did not live in virtual isolation from the rest of the continent and conducted valuable geographical explorations centuries before the first Europeans established contact in Africa.

THE MEDITERRANEAN WORLD. Egyptian trade with the Mediterranean world also facilitated the opening of Africa's frontiers. As indicated by the archaeological evidence uncovered at the city of Byblos, the pharaohs obtained valuable shipbuilding technology from the Phoenicians and maintained a prosperous link between the North African coast and the eastern Mediterranean Sea. These ties were expanded after the Phoenicians moved westward and founded the city of Carthage in approximately 813 B.C.E. Located near the present-day city of Tunis, Tunisia, Carthage's success led to other

settlements along the Maghreb, or northwestern coastline, and eventually generated movement into both Morocco and Algeria.

African textiles, foodstuffs, and mercenaries fueled Carthage's economy, and the wealth from gold, tin, and silver deposits was exported out of Africa in exchange for cheap manufactured goods. According to the Greek historian Herodotus, the Egyptians also benefited from Carthage's success, and one pharaoh even financed a Phoenician expedition to circumnavigate the African coast. Although Herodotus claims that these explorers sailed from the Red Sea along the southern cape and back north through the Strait of Gibraltar, the mission's accomplishments remain questionable. However, by the fifth cen-

Gibraltar
Page 1100

When this map was published in 1570, Europeans knew very little about the inland regions of Africa. (Corbis)

tury B.C.E., navigators were compiling systematic charts that outlined the continent's vast coastline.

Alexander the Great of Greece invaded and conquered Egypt in 332 B.C.E. The Hellenistic period lasted for only three centuries, but it had a tremendous impact upon the geographical exploration of Africa. The Greeks centered their power in the new city of Alexandria and forever linked the Nile River and North Africa with Europe. Since this city served as such a vital trade center for the growing regional economy, both merchants and statesmen hoped that the river could be used to exploit the interior of central Africa. Many Greeks began to search for the river's origins.

In approximately 500 B.C.E., Hecataeus, the first Greek geographer to visit Egypt, wrote in his text that the Nile River flowed into the River Oceanus and encircled the entire world. Other writers outlined the landscape in the southern Aswan region. The historian Diodrus Siculus traveled to Egypt in 59 B.C.E. and wrote a book describing the topographical conditions in both the Sudan and Ethiopia. Later scholars spent considerable time exploring these ideas, but the theoretical framework that would later inspire adventurers such as David Livingstone and Henry Stanley had been firmly laid down by Greek geographers during the Hellenistic period.

Roman amphitheater
Page 1039

The Romans eventually eliminated Greek power in Africa. Using information that had been gathered from early explorers, they were able to secure control over the entire northern coast by the third century B.C.E. Local businessmen profited from this relationship and established trading headquarters in Ostia, Rome's outlet to the sea. Financial and military concerns also led to the building of a centralized road system in northern Africa. Surviving records indicate that the Ro-

mans constructed an elaborate highway system that linked Carthage with both the southeast and southwest. This network inexorably linked Africans together through a sophisticated internal trade system and exposed various peoples to the goods and services of other Africans. Instead of being isolated from the wider world, North Africa and the Red Sea were already systematically connected to economic and military systems of the wider Mediterranean world.

ISLAMIC INFLUENCE. The Muslim invasion of Africa drastically altered the religious, cultural, and territorial landscapes of Africa. Islam quickly spread during the seventh and eighth centuries C.E. and became the continent's dominant faith; its influence spread much farther south than the Greeks or Romans into modern-day Nigeria, Uganda, and the Congo. When the Arabs moved across the Sahara, they encountered considerable resistance, but by 711 C.E., all of Northwest Africa was under Muslim control. In the process, they captured and destroyed Carthage, built the new Arab city of Tunis, and severed the region's ties with the Mediterranean world. These actions sparked an initial clash between Hellenistic and Islamic culture, but approximately 90 percent of the people ultimately embraced Islam and adopted Arabic speech.

The Muslims also had a historic impact upon Africa's eastern coastline. They established several colonies that evolved into flourishing export cities. Drawn by trade and profits, the Arabs entered into a trade agreement with the Nubian Christian kingdom of Dongola that lasted until the fourteenth century. This agreement secured the Egyptian-Nubian border and granted the Arabs special trade privileges.

Under Islamic influence, Cairo emerged as one of the principal port cities in the world's economy. African natural resources—such as gold and ivory, as well as slaves—were exported in exchange for Arabian textiles and porcelain goods. Most important though, the Arabs opened trading routes between Africa and the Indian Ocean and increased Africa's integration into a world system. Muslim merchants controlled the Indian Ocean until the Portuguese arrived in the fifteenth century, and during this period, they initiated contact between India and the African coast. Navigators sailed from the Arabian Sea and launched excursions into Mozambique, Madagascar, and the islands of Pemba, Zanzibar, and Mafia. While most Muslims stayed close to the coast, their trade in gold from the interior gradually opened up additional African frontiers. By the time the first great wave of European voyagers visited Africa, both the northern and eastern coastal regions had been thoroughly explored.

WESTERN EUROPE AND THE SLAVE TRADE. By the end of the sixteenth century, Western European economic and military power dominated the world system. The quest for new commercial markets coincided with new scientific, naval, and technological advancements, which allowed some countries to obtain a commanding influence in Africa. For the first time, Europeans crossed the sub-Saharan frontier and explored the western coastline. To say that these expeditions had an impact on Africa is a gross understatement; some scholars argue that the emergence of the European slave trade destroyed any chance for either African statehood or industrial and commercial takeoffs.

While the institution of slavery existed in many African civilizations, the European model quickly surpassed all others in intensity, brutality, and specialization. Approximately 10 million Africans were enslaved and sold in South America, the Ca-

ribbean, and the United States. Since slaves were valued based on their capabilities, slave traders focused on the most able-bodied members of a community. This forced migration began a destructive process that, from a geographical perspective, had severe sociological, cultural, and political consequences for Africa.

European exploration was driven by a number of factors. Mediterranean merchants had recently regained control of their sea lanes. Profits from Marco Polo's Asian trade motivated others to seek an alternative route to India that would circumnavigate the entire African coast. Europe's Christian Crusades in the Holy Land had generated considerable European interest in Saharan markets, and some Europeans believed that Islamic power could be bypassed and outflanked by exploring southward.

Most important, however, European cartographers had made considerable progress in their mapmaking, and their work generated promising expectations for a new age of explorers. Drawn in 1375 by Abraham Cresques for Charles V of France, the Catalan Atlas identified oases in the desert for launching trade caravans, salt deposits in the Sahara, and gold in Guinea. It provided geographical information on new areas such as Mali and medieval Ghana and accurately pinpointed the major cities of Niani, Timbuktu, and Gao.

The first patron of exploration to benefit from this knowledge was Prince Henry the Navigator of Portugal. Hoping to find a practical trade route to Asia, he initiated a number of voyages into the southwestern Atlantic Ocean. In 1419 an expedition he sent out discovered Madeira Island off the northwestern coast. Another reached the Azores in 1439. In 1443 Henry launched a series of annual expeditions further south along the coast. His captains ob-

Slave trade fort
Page 1040

Seventeenth century map
Page 1039

Caravan
Page 1038

Portugal's Prince Henry the Navigator. (Library of Congress)

Fernando Po and São Tomé islands, established contact with African rulers in what later became Ghana, and collected gold in such large amounts that the Europeans would later call this area the Gold Coast. This resource, however, prompted a shift in tactics. Lisbon assumed direct control over African trade and established a military presence in Africa.

Portugal continued to expand its awareness of Africa's geography by using foreign agents and launching new naval expeditions. King João II sent Pero de Covilha on information-gathering missions to Ethiopia, East Africa, and the Persian Gulf. At the same time, mariner Bartolomeu Dias rounded the Cape of Good Hope in a storm and anchored in Mossel Bay. He went another 170 miles (275 km.) eastward to Algoa Bay before returning to Lisbon.

Cape of Good Hope Page 1156

tained helpful information on hydrography, people, culture, and economics.

All of Henry's findings were cataloged by the leading geographers, cartographers, and astronomers of his time and substantially improved the next mission's chances for success. His death signified a shift by Portugal back toward Morocco, but his ventures transformed knowledge of Africa's geography. Portuguese navigators now had information on the African coast, stretching from Gibraltar to Sierra Leone.

Their efforts continued in 1469, when the Portuguese government granted merchant Fernão Gomes a five-year lease to explore trade possibilities south of Sierra Leone. Gomes agreed to open up four hundred miles (about a thousand sq. km.) of coast per year. By 1475 Gomes had navigated an additional two thousand miles (3,200 km.) of Africa's coastline. He found

Both of those missions undoubtedly provided explorer Vasco da Gama with priceless details that allowed him to chart almost the entire African coastline before venturing south for his infamous mission to India in 1497. Fulfilling Henry the Navigator's dream for a route around Africa, da Gama set anchor north of the cape and visited Mozambique and Mombasa before proceeding on to India in 1498. After he persuaded the government to finance additional voyages to east Africa, Portugal, and ultimately the rest of the Western world, possessed sufficient geographical evidence to circumnavigate the entire African continent.

Portugal's decision to build fortresses and practice economic imperialism set a dangerous historical precedent in Africa. Force, rather than diplomacy, would guide affairs. When the Dutch supplanted the

Portuguese during the seventeenth century, a thriving slave trade was already in place. Over the next two centuries, this system ignited one of the greatest population movements in history. More than 10 million Africans were uprooted from their homes and enslaved in plantation economies in Brazil, the Caribbean, and later North America. This process, moreover, increased tensions among indigenous peoples, disrupted traditional home life, and stymied African economic development.

THE SEARCH FOR THE NILE. With the coastline charted and settled, European explorers undertook several land expeditions in an attempt to unlock the mysteries of Africa's interior. Many geographers speculated about the source of the Nile River and whether a single river or body of water flowed continuously throughout the continent.

From 1768 to 1773, Scottish adventurer James Bruce retraced the source of the Blue Nile. Mungo Park navigated much of the Niger River from 1805 to 1806; English explorer Hugh Clapperton became the first European to cross the Sahara, in the 1820's; and Frenchman René Caillie visited Timbuktu and surveyed much of West Africa. German Heinrich Barth traveled from Tripoli southward to Lake Chad, Gao, and Timbuktu. However, the sources of the Nile River and the Congo Basin were still largely unknown to world geographers.

During the 1850's, two British explorers attempted to locate the origins of the Nile River by traveling west from Zanzibar. Sir Richard Francis Burton served in Great Britain's Indian army, studied several foreign languages, and was well known as an Islamic scholar for his translation of *The Arabian Nights' Entertainment.*

John Hanning Speke and James Grant interview King Mutesa I in Uganda in 1862. (Arkent Archive)

Headquarters of the Royal Geographical Society in London. (Ray Sumner)

Lieutenant John Hanning Speke was a well-disciplined soldier with extensive experience surveying the Himalayan Mountains and Tibet. He also had considerable communication skills that proved useful when negotiating passage from a hostile African chief into a secluded area. During a joint venture to Somalia in the 1850's, Speke and Burton were ambushed on the coast of Berbera. Both men managed to escape unharmed, but another Indian army officer was killed. Since conditions remained volatile on the Ethiopian coast, they shifted their focus to the Nile's roots.

Three German missionaries had produced a map that sparked considerable interest in Europe. It charted the interior of East Africa, and based on evidence from merchants who traded in the interior, there were reports of a huge inland lake—Lake Tanganyika. Burton and Speke analyzed this data, presented it to the Royal Geographical Society in London, and ob-

tained funding for a Nile expedition. The men, however, disagreed over which direction they should take. Burton maintained that Tanganyika was the home of the Nile River, while Speke argued that they would find the source at another lake located further north.

Speke conducted his own investigation and concluded that the river's source must be north of Kazeh. He reached Mwanza on the southern shores of Lake Victoria in 1858, and from 1860 to 1861, he scouted the lake's southern banks until he uncovered the Nile's source. Neither man, however, circumnavigated either inland lake. They eventually parted company and often disagreed over whose contributions unlocked these mysteries, but their expeditions led to two critical geographical discoveries in Africa. As a result, it was now possible to chart one of Africa's major waterways from the Mediterranean Sea to the interior of central Africa.

DAVID LIVINGSTONE. Scottish missionary David Livingstone also searched for the Nile's origins. Like others, he believed that the Nile emanated from a source deep in the heart of Africa, and while he proved to be unsuccessful, his efforts generated considerable information regarding Africa's interior geography. Born in Scotland, Livingstone attended the University of Glasgow and earned a medical degree. He joined the London Missionary Society and traveled to Southern Africa to work on converting the people to Christianity.

Livingstone's desire for exploration, however, remained his top priority, and during his stay on the continent, he emerged as Europe's leading authority on African geography, customs, and life. He argued against the continuation of the slave trade, and his successes were largely attributed to his willingness to conduct his affairs in a fair and humane fashion. Upon his death, he was venerated as a true friend of Africa.

Livingstone was the first European to visit certain areas on the continent. Although Central Africa previously had been viewed as an arid desert, Livingstone revealed that the region contained awe-inspiring lakes, rivers, and waterfalls. In 1849 he uncovered Lake Ngami in what later became Botswana. In 1855 he became the first European to witness the beauty of the falls on the Zambezi River, and because of their majestic presence, Livingstone decided to name the waterfalls Victoria, in honor of England's

Mission station Page 1040

Victoria Falls Page 1166

Muslim slave traders marching their captives to the East African coast in the early 1870's. (David Livingstone, *Last Journals,* 1874.)

queen. He furthered his exploration of this river and ultimately charted a course across the central Zambezi valley through Angola to Luanda on the Atlantic coast. He organized another mission from 1858 to 1864, discovering Lake Nyasa in 1859.

During Livingstone's last expedition in the early 1870's, he found the river Lualaba. He incorrectly identified it as part of the Nile River system and failed to appreciate the enormity of his findings. While it would take the work of future explorers to recognize that the Lualaba River was actually the Congo River, Livingstone's struggles unveiled another one of Africa's geographical mysteries. Although he eventually succumbed to disease and died in Africa in 1873, his achievements sparked an enthusiastic response among Europe's statesmen.

HENRY MORTON STANLEY. Born to Welsh parents who rejected him, Henry Morton Stanley fled to America and fell into the good graces of an English cotton merchant named Henry Hope Stanley. The Englishman gave the young immigrant his name, helped him finish his education, and provided the guidance that finally resulted in a job as a foreign correspondent for *The New York Herald*. Motivated by fame and fortune, Stanley devised a plan to find Livingstone in the interior in 1871.

Due to his increasing fame and perilous profession, there was often speculation that Livingstone had perished in the jungle. Some of his former workers had started death rumors, and Stanley hoped to scoop the world by either contacting the explorer or verifying his death. He traveled to Livingstone's base camp at Ujiji, on the northeastern coast of Lake Tanganyika, and waited. When Livingstone returned in November, 1871, he found Stanley willing to attend to his needs. The reporter produced extra porters and pro-

vided the camp with critical supplies, including cotton, cooking pots, medicine, and ammunition.

Livingstone was grateful to Stanley, since his supplies were at a critical stage. He had recently faced a near disaster at Nyangwe on the Lualaba River while traveling under Swahili protection. When he reached the settlement, the Swahili unleashed a violent attack upon the people. They let loose with a barrage upon the marketplace, torched villages, captured slaves, destroyed canoes, and killed hundreds of innocent people. Livingstone felt hopeless to act, especially since he needed supplies from the Swahili in order to return to Ujiji. His friends warned him that Stanley was only interested in profiting off his name, but Livingstone was extremely thankful. Over the next four months, both men developed a deep respect for one another.

Although Stanley subsequently published a book, *How I Found Livingstone* (1874), he also became a loyal disciple and served as Livingstone's representative to the press. After Livingstone died in 1873, Stanley arranged to continue his explorations of Africa's inland lakes and the Congo Basin and ultimately helped to find the final pieces of the puzzle surrounding Africa's geography. Many professionals criticized his motives and credibility, but Stanley pursued Livingstone's dream with a vengeance from 1874 to 1877. After leaving from Zanzibar, he traveled north and completed the first successful circumnavigation of Lake Victoria. In the process, however, he swiftly adopted tactics that radically differed from Livingstone's conciliatory approach toward African people. In April, 1875, after being threatened by people at Bumbireh Island, he killed fourteen in a skirmish. Barely escaping without any casualties, he returned and fired a series of rifle volleys into the tribe, while remaining beyond the range of the tribe's spears and arrows.

Stanley reached Nyangwe, the Swahili trading post and Livingstone's farthest point on the Lualaba, in October. He persuaded the local leader, Tippu Tip, to guide him on the river and accompany him with 140 soldiers and porters. Tippu Tip was reluctant, but Stanley offered $5,000 and later added $2,600 during the journey. The trip, however, was extremely costly. Stanley's boat had to be disassembled and carried over stretches of jungle, food supplies were inconsistent, and typhoid, dysentery, and smallpox decimated the group. On December 19, 1876, Stanley and Tippu Tip survived an attack upon their fortress at Vinya-Njara because of superior firepower, but Stanley lost four men and thirteen were wounded in the battle. The conflict persuaded Tippu Tip to return home.

Stanley managed to resupply and push further into the interior. Arriving at a series of menacing waterfalls he would later name the Stanley Falls, several members of his expedition drowned. He lost his boat at the Isangila Falls, yet the surviving members of the party trudged toward the sea. When he arrived at the Atlantic coast in 1877, he had lost 250 women, men, and children to the river, war, and disease. However, he had unlocked the secrets of the fifth-largest river in the world and more or less completed the geographical exploration of Africa. While he clearly demonstrated that the Nile and Congo Rivers were not an integrated system, his work indicated that the Congo River surpassed the Nile River in capabilities and could be used to transport goods, services, people, and Christianity into the heart of Africa.

OTHER EXPLORERS. Other expeditions also contributed to Europe's comprehensive understanding of Africa's ge-
ography. British army lieutenant Verney Cameron headed a relief party that failed to arrive before Livingstone's death. Cameron found some of Livingstone's materials and decided to explore the river. Unlike Stanley, he was unable to stay on the river and was forced south, but when he arrived in Benguela off the coast of Angola in 1875, he became the first European to cross Central Africa.

French explorer Pierre Savorgnan de Brazza—after whom Brazzaville was later named—ventured into the uncharted rain forests on the Ogowe River. He was forced to retreat before he could discover where the Ogowe River met the Congo River, but his findings provided more insight into the difficulties surrounding the use of river transportation in central Africa.

These successes generated a considerable degree of interest in Africa by the European powers. Once the powers obtained a clear understanding of the land, Africa was carved up into foreign colonies, valuable natural resources and profits were channeled away from local merchants and into the hands of European businesses, and military rule destroyed tribal governments. As a result, the nineteenth century scramble for Africa ushered in an imperial system that undermined African political and economic development throughout the twentieth century.

Robert D. Ubriaco, Jr.

FOR FURTHER STUDY

Davidson, Basil. *Africa in History: Themes and Outlines.* New York: Collier Books, 1991.

Fage, J. D. *A History of Africa.* Reprint. New York: Alfred A. Knopf, 1983.

Lipschutz, Mark R., and R. Kent Rasmussen. *Dictionary of African Historical Biography.* 2d ed. Berkeley: University of California Press, 1986.

Mokhtar, G., ed. *Ancient Civilizations of Africa*. Berkeley: University of California Press, 1990.

Pakenham, Thomas. *The Scramble for Africa: The White Man's Conquest of the Dark Continent from 1876 to 1912*. New York: Random House, 1991.

Rodney, Walter. *How Europe Underdeveloped Africa*. London: Bogle-L'Ouverture, 1972.

Rotberg, Robert I., ed. *Africa and Its Explorers: Motives, Methods, and Impact*. Reprint. Cambridge, Mass.: Harvard University Press, 1973.

Stanley, Henry M. *Through the Dark Continent*. New York: Harper & Brothers, 1879.

Stanley, Richard, and Alan Neame, eds. *The Exploration Diaries of H. M. Stanley*. New York: Vanguard Press, 1981.

Thompson, Leonard. *A History of South Africa*. New Haven, Conn.: Yale University Press, 1995.

URBANIZATION

Map
Page 1089

Urbanization involves the movement of people from rural to urban areas. "Urban" generally implies a nonagricultural settlement; with regard to minimum population size, its definition varies from country to country. It is not easy to generalize about Africa, since there is so much diversity among its peoples. However, African societies have continually changed, at an ever-increasing rate in modern times. Cities have grown and people have moved back and forth between village and town, resulting in new social groups, occupations, institutions, and forms of communications.

HISTORICAL DISTRIBUTION OF URBAN CENTERS. African scholars have been trying to reconstruct much of Africa's history, traditions, customs, and artifacts, which were lost during colonialism. Efforts in the last three decades of the twentieth century, using folklore, poetry, art objects, archaeological sites, carbon-dating techniques, buildings, and linguistics, have begun reconstructing Africa's past. Evidence suggests that towns and cities have existed for several millennia in Africa. Towns that were major centers of religion, learning, cultural, and commercial exchange included Meroë, Napata, Axum, Jenne, Gao, Timbuktu, and Great Zimbabwe. Precolonial towns and cities exhibited rules of social behavior, codes of law, and organized communities. Such centers were characterized by division of labor, class structures, and communication networks.

African scholars generally agree that the earliest known cities in Africa emerged around the central part of the Nile River. For example, Meroë was the capital of the black kingdom of Kush and existed from the fourteenth to the fourth century B.C.E. Iron technology, stone masonry, and other crafts and skills diffused from this region to the west and south of Africa. Meroë also had an agricultural economy, which included pastoralism and irrigation agriculture. This early urban civilization also had building and construction technologies, pottery works, textiles, sculptures, and woodwork.

Few precolonial cities survived the colonial era. Among those that did endure the ravages of colonialism and still thrive as historic centers, preserving remnants of Africa's rich heritage, are Ibadan and Ife in Nigeria; Mogadishu, Somalia; Kumasi, Ghana; and Addis Ababa, Ethiopia.

Colonial cities invariably sprung up along the coast to facilitate exploitation of resources in the interior. Therefore, most African capitals are coastally located. Modern African cities have a physical structure and design combining features of both indigenous and colonial times, and the characters of cities are a function of their historical legacy. Based on their history, seven types of African cities can be distinguished: indigenous, Islamic, colonial, European, apartheid, dual, and hybrid.

Addis Ababa, in Ethiopia, and the Yoruba cities of southwest Nigeria are the best documented indigenous cities. Yoruba towns of the twelfth and thirteenth centuries were designed around a central palace, encircled by compounds of rectangular courtyards. Such towns were surrounded by high walls and gates that linked main routes to central places.

The impact of urban Islam is still visible in North Africa. Moroccan Islamic cities include Rabat, Marrakesh, and especially Fès, the world's largest intact medieval city. Islamic cities south of the Sahara include Merca, Somalia; N'Djamena, Chad; Niamey, Niger; and Kano, Zaria, and Sokoto in northern Nigeria. Islamic cities have a permanent central market, mosques, shrines, a citadel, and public baths.

Koutubia Mosque in Marrakesh, Morocco. (Corbis)

Fès
Page 1160

IMPACT OF EUROPEAN COLONIZATION. Colonial cities performed several port functions and developed primarily as administrative outposts and trade centers. Social, spatial, and functional segregation of people and land uses were dominant features of the urban colonial landscape. Such coastal capital cities include Freetown, Sierra Leone; Dakar, Senegal; and Conakry, Guinea.

Cities depicting European culture were transplanted into Africa and were developed mainly for European settlement. Africans in those cities were marginalized, took up menial jobs, and did not regard those urban centers as their permanent home. For example, Nairobi, Kenya, catered specifically to Europeans. Other European cities included Harare (originally Salisbury), Zimbabwe, and Lusaka, Zambia.

Apartheid cities were common in South Africa, and their character reflected the segregation of residential areas for Whites, Coloureds, Asians, and Africans. Some commercial and industrial zones also reflected this segregation. Durban, for example, had a White and nonwhite downtown area. Other apartheid cities included Cape Town, Johannesburg, Pretoria, and Bloemfontein.

Dual cities result from a juxtaposition of two or more characteristics defined above. Sudan's capital Khartoum (colonial)—Omdurman (indigenous) is an example of a dual city. Hybrid cities integrate indigenous and foreign elements. Most modern cities in Africa are hybrids of indigenous, modern, foreign, and

Apart from coastal ports, East Africa had no tradition of true urban centers before the colonial era. The nearest thing to towns in the interior regions were villages in Uganda's highly organized kingdoms. (Arkent Archive)

colonial development, for example, Accra, Ghana.

IN-MIGRATION AND PUSH/PULL FACTORS. On a simple level, migration results when a new location pulls on a person, with good wages, freedom, land, or peace, while the location where the person lives pushes him or her away because of low income, repression, overcrowding, or war. However, there is a more complex side to why and where people move, which embraces such factors as a person's culture, traditions, beliefs, and history, and local, national, and international relationships.

Four basic classes of migration can be distinguished: primitive, forced, free, and illegal. Primitive migration is associated with preindustrial peoples and includes hunting and gathering groups in Africa that might migrate on a regular basis as the resources of an area are depleted or as game moves. Forced migration refers to situations in which people have little or no alternative but to move. Slavery is an example of such a movement.

In free migration, people make their own decisions and have the option of staying or moving. European overseas expansion to temperate areas such as South Africa involved free migration. Illegal migration results when a country prohibits emigration (moving out) or when people immigrate (enter) into a country without official approval. Generally, illegal migrants consciously violate immigration laws, but illegal migrants can be created as a result of policy changes. For example, several million West Africans who legally emigrated to Nigeria during the 1970's and early 1980's found their legal status changed as a result of new regulations related to a change of government and economic problems in Nigeria.

REGIONAL PATTERNS. In the United States in the 1990's, the minimum population size for a region to be classified urban is 2,500, whereas in Ghana and Nigeria, it is 5,000. Sub-Saharan Africa and some southern and southeastern regions of Asia are the least urbanized regions of the world. Overall, 30 percent of Africa's people are urban. North Africa is the most urban (46 percent), followed by Southern Africa (42 percent), Middle Africa (33 percent), West Africa (24 percent), and East Africa (20 percent). The degree of urbanization by country ranges from a low of 5 percent in Rwanda and Burundi to highs of 83 percent in tiny Djibouti and 86 percent in Libya.

The urbanized northwestern fringe of Africa, encompassing Morocco (and the disputed Western Sahara), Algeria, and Tunisia, is known as the Maghreb (place of the west) of the Arab World. The three largest seaport cities there are Algiers, the capital of Algeria, with a population of nearly 4 million; Casablanca, the capital of Morocco, with 3.5 million; and Tunis, the capital of Tunisia, with just over 2 million.

Maghreb Page 1091

Other cities with about a million people at the end of the twentieth century include Oran, Algeria; Rabat and Fès, in Morocco; and Sfax, Tunisia. Libya's two largest cities include the seaport capital of Tripoli (about 3 million) and Benghazi (about 1 million). More than half of Egypt's population live in towns and cities. Cairo, Egypt's capital, has expanded to the foot of the pyramids and its population is about 13 million. Alexandria, the main Egyptian port, has nearly 4 million people.

Cairo Page 1155

WEST AFRICA. Urban population has been increasing in West Africa, and Nigeria has the most impressive urban development in this region. Three of the eleven largest metropolitan cities in West Africa are clustered in the Yoruba-dominated southwestern portion of Nigeria, in the vicinity of the densely populated belt of commercial cacao production. The largest of these three is Lagos (population, 4 mil-

Nigerian cities Pages 1090, 1092

lion). Lagos was Nigeria's capital until 1992, when most governmental functions were moved to a new capital at Abuja in the interior of the country.

Immediately west of Nigeria on the Guinea Coast lies Benin's de facto capital, main city, and port, Cotonou (1.06 million). To the northeast is Porto-Novo, the official capital of Benin. Further west, in southern Ghana, is that country's national capital, Accra (1.67 million). The world's largest cacao producer and exporter in the 1990's was Côte d'Ivoire, whose economic capital and main seaport is Abidjan (2.79 million). Also on the Guinea Coast is Conakry (1.56 million), the seaport capital of Guinea.

CENTRAL AFRICA. The Central African region has three cities that exceed the million mark in population. The largest of these is Kinshasa (4.24 million), capital of the Democratic Republic of the Congo, which covers an area one-quarter the size of the United States. Brazzaville, located directly across the Congo River from of Kinshasa, is the capital of the Republic of the Congo, with a population of 1 million. Cameroon's inland capital of Yaoundé, with a population of 1.2 million, is connected by rail to the country's seaport of Douala.

EAST AFRICA. The most productive parts of East Africa are bound together by railways that form a network moving toward the interior from the seaports of Mombasa in Kenya and Dar es Salaam and Tanga in Tanzania. From Mombasa, the main line of the Kenya-Uganda rail link leads inland to Kenya's capital, Nairobi (population, 2 million), the most important industrial center in East Africa.

Dar es Salaam is the capital, main industrial center, main city, and main port of Tanzania. The city has a population of 1.75 million and rail connections to Lake Tanganyika, Lake Victoria, and Zambia. Located in the interior of Tanzania is Dodoma, with a population of 1.24 million, which has been selected as the new capital of the country.

In predominantly rural Sudan, the largest urban district is formed by the capital city of Khartoum (2.25 million). Addis Ababa (2.43 million), the capital of Ethiopia, accounts for the bulk of that country's manufacturing. Nestled in the central highlands of Madagascar (the fourth largest island in the world) is Antananarivo (1.1 million), its capital and largest city.

SOUTHERN AFRICA. The most urbanized country in sub-Saharan Africa is South Africa, which has four cities exceeding 1 million in population: Johannesburg, Cape Town, Durban, and Pretoria. Cape Town (2.73 million) is the legislative capital of South Africa; Pretoria (1.31 million) is its administrative capital. The county's leading seaport is Durban (2 million), and its largest city is Johannesburg (3 million).

The former Portuguese African possessions of Angola and Mozambique have large coastal cities along the west and east coast of Southern Africa. The seaport, capital, and largest city in Angola is Luanda (2.08 million). Mozambique has the two major port cities of Beira and Maputo (2.1 million), the latter being the capital.

The middle course of the Zambezi River separates the former British colonies of Zimbabwe and Zambia. The main axis of economic development in Zimbabwe straddles the railway line connecting the largest city and capital, Harare (1.4 million), in the northeast with the second-largest city, Bulawayo, in the southwest. The Copperbelt region contains the majority of Zambia's manufacturing plants and copper mines and is linked by railway to Zambia's capital and largest city, Lusaka (1.32 million).

PRIMATE CITIES. Rapid urbanization in African cities triggered the growth of primate cities. Primate cities are those with population many times larger than those of any other city in the country. Urban primacy can be measured in various ways where capital cities dominate the urban landscape, especially in small countries such as Togo, Gambia, and Burundi. Primate cities also are found in larger countries, such as Tanzania and Mozambique, where they previously served as former colonial administrative centers.

The following are some examples of primate cities: Lomé (population, 513,000) is the largest city in Togo, a country about the size of West Virginia. In Gambia, a country about twice the size of Delaware, Banjul, with a population of 42,400, is the capital. Bujumbura has a population of about 300,000 and is the capital of Burundi, a country close to the size of Maryland. Located on West Africa's finest natural harbor is Freetown (669,000), the capital of Sierra Leone, which is about the size of South Carolina.

*Cape Town
Page 962*

*Johannesburg
Page 1161*

In most of Africa, European colonists founded a single city in each colony that served as a "head link" to the rest of the colony. A head link is a city that links a country to the rest of the world, as imports and exports flow through it. Roads and railroads from head-link cities gave access to the minerals of Africa or to areas producing tropical crops of cacao (cocoa), peanuts, cotton, or palm oil. Consequently, European-based cities became focal points of each colony in African countries and emerged as primate cities.

The major cities and capitals in African countries are still those that Europeans founded to exploit the continent. Examples include Lagos in Nigeria, Dakar in Senegal, Dar es Salaam in Tanzania, Nairobi in Kenya, and Luanda in Angola.

Besides having a relatively large population size, primate cities generally are characterized by the disproportionate amount of social, cultural, economic, and administrative resources. For example, more than half the jobs in Tanzania's manufacturing sector are concentrated in Dar es Salaam.

CHARACTERISTICS OF AFRICAN CITIES. In many African cities, the greater part of the urban population did not live in formal settlements in the 1990's. Many cities had up to 40 to 70 percent of their populations in informal settlements. In some parts of Africa, these settlements are considered to be illegal, but they seem to have become a permanent imprint on the African landscape.

Terminology used to describe informal settlements varies throughout Africa, and includes "squatter communities," "shanty-towns," "slums," and other such descriptors. Late-twentieth century trends reflect the lack of basic services and infrastructure in these informal communities. Problems in these areas include poverty, lack of potable water and sanitation, inadequate health and education services, and other site-specific habitation problems. Nongovernmental organizations and community-based organizations have played an increasing role in providing services to the urban poor. In some of the better-developed areas, such as parts of Southern Africa, there has been an associated increase in the role of private sector assistance for informal communities

FUTURE CHALLENGES. Generally, African cities are in a crisis situation as a result of the problems associated with rapid and uncontrolled growth. United Nations statistics indicate that urban population growth rates in sub-Saharan Africa in the 1990's were among the highest in the world. The average annual growth rate for sub-Saharan cities during that period was 6.2 percent, compared with 4.0 percent for Asian cities. Some of the world's fastest-growing cities are in Southern Africa; these include cities in Botswana (13.5 percent annual growth rate), Swaziland (10.5 percent), and Mozambique (9.5 percent). Other cities with high urban growth rates include those in Tanzania (10.3 percent), Benin (7.4 percent), and Niger (7.4 percent).

African governments are exceptionally centralized and face many challenges to effectively managing urban areas. Decentralization will allow local communities to participate more effectively in the decision making process. Local government institutions need to enhance their administrative and technical capacity to coordinate the delivery and operation of services. The financial capability of cities needs to be improved to allow for the provision of adequate urban services. In addition to these city-planning initiatives, regional strategies need to be devised to maximize the benefits of people outside the dominant city, and to retard the flow of migrants to urban areas.

Hari P. Garbharran

FOR FURTHER STUDY

Aryeetey-Attoh, Samuel, ed. *The Geography of Sub-Saharan Africa.* Englewood Cliffs, N.J.: Prentice Hall, 1997.

Banjo, Adegboyega G. "Deregulation of Urban Public Transport Services: Some Realities for Policy Makers in African Cities." *Third World Planning Review,* 16 (4): 411-428.

Grove, A. T. *The Changing Geography of Africa.* 2d ed. Oxford, England: Oxford University Press, 1993.

Swilling, Mark, ed. *Governing Africa's Cities.* Johannesburg: Witwatersrand University Press, 1997.

Theroux, Peter. "Cairo—Clamorous Heart of Egypt." *National Geographic* (April, 1993): 38-69.

POLITICAL GEOGRAPHY

Africa is probably the continent least understood by the Western world, due to its variety of beliefs, cultures, religions, and language patterns. In fact, it has been referred to as the Dark Continent.

Africa, with a population of about 800 million in the 1990's, can be divided into two regions, separated by the Sahara Desert: North, or Arab, Africa, which is culturally part of the Middle East, and sub-Saharan, or black, Africa. North Africa extends from the small nation of Western Sahara to Egypt, with the Mediterranean Sea to the north and the Sahara to the south. Sub-Saharan Africa is generally seen as having three broad regions: East Africa, West Africa, and Southern Africa.

EARLY KINGDOMS. Many empires rose and fell throughout Africa before European colonization. In North Africa, ancient Egypt under the pharaohs conquered vast areas and spread civilization beyond the Nile River valley. The Egyptian empire eventually was taken over by Arabs, Ottoman Turks, and finally Europeans. In East Africa, Ethiopia achieved political power at an early date. Its imperial roots can be traced back to biblical times when Menelik—the son of King Solomon and the queen of Sheba, according to legend—founded the kingdom of Axum. Ethiopia benefited from the Red Sea trade in gold, ivory, and other products.

West Africa saw the rise and fall of several empires, especially along the Niger River. The Ghana Empire lasted nearly a thousand years, at one time covering more than 150,000 square miles (400,000 sq. km.), and controlled the trans-Sahara caravan trade. The empire crumbled in the eleventh century, and the Mali Empire became powerful, especially during the reign of Mansa Musa. Mali leadership accepted Islam around 1050, and took control of the rich caravan trade. However, it weakened by 1400, as a result of the expansion of territories. It was replaced by the Songhai Empire, which flourished for a time but declined in the seventeenth century. The Kanem-Bornu, Yoruba, and Benin empires soon followed.

Caravan
Page 1038

Powerful kingdoms in Southern Africa established governments rich in culture, music, and traditions, such as the Kongo Kingdom. In the fifteenth century it stretched out from the mouth of the Congo River, and lasted until the early sixteenth century. The Karanga people of what later became Zimbabwe created another empire around the fifteenth century in Mwana-Matapa (Monotapa). By the late fifteenth century, the Changamire Empire had conquered Mwana-Matapa. During the early nineteenth century, the Zulu Kingdom's strong armies dominated much of southeastern Africa.

It took Europeans hundreds of years to gain effective control of Africa, in contrast to their rapid colonization of the Americas. Portuguese traders were the first Europeans to discover Africa's potential in ivory, gold, pepper, and slaves, arriving on the coast of West Africa in the mid-fifteenth century. The Dutch, British, and French later joined the Portuguese traders. Because of its huge potential for profit, trans-Atlantic trade soon replaced the trans-Sahara trade. The availability of

European and Asian goods led to the deterioration of African handicraft industries and innovations. As Africa gradually became a political and economic appendage of Europe, the trans-Atlantic trade affected indigenous African development and altered the political, economic, and cultural composition of the continent. Probably the greatest European impact on Africa during this period was the slave trade.

SLAVE TRADE. The slave trade did not start with Europeans. Africans and Asians sold and used slaves before the time of Christ. In the African savanna, kings, chiefs, and wealthy families took slaves. However, the number of slaves in early times was small compared to the later trans-Atlantic slave trade. Initially, the Europeans bought a small number of slaves for domestic and farm work. The slave trade increased in size as labor demands grew in the New World, particularly the Caribbean.

By 1600 approximately seventy-five thousand African slaves had been brought to the Spanish areas of the New World, and another fifty thousand had been brought to Portuguese Brazil. Through another two hundred years, the New World provided the major market for African slaves. Most of those slaves came from the western part of Africa, although large-scale slave trading was introduced in East Africa long before the Europeans brought it to West Africa. Slavery caused a decline in power of the states in the interior savanna and increased the power of the coastal forest states. The demand for more slaves also ravaged the interior population.

Estimates of the numbers of Africans taken to the New World as slaves between 1701 and 1810 have ranged from around nine million to as many as thirty million. About a third of them perished while being transported across the Atlantic Ocean.

Slave trade fort Page 1040

Slavery destroyed families, villages, and cultures. It also created a tremendous degree of misery for the Africans.

EUROPEAN COLONIALISM. The slave trade declined at the beginning of the nineteenth century, affecting the overall trade between Africa, Europe, and the Americas. Europeans then turned their attention to the exploration of Africa. For the first time, European explorers began to penetrate the interior of the continent, followed by missionaries and merchants. The missionaries wanted to spread Christianity; the merchants wanted to develop new trade links based on palm oil, and other raw materials for European industries. Antislavery groups in Europe were able to use this new relationship between Africa and Europe to demand an end to slavery. In 1807 Great Britain outlawed the slave trade; a year later, the United States began prohibiting the importation of African slaves.

Through military means, Europeans were able to push farther into the interior of Africa and soon gained influence and control over a large area. France gained Tunisia and Algeria, while Great Britain took control of Egypt in the nineteenth century. The Dutch moved inland from their settlement at Cape Town, South Africa, after conquering several African groups. Spain and Portugal joined other Europeans in extending their old coastal holdings.

Europeans gained more political control over parts of Africa as a result of their involvement in trade. The intense competition among European colonialists, who staked claims to profitable parts of Africa, was the beginning of the colonial scramble for Africa. In November, 1884, Germany called for the Berlin Conference to settle peacefully the political partitioning of Africa among Europeans. The conference allowed the French to dominate most of

West Africa and the British to control East and Southern Africa. The vast Congo area was given to Belgium's King Leopold II as his private domain. Portugal was given a small dependency in West Africa and two colonies in Southern Africa—Angola and Mozambique. Germany held on to four colonies, the largest being in Southern Africa. Spain and Italy retained small areas.

By 1914 Belgium, Britain, England, France, Germany, Italy, Portugal, and Spain had divided most of Africa among themselves. Ethiopia and Liberia were the only independent African nations remaining. In some areas, colonial rule in Africa was established peacefully through treaties between the Europeans and the African kings and chiefs. In other areas, there

was organized resistance. For example, there was resistance against British rule in Nigeria and Ghana and revolts against French rule in Western and Northern Africa.

COLONIAL ADMINISTRATIVE PROCEDURES. European colonial powers employed different methods to govern their colonies. This was evident in that many of the colonial powers themselves did not have the same types of government when they were building their colonial empires. For example, Britain and France were democratic countries, while Portugal and Spain were dictatorships through most of the twentieth century.

Most British colonies had a system of indirect rule that was similar to British rule

The only major sub-Saharan state to escape European colonialism was Ethiopia. However, Italy occupied Ethiopia in 1935 and remained there until driven out by the British in World War II. Meanwhile, Ethiopian emperor Haile Selassie (right) and his family went into exile in England. (National Archives)

Much of the physical evidence of Germany's brief presence in what is now Tanzania is being reclaimed by the tropical flora. (R. Kent Rasmussen)

in colonial America before 1776. Indigenous power structures were left in place, and the British ruled through the African chiefs or kings in charge of the areas. Portugal and France used a system of direct rule. This meant that the Africans were ruled directly by the European administrators, who lived in the colonies.

Portugal's direct rule was much harsher than that of France. The French believed in creating culturally assimilated African elites who would represent French ideals. Hence, France administered the colonies as overseas territories with representation in the French Parliament. The Portuguese also encouraged the idea of assimilation, and considered the colonies as provinces.

The Europeans, usually in collaboration with church missionaries, created schools to educate the Africans. In most cases, this was to ensure that the Europeans had a suitable labor force to administer the day-to-day activities of the colonies. For effective control, Europeans employed the divide-and-rule method. Colonial governors commonly used rivalries between African tribes to achieve their objectives. These rivalries often turned violent, and the governors served as peacemakers.

COLONIAL IMPACT. Colonial rule did not last in Africa. Most African states did not become colonized until the late nineteenth century. By the mid-twentieth century, nearly all of them had become independent. However, colonialism created new political units with boundaries that cut across ethnic homelands in many regions. Colonial rule disrupted African populations and increased ethnic conflicts. It tied Africa to an economic system based on world needs rather than on local needs. African miners and farmers produced raw materials for European and world markets. The system created Africa's economic dependency on the industrialized nations, poverty, and underdevelopment.

The missionaries who came to Africa with the colonists challenged and changed some of the religions and social traditions that had long been part of African life. As a result, individualism and competition replaced family and community spirit. Colonial rule gave control of African governmental affairs to foreigners.

RESISTANCE TO COLONIALISM. From the beginning, many Africans resisted colonial rule. In several areas, organized groups demanded independence. After World War II, many Africans who had

NEOCOLONIALISM

Kwame Nkrumah, the first prime minister and president of independent Ghana (1957-1966), called neocolonialism the last stage of imperialism. The term "neocolonialism" is used most frequently to describe the relationship between European powers and their former colonies in Africa and Asia. Replacing colonialism in Africa, neocolonialism is a process whereby powerful states in the Western world exercise their economic and political authority directly or indirectly over weaker states. The stronger, outside powers attempt to tie the new nations closely to the interests and needs of the outside power. This dynamic creates unequal trade and underdevelopment for the weaker states, because the powerful states dictate the terms of world trade. A state that is subject to neocolonialism appears to be independent and sovereign, but in actuality its political and economic systems are directed externally.

fought with their colonial masters against Germany came home to organize independence movements across Africa. In an attempt to present a strong force against colonialism, most of them organized the pan-African movement. Many of the African leaders of this movement were educated in the United States or Europe; chief among them was Kwame Nkrumah of Ghana. Other leaders of the pan-African movement had lived in the United States and the West Indies.

Pan-Africanism is a force of unity in Africa that promotes independence or self-determination for all colonies in Africa. In 1963 pan-Africanism led to the creation of the Organization of African Unity (OAU). The aims of the organization were to defend the newly independent countries and, when needed, settle conflicts between them.

INDEPENDENCE. Independence came earlier to North African states than to black Africa. In 1922 Egypt became the first African state to become independent (from Great Britain). Libya gained its independence from Italy in 1951. Tunisia and Morocco got their independence from France in 1956. Algeria achieved independence from France in 1962 after an eight-year-long war, in which almost a million people on both sides died. Western Sahara, the last of the North African states, became independent in 1975, from Spain. Shortly thereafter, Morocco annexed the country, claiming it was part of Greater Morocco. A national liberation organization, called the Polisario, resisted the annexation.

In 1957 the Gold Coast became the first black African colony to win its indepen-

ORGANIZATION OF AFRICAN UNITY

In May, 1963, the Organization of African Unity (OAU) was founded in Addis Ababa, the capital of Ethiopia. Of the thirty-two African countries independent at that time, only Morocco did not attend, but it agreed to join the OAU. The thirty-one members agreed on the following six principles.

- To rid Africa of colonialism

- To work for unity among African states

- To defend the sovereignty of African states

- To maintain respect for existing borders of member states and noninterference in the internal affairs of members

- To work for common actions in world organizations like the United Nations

- To remain loyal to the policy of nonalignment

dence, from Great Britain, and renamed itself Ghana. In 1958 Guinea became the first French colony in black Africa to become independent. So many African nations became indpendent in 1960 alone, that that date became known as the "year of independence." By 1966 a majority of the African colonies were independent.

European responses to African liberation struggles varied from peaceful negotiations to armed conflict. In most cases, Europeans were too weak to fight after the problems created by World War II. As a result, they were forced to negotiate with the African leaders. Many black African states, led by Ghana, Nigeria, Tanganyika, and Uganda, attained independence in this way.

In other parts of black Africa, armed struggle was organized. For example, in Kenya the British were not willing to grant independence because of the large number of British settlers in the country. Central Kenya's Kikuyu people, who had been most heavily disrupted by British settlement, formed the Mau Mau movement, which fought Great Britain for independence. The bloody struggle lasted fourteen years and in December, 1963, Kenya became independent under the leadership of Jomo Kenyatta.

Liberation struggles in Southern Africa proved to be difficult due, in part, to the large number of white settlers and the great natural wealth in the region. In Angola and Mozambique, the Portuguese refused to grant independence. Portugal, like Belgium, ruled its colonies with dictatorships, allowing colonial authorities to rule everything. There was no way to achieve independence peacefully. In 1956 African nationalists in Angola formed the People's Liberation Movement of Angola (MPLA), and in 1962 the Mozambique Front of Liberation (FRELIMO) was formed. The MPLA fought Portugal in An-

gola for fourteen years before achieving independence in 1975. FRELIMO did the same in Mozambique for ten years and became independent the same year as did Angola.

In Southern Rhodesia (later known as Rhodesia), white settlers who refused to accept African majority rule demanded independence from Britain in 1961. By 1965 under the leadership of Ian Smith and influenced by South Africa, Rhodesia declared independence. Initially, several African nationalists who joined forces to fight the minority regime of Ian Smith failed because of lack of political experience. The Zimbabwe African National Union (ZANU) took over the struggle in the early 1970's and by 1978, controlled a large part of Rhodesia. Consequently, Smith's regime was forced to negotiate with ZANU. Victory came to the African majority in a 1980 one-person, one-vote election won by Robert Mugabe, leader of ZANU. As long expected, the country's name was changed to Zimbabwe.

SOUTH AFRICA. South Africa has a unique political history within Africa. It was one of the oldest colonies and the first to achieve independence from Great Britain. It is the most industrialized nation in Africa. Its minerals are vital to the United States' military needs. Half the world's supply of gold and diamonds comes from South Africa.

The Dutch were the first Europeans to form permanent settlements in South Africa, beginning in the mid-seventeenth century. The British arrived in the early nineteenth century. As a result of the discovery of gold and diamonds in the interior of South Africa, the British and the Dutch (Boers) went to war. The British won the Boer Wars of 1880 and 1899-1902 and were able to colonize all of South Africa. In 1910 they granted independence to the country under the leadership of the white settlers, who made up a small percentage of the country's population.

In 1948 the Afrikaner Nationalist Party gained control of the government and introduced the policy of apartheid, which was even harsher than Jim Crow laws in the United States. Apartheid meant the separation of races, with all privileges given to whites. Opposition to this policy began immediately, with peaceful protest. The opposition, led by the African National Congress (ANC), intensified in the 1970's and became increasingly violent as the government continued to oppress the black majority. The ANC, led by Nelson Mandela, was increasing in power in the 1980's. The United States and Western Europe imposed economic sanctions on South Af-

rica, aimed at bringing both sides to the negotiating table. In 1990 the South African government, under the leadership of President F. W. De Klerk, recognized the ANC and released Nelson Mandela after twenty-seven years of imprisonment. In 1994 the first election in which all races could vote was held, and the ANC, under Nelson Mandela, won. Mandela became the first black president of South Africa. In 1999 another free election was held and Thabo Mbeki (ANC) succeeded the retired Mandela as the country's president.

Namibia, formerly South West Africa, was Africa's last colony to gain its independence, which it won from South Africa in 1990. It had been a German colony until after World War I, when South Africa, with

Nelson Mandela (left) and South Africa's then-president F. W. de Klerk accepting the UNESCO peace prize in 1992 for their work in democratizing South Africa. Mandela's elevation to the national presidency two years later capped one of the most remarkable political revolutions in modern history. (AP/Wide World Photos)

British support, took it over. In the 1950's, African nationalists in Namibia asked the United Nations for help, but were ignored until 1971, when the United Nations asked South Africa to withdraw. The South African government ignored this call, leading to the intensification of an armed struggle by the South West African People's Organization (SWAPO). SWAPO was formed in 1960, but did not become a force to be reckoned with until the 1980's, when it gained support from Angola and Cuba. The militant actions of SWAPO and mounting international pressure persuaded South Africa to give up Namibia. In 1990 Sam Nujoma, the leader of SWAPO, was elected as the first president of the country.

AFRICA AFTER INDEPENDENCE. African states won the opportunity to govern themselves after independence. These gains were not only political but also economic, social, and cultural. These new nations now could control their wealth and use it to benefit their own people, and be directly involved in world politics.

These gains were limited, however, in part because of the legacy of colonialism and neocolonialism. The former rulers did little to prepare the new nations for independence. As a result, many countries lacked the institutional framework for an independent government. The major problem facing these states was their political-geographical structure. European colonialists had ignored ethnic and political boundaries when dividing Africa among themselves and creating their own administrative divisions.

Africa's boundaries divide some ethnic groups among two or more nations. For example, most of the Yoruba people live in western Nigeria, but a significant number of them live in neighboring Togo and Benin, which formerly were French colonies. In central Africa, the Kongo people were colonized by Belgium, France, and Portugal. Today they live in three different nations—Angola, Congo-Kinshasa, and Congo-Brazzaville.

Throughout Africa, different ethnic groups found themselves in states with peoples of different languages, cultures, and religious backgrounds. These imposed political boundaries have made it difficult for many African countries to generate a common sense of national identity or establish stable political institutions.

ETHNIC CONFLICTS. During colonial rule, many ethnic groups worked together for independence. Once independence was achieved, nation-building became a difficult task. Ethnic allegiances frequently disrupted national unity. Ethnic competition for political positions, government programs, and other benefits were common. Many African leaders who participated in pre-independence politics were mainly concerned about acquiring political power and amassing wealth. They achieved these mostly through compromise and sometimes by injecting ethnicism into every aspect of African politics. It soon became clear that most of the political parties in black Africa were ethnic-biased.

In Nigeria, for example, the three major ethnic groups—Yoruba, Ibo, and Hausa—formed their own political parties although minorities and others were encouraged to join. In most cases, military regimes were as guilty of ethnicism as their civilian counterparts. Ethnic rivalries soon gave way to ethnic conflicts and civil wars in black Africa. In 1967 the Ibo of eastern Nigeria decided to secede and create the Republic of Biafra. The rest of Nigeria united against them, and by 1970, the Nigerian government won the civil war. However, the defeat of the Ibo did not mean that Nigeria had resolved its ethnic strife.

Early Liberian settlements, such as this mission station at Cape Palmas, were modeled on the plantations of the pre-Civil War American South. (Library of Congress)

Regionalism arising from past history and the colonial legacy also brought trouble to Sudan. About 75 percent of the people of Sudan are Muslims, the majority of whom live in the northern and western part of the country. The rest are Christians and animists living in the south. The northern Sudanese took over after independence in 1956, with little southern participation. The south, led by the Sudanese People's Liberation Army (SPLA) under the leadership of John Garang, took up arms in the 1970's to demand a separate state. The civil war has been ongoing.

Burundi and Rwanda gained independence from Belgium in 1962, but were ruled by the chiefs of Tutsi. The Tutsi are a minority in both countries, with the Hutus the dominant group. After independence, the Tutsi stayed in power in Burundi through repression of the Hutu. A 1972 Hutu rebellion was met with severe Tutsi repression in which thousands died. In Rwanda, the Hutu majority won control after independence at the ex-

pense of the Tutsi. In 1994 Tutsi rebels shot down an airplane carrying the Hutu president, leading to a mass slaughter of the Tutsi. At the end of the twentieth century, Tutsi rebels again controlled the government.

In Somalia, the parliamentary system left by the Italians after independence was a disaster, since it emphasized proportional representation—the idea that each social class in the society could have a party with seats in parliament. However, Somalia, unlike Italy, is divided into clans, rather than having a class structure. Since colonialism destroyed the old clan division, it has been difficult to rule. In the early 1990's, the government disintegrated, and rival clans began to run the country.

Liberia has seen competition between the Americo-Liberians and the ethnic majority. The Americo-Liberians are descendants of slaves from the United States, who make up approximately 5 percent of the population but control 60 percent of the wealth. In 1980 a military coup sought to distribute that wealth among many ethnic groups. The coup led to years of civil war, with Nigeria, Ghana, and other African states sending troops to end the crisis.

Ethiopia Page 1093

Ethiopia erupted into civil war in the mid-1980's, expelling the communist government in power. The new leadership allowed the former province of Eritrea to secede in 1993. Border disputes between the two countries followed in 1999. The crisis has created severe problems of refugees in Africa, which have proven difficult for individual states to solve.

The lack of leadership is another problem for Africa. Since independence, many African leaders have been ethnic or regional leaders rather than national leaders. Several have served the interests of their ethnic groups or regions over those of the entire nation.

Political leaders Page 1093

The political geography of Africa has been greatly influenced by the colonial experience. The unification of ethnic groups with old relationships involving conflict, deep ethnic loyalties, diverse languages, and different traditional values has made it difficult to build modern nation states. Nevertheless, many African nations are working together to solve common problems, at times forming regional organizations. One hopes that these regional organizations will help Africa develop in the new millennium.

Femi Ferreira

FOR FURTHER STUDY

Achebe, Chinua. *The Trouble with Nigeria.* London: Heinemenn, 1983.

Bradshaw, Michael. *World Regional Geography: The New Global Order.* Boston: McGraw-Hill, 2000.

Davidson, Basil. *Modern Africa: A Social and Political History.* New York: Longman, 1992.

De Blij, H. J., and Peter Mullerr. *Geography: Realms, Regions, and Concepts.* New York: John Wiley and Sons, 1998.

Drysdale, Alasdair, and Gerald H. Blake. *The Middle East and North Africa: A Political Geography.* New York: Oxford University Press, 1985.

Grove, A. T. *The Changing Geography of Africa.* 2d ed. Oxford, England: Oxford University Press, 1993.

Rasmussen, R. Kent. *Modern African Political Leaders.* New York: Facts On File, 1998.

Reader, John. *Africa: A Biography of the Continent.* New York: Alfred A. Knopf, 1997.

Rowntree, Les, et al. *Diversity Amid Globalization: World Regions, Environment, Development.* Upper Saddle River, N.J.: Prentice Hall, 2000.

INFORMATION ON THE WORLD WIDE WEB

A wide range of information sources on the political geography of Africa appears at the Africa Online Web site. (www.africaonline.com)

ECONOMIC
GEOGRAPHY

AGRICULTURE

Africa's fifty-six countries can be grouped into seven regions on the basis of geographic and climatic homogeneity: Northern, Sudano-Sahelian, Gulf of Guinea, Central, Eastern, Indian Ocean Islands, and Southern. Rainfall—the dominant influence on agricultural output—varies greatly among Africa's countries. Without irrigation, agriculture requires a reliable annual rainfall of more than 30 inches (75 centimeters). Portions of Africa have serious problems from lack of rainfall, such as increasing desertification and periods of drought.

Food output has declined, with per capita food production 10 percent less in the 1990's than it was in the 1980's. In most African countries, however, more than 50 percent, and often 80 percent, of the population works in agriculture, mostly subsistence agriculture. Large portions of the continent, such as Mali and the Sudan, have the potential of becoming granaries to much of the continent and producing considerable food exports.

TRADITIONAL AFRICAN AGRICULTURE. Traditionally, agriculture in Africa has been subsistence farming in small plots. It has been labor-intensive, relying upon family members. New land for farming was obtained by the slash-and-burn method (shifting agriculture). The trees in a forested area would be cut down and burned where they fell. The ashes from the burned trees fertilized the soil with needed minerals. Both men and women worked at such farming. Slash-and-burn agriculture is common not only in Africa, but also in tropical areas around the world where heavy rainfall removes nutrients from the soil. In areas of heavy rainfall, the rains wash out the nutrients from the burned trees in a period of two to three years.

The crops grown depend upon the region. In the very dry, yet habitable, parts of Africa—such as the Sudano-Sahelian region that stretches from Senegal and Mali in the west of Africa to the Sudan in the east—a key subsistence crop is green millet, a grain. It is ground into a type of flour and can be made into a bread-like substance. In moister areas, traditional crops are root and tuber crops, such as yams and cassava. Cassava has an outer surface or skin that is poisonous, but it can be treated to remove the poison. The tuber then can be ground and used to make a bread-like substance. Other important traditional crops are rice and maize (corn), which were introduced by the Europeans when they came to Africa.

Animal husbandry, or seminomadic herding, is another form of traditional agriculture. Cattle are herded in the Sudano-Sahelian region and in the eastern and southern regions of Africa. Problems that have arisen with this type of agriculture are the availability of water and grass or hay for the cattle. In some areas, goats and sheep are herded. Regions that are very moist, such as the Gulf of Guinea, which has rain forest, are not good for cattle because of the tsetse fly, which carries diseases such as sleeping sickness.

CROPS. The most widely grown crop is rice, which is grown on more than one-third of the water-managed or irrigated

*Map
Page 1094*

*Drought
Pages 975,
1033*

*Cattle
Page 1033*

LEADING AGRICULTURAL PRODUCTS OF AFRICAN COUNTRIES WITH MORE THAN 15 PERCENT OF ARABLE LAND

Country	Products	Percent of Arable Land
Burundi	Coffee, cotton, tea, corn, sorghum, sweet potatoes, bananas, manioc, meat, milk, hides	44
Comoros	Vanilla, cloves, perfume essences, copra, coconuts, bananas, cassava	35
Gambia	Peanuts, millet, sorghum, rice, corn, cassava, palm kernels, cattle, sheep, goats	18
Malawi	Tobacco, sugarcane, cotton, tea, corn, potatoes, cassava, sorghum, pulses, cattle, goats	18
Mauritius	Sugarcane, tea, corn, potatoes, bananas, pulses, cattle, goats, fish	49
Morocco	Barley, wheat, citrus, wine, vegetables, olives, livestock	21
Nigeria	Cocoa, peanuts, palm oil, corn, rice, sorghum, millet, cassava, yams, rubber, cattle, sheep, goats, pigs	33
Rwanda	Coffee, tea, pyrethrum (insecticide made from chrysanthemums), bananas, beans, sorghum, potatoes, livestock	35
Togo	Coffee, cocoa, cotton, yams, cassava, corn, beans, rice, millet, sorghum, meat, fish	38
Tunisia	Olives, dates, oranges, almonds, grain, sugar beets, grapes, poultry, beef, dairy products	19

Source: *The Time Almanac 2000*. Boston: Infoplease, 1999.

crop area in Africa. Cultivated mostly in wetlands and valley bottoms, rice is the most common crop in the humid areas of the Gulf of Guinea and Eastern Africa. It is also commonly grown on the plateaus of Madagascar. In the northern and southern regions, rice represents only a small portion of the total crops under water management. Wheat and corn are cultivated and irrigated, mostly in Egypt, Morocco, South Africa, Sudan, and Somalia.

In 1997 rice was grown in forty-two countries. Rice is the staple food of the population in Cape Verde, the Comoros, Gambia, Guinea, Guinea-Bissau, Liberia, Madagascar, Senegal, and Sierra Leone. It is important in the diet of Côte d'Ivoire

(Ivory Coast), Egypt, Mali, Mauritania, Niger, Nigeria, and Tanzania. The availability of rice has become an important factor of food security in Angola, Benin, Burkina Faso, Chad, and Ghana.

The growing conditions and the process of rice production in Africa north of the Sahara (the northern region) are different from those south of the Sahara (sub-Saharan Africa). In North Africa, rice is grown mainly in the delta of the Nile River in Egypt and in small areas in Algeria and Morocco. The japonica subspecies is dominant there, and rice is grown only under irrigation. Rice yields in Egypt were the world's highest in 1997. Production increases in North Africa have come both from improvements in productivity and increases in harvested area. On average, the rice yield in the region increased from about 2.21 tons to 3.28 tons per acre in 1997. The harvested rice area increased by about 35 percent during the same period.

Vegetables, including root and tuber crops, are present in all regions and almost every country. Vegetables are grown on about 8 percent of the cultivated areas under water management in Africa. In Algeria, Mauritania, Kenya, Burundi, and Rwanda, they are the most widespread crops under water management. Arboriculture (growing of fruit trees), which represents 5 percent of the total irrigated crops, is concentrated in the northern region and consists mostly of citrus fruits. Commercial (cash and export) crops are grown mostly in the Sudan and in the countries of the southern region and consist mostly of cotton and oilseeds. Other commercial crops in Africa are sugarcane, coffee, cocoa, oil and date palm, bananas, tobacco, and cut flowers. Sugarcane is grown in all countries except in the Northern region. The other commercial crops are concentrated in a few countries.

NORTH AFRICA. This region comprises Morocco, Algeria, Tunisia, Libya, and Egypt. This region's agricultural and timber resources are limited by its dry climate. Its agricultural products are those typical of the Mediterranean, steppe, and desert regions: wheat, barley, olives, grapes, citrus fruits, some vegetables, dates, sheep, and goats. It is not a region noted for its timber resources, although cork is produced.

Agriculture employs between 20 and 25 percent of the working population in Algeria and Tunisia and less in Libya, but about 40 percent in less-urbanized Morocco and as much as 55 percent in Egypt. From about the middle of the twentieth century, North Africa's production failed to keep pace with its population growth and remained susceptible to large annual fluctuations. All four countries have only small areas of prime arable land and no large reserves suitable for expansion. Cropland occupies about 33 percent of Tunisia and 20 percent of Morocco, but less than 3 percent of Algeria and Egypt, and 2 percent of Libya. Some export crops, such as wine grapes, citrus fruits, tobacco, and cotton, have suffered from strong international competition. Sugar beets, among other crops in Morocco, have expanded.

*Tunisia
Page 1095*

The northern region is not a major contributor to the continent's fish catch. Morocco, however, with its cool, plankton-rich Atlantic waters and access to the Mediterranean Sea, is one of the largest fish producers in the world. Pilchards, sardines, bream, hake, sea bass, anchovies, and mullet are the principal species landed, with the unusual addition of sponges in Tunisian waters.

SUDANO-SAHELIAN REGION. This region comprises Mauritania, the Western Sahara, Senegal, Gambia, Mali, Burkina-Faso, Niger, Chad, and the Sudan. This part of Africa is very dry and has mostly subsistence farming and seminomadic herding. For many people in this region, the primary crop is green millet. In the late twentieth century, this region was devastated by long droughts that caused famine and starvation. Mali and the Sudan have the Niger and Nile Rivers flowing through them. These great rivers provide plenty of water for irrigation of fields. During the very rainy season in Mali—mostly June through September—the Niger River widens into a great, extensive floodplain. This area is good for the growing of rice. The situation in the Sudan is similar with regard to the Blue and White Niles, which meet at Khartoum to form the Nile River and flow north into Egypt.

*Niger oasis
Page 1163*

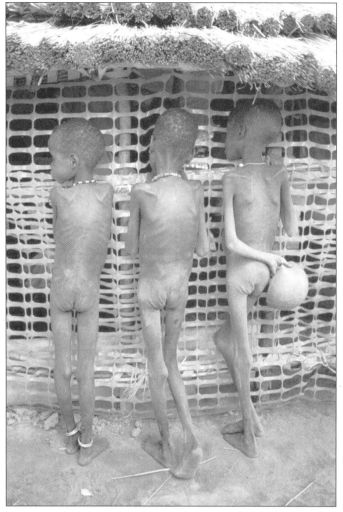

Sudanese boys suffering from severe malnutrition in 1998. Wars, political instability, and recurrent droughts have made famine an ever-present threat in Africa, particularly the arid northern regions. (AP/Wide World Photos)

GULF OF GUINEA. This region comprises Guinea-Bissau, Cape Verde, Guinea, Liberia, Sierra Leone, Côte d'Ivoire, Togo, Ghana, Benin, and Nigeria. With the exception of Nigeria, agriculture there is dominated by the cultivation of rice. The percentage of total land area that is arable ranges from 3.6 percent in Guinea to 44.6 percent in Togo and 50 percent in Nigeria. The percentage of arable land that is under cultivation ranges from 60 percent in Liberia to just 9 percent in Sierra Leone.

The total cultivable area of Ghana is 39,000 square miles (100,000 sq. km.), or 42 percent of its total land area. Only 4,500 square miles (11,500 sq. km.) were under cultivation at the end of the twentieth century. This is 4.8 percent of the total land area and 11.4 percent of the total cultivable land of Ghana. Much of the cultivation is subsistence farming of yams and other crops. Ghana is increasingly producing and consuming rice, but much of the rice used there is imported (106,000 tons in 1995). Ghana's efforts in agriculture have been hampered by droughts. Additional problems are that organic matter has been leached out of the soils by heavy rainfall and that increasing deforestation has led to additional erosion. This is the situation in much of the Gulf of Guinea and the central regions.

It is estimated that Nigeria has about 176 million acres of available agricultural land, about half of which is being used. Increasing rainfall from the semiarid north to the tropically forested south allows for great crop diversity. The crops include short-season cereals, sorghum, millet, and wheat in the north and cassava, yams, and rice in the wetter areas. In the drier regions, cotton, peanuts, and tobacco are the predominant commercial cash crops. In the south, cocoa, coffee, rubber, oil palm, and sugar are grown.

Estimates of production output for Nigeria's principal staple crops in 1997 were 6.3 million tons of corn, 8 million tons of sorghum, 6 million tons of millet, 3.2 million tons of rice, 33.5 million tons of cassava, 24.7 million tons of yams, 1 million tons of potatoes, and 3.8 million tons of vegetables. Among the agricultural cash crops, only cocoa made a significant contribution to exports. Nigeria was the world's fourth-largest exporter of cocoa beans in 1990-1991, with sales of 135,000 tons accounting for about 7.1 percent of

NATURAL HAZARDS OF DEFORESTATION AND DROUGHT

The greatest obstacles to African agriculture are deforestation and drought. Deforestation is the reduction of the amount of land covered by forests. Deforested land usually receives less rain, and the rain it does receive causes more erosion because there are fewer root systems to hold soil in place. Africa was hard hit by droughts in the last three decades of the twentieth century. Droughts in 1970, 1975, 1979, and 1984 devastated much of the Sudano-Sahelian and eastern regions. Famine and death accompanied the drought in many countries, especially Ethiopia. In the drought regions, several hundred thousand people died due to starvation. The eastern region was hit again by drought in the late 1990's. Droughts have prevented agricultural progress in these regions.

world trade in this commodity. Nigeria's share of the world cocoa market has been substantially reduced because of aging trees, low prices, black pod disease, smuggling, and labor shortages.

Cocoa (cacao) beans. (PhotoDisc)

Nigeria was also the world's leading exporter of palm oil until it was overtaken by Malaysia in 1971. As Nigeria's production and export of palm products declined dramatically, the country has become dependent on imports to satisfy domestic needs. In 1990 Nigeria overtook Liberia as the largest rubber producer in Africa. Production rose from 55,000 tons in 1986 to 147,000 tons in 1990, 255,000 tons in 1995, and 250,000 tons in 1997. Production of cottonseed increased from 276,000 tons in 1990 to 309,000 tons in 1997.

CENTRAL REGION. This region comprises the Central African Republic, Cameroon, Congo-Brazzaville, Congo-Kinshasa, Gabon, Equatorial Guinea, Burundi, Rwanda, and São Tomé and Príncipe. Cameroon has 14.7 million acres of arable land. In 1997, 55,000 tons of rice were produced there from 30,000 acres under cultivation, but the country imported 124,000 tons in 1995. In the central region, the percentage of arable land ranges from 0.4 percent for the Congo-Brazzaville to 43 percent for Burundi and 47 percent for Rwanda. Cassava is harvested from 72.4 percent of the cultivated land in Congo-Brazzaville, 30.25 percent in Congo-Kinshasa, 14.6 percent in Equatorial Guinea, and 13.2 percent in Gabon. Corn is harvested from 19.3 percent of the cultivated land in Congo-Brazzaville, 19.2 percent in Congo-Kinshasa, and 12 percent in Burundi. In Rwanda, 17 percent of the harvested land is used to grow sweet potatoes. Agriculture is not important in the economy of São Tomé and Príncipe.

EASTERN REGION. This region comprises Eritrea, Djibouti, Ethiopia, Somalia, Kenya, Uganda, and Tanzania. Agriculture employs about 80 percent of the labor force in Uganda and Ethiopia. Small farms, approximately 2.5 million, dominate agriculture in both countries, of which 80 percent have less than five acres of land. About 84 percent of Uganda's land is suitable for agriculture—a high percentage compared to the majority of African countries. Only 12 percent of Ethiopia's land is suitable for agriculture, however. Forests cover about 8 percent of its land. Food crops account for about 74 percent of agricultural production. Only one-third is marketed; the rest is for home consumption.

In four years out of five, the minimum needed rainfall may be expected in 78 percent of Uganda and 51 percent of Tanzania, but in only 15 percent of Kenya. Somalia receives almost none of the needed minimum. Ethiopia does not fare much better. The three countries in the area of Lake Victoria—Kenya, Tanzania, and Uganda—share a large area of strong agriculture. This is especially true in an arc from western Kenya through Uganda to Bukoba in Tanzania. Food crops here include bananas, sweet potatoes, taro, and yams. Robusta coffee and cotton are important cash crops. The uplands and mountains also are cultivated intensely. In

Kenya, Tanzania, and Uganda, cultivation has spread upward in such highlands. The Irish potato, species of peas and beans, and wheat and barley are grown there. The lower slopes are suited to Arabica coffee and the higher ones to tea and pyrethrum.

Distinct agricultural zones at different elevations are most common in Ethiopia. There, the distinctive ensete ("false banana") is grown at medium elevations in the forest belt of the south. Mediterranean fruits and vines are grown at higher elevations. Barley, wheat, and the native cereal teff are grown in plowed fields on the high plateau.

Tanzania has almost four million farms. Traditional export crops include coffee, cotton, cashew nuts, tobacco, tea, sisal, and pyrethrum; oilseeds, horticultural items, spices, livestock, sugar, cardamom, and coca beans are sometimes exported too. Major staple foods are exported in times of surplus. Coffee production has remained constant at around 50,000 tons per year.

Tanzania's climatic growing conditions are favorable for the production of a wide range of fruits, vegetables, and flowers. The most important fruits include pineapple, passion fruit, citrus fruits, mangoes, peaches, pears, and bananas, while vegetables include tomatoes, spinach, cabbage, and okra. Flowers include both tropical and nontropical varieties. Oilseed crops include both industrial oilseeds (castor seeds) and edible oilseeds (sunflower, peanut, sesame, copra, cottonseed, and soybean). Spices grown include black, sweet, and hot peppers, chilies, ginger, onion, coriander, garlic, cinnamon, and vanilla. Major staples (maize, rice, and wheat), drought-resistant crops (sorghum, millet, and cassava), and other substaples such as Irish potatoes, sweet potatoes, bananas, and plantains are also produced. Sugar

Sorghum
Page 1033

production averages around 120,000 tons per year.

Regions with a smaller annual rainfall or a long dry season can support only drought-resistant crops such as sorghum, millet, and cassava. Areas that have 20-30 inches (50-75 centimeters) of rainfall per year rely on a mixture of agriculture and livestock herding. The livestock population in 1991 for Tanzania was estimated to be 4.3 million head of cattle, 1.2 million pigs, 3 million goats, 800,000 sheep, 620,000 pigs, and a count of poultry 10-12 million.

Over large areas of eastern Africa, rainfall is inadequate for crop cultivation. This applies to the whole of Somalia and to 70 percent of Kenya, areas that receive less than 20 inches (50 centimeters) of rain four years out of five. In these areas, the only feasible use of land is pastoralism. In the driest areas along the Red Sea coast, the whole of Somalia, and northeast Kenya, the principal animal is the Arabian camel. In other areas, cattle are found, along with herds of sheep and goats and a few donkeys. Agriculture is not an important factor in the economies of Eritrea and Djibouti. In Djibouti, only 20 percent of the population is rural.

SOUTHERN REGION. This region comprises Angola, Namibia, Zambia, Zimbabwe, Malawi, Mozambique, Botswana, Lesotho, Swaziland, and South Africa. There, the arable percentage of the total land area ranges from 14 percent in Malawi to just 1 percent in Namibia. The percentage of arable land under cultivation ranges from 14 percent in Angola to 0.8 percent in Namibia. With the exception of Mozambique, where cassava predominates, corn is the single major crop in all countries in this region. In Malawi, 63 percent of the area harvested is used for corn.

Camel caravan en route to market in Cairo, Egypt. In the dry areas of North and Northeast Africa, the Arabian camel is the principal farm animal. (American Stock Photography)

Sunflower plants. (PhotoDisc)

About 13 percent of South Africa's land area can be used for crop production. High-potential arable land comprises only 22.5 percent of the total arable land. Slightly more than 2.8 million acres are under irrigation. The most important factor limiting agricultural production is the availability of water. Rainfall is distributed unevenly across the country, with humid, subtropical conditions occurring in the east, and dry, desert conditions in the west. Almost 50 percent of South Africa's water is used for agricultural purposes. Varied climatic zones and terrains enable the production of almost any kind of crop. The largest area of farmland is planted for corn, followed by wheat and, on a lesser scale, oats, sugarcane, and sunflower.

South Africa is self-sufficient as far as most primary foods are concerned, with the exception of wheat, oilseeds, rice, tea, and coffee. Of the 10.2 million tons of corn produced in 1996, approximately 3.1 million tons were used for local human consumption and 1.2 million tons were processed as farm feed. The remainder of the corn crop was exported to neighboring countries. Wheat production usually amounts to 2.3 million tons, of which 1.8 million tons are for human consumption. On average, 500,000 pounds of sunflower seed are produced annually. In 1996 the production of sunflower oil cake was estimated at 215,040 tons. Approximately 18 million tons of sugar were produced annually. South Africa is well known for the high quality of its fruits, such as apples and citrus. During 1996, 1.2 million tons were produced. In 1996 the country produced 63,829 tons of wool and 106,000 tons of mutton. South Africa's national commercial cattle herd was estimated at 13.4 million head. Almost 480,000 tons of beef were produced in 1996.

Agriculture is the predominant economic activity in Zimbabwe, accounting for 40 percent of total export earnings—about 22 percent of the total economy—and employing more than 60 percent of the country's labor force. The main export crops are tobacco, cotton, and oilseeds. Zimbabwe was the world's third-largest tobacco producer, after the United States and Brazil, with output of 205,000 tons annually at the end of the twentieth century. Cotton production was 106,000 tons in 1995. Zimbabwe is usually self-sufficient in food production. Its main food crops are corn, soybeans, oilseeds, fruits and vegetables, and sugar. Mozambique's agriculture has been badly hindered by civil war. However, the country has considerable potential for irrigation due to the Zambezi and Limpopo Rivers. The irrigation potential is estimated to be 7.5 million acres. In the 1990's, only 110,000 acres were irrigated, growing rice, sugarcane, corn, and citrus.

Agriculture and livestock production employ about 62 percent of Botswana's labor force. Most of the country has semi-desert conditions with erratic rainfall and poor soil conditions, making it more suitable to grazing than to crop production. The total amount of livestock—cattle, sheep, and goats—is about 3.2 million head, which is considered to be the land's capacity. The principal food crops are sorghum, of which 16,500 tons were produced in 1993, and corn, with 4,250 tons produced in 1993.

Namibia's cultivable land area is estimated to be 62 million acres, about 30 percent of its total area. The cultivated area is only 506,000 acres—only 0.8 percent of the cultivable area and 0.25 percent of the total area. Agriculture makes up approximately 10 percent of the economy, but employs more than 80 percent of the population. The major irrigated crops are corn, wheat, and cotton. Corn is the country's major crop.

INDIAN OCEAN ISLANDS. This region comprises Madagascar, Mauritius, the Comoros, and the Seychelles. During the 1990's an estimated that 8.7 million people lived in the rural areas and that 65 percent of the people within these areas lived at the subsistence level. Average farm size was about 3 acres, but irrigated rice plots in the central highlands were often only 1.2 acres. Only 5.2 percent of Madagascar's total land area (7.4 million acres) was under cultivation, and less than 5 million acres were permanently cultivated. Of the total land area, 50.7 percent supported livestock rearing, while 16 percent (1.2 million acres) of the land under cultivation was irrigated.

Rice production grew by less than 1 percent per year during the 1970's, but the cultivated area for rice grew by more than 3 percent per year during the same time period.

Some food crops had small increases in production from 1985 to 1992, while others decreased. Cassava, the second major food crop in terms of area planted (almost everywhere on the island) and probably in quantity consumed, increased in production from 2.14 million tons in 1985 to 2.32 million tons in 1992. During this same period, corn production increased from 140,000 tons to 165,000 tons, sweet potato production increased from 450,000 tons to 487,000 tons, and bananas dropped slightly from 255,000 tons to 220,0000 tons. Cotton output rose from 27,000 tons in 1987 to 46,000 tons in 1988, but gradually declined to only 20,000 tons in 1992. Cloves declined from a high of 14,600 tons in 1991 to 7,500 tons in 1993. Vanilla declined from a high of 1,500 tons in 1988 and 1989 to only 700 tons in 1993.

The fisheries sector, especially the export of shrimp, has been the most rapidly growing area of the agricultural economy in the Indian Ocean Islands region. This

Zimbabwe farm
Page 1034

Tobacco plants
Page 1095

makes up for lost revenues due to the ailing coffee, vanilla, and clove trade. Between 1988 and 1993, total fish production expanded nearly 23 percent, from 92,966 tons to 114,370 tons. In 1990 the Food and Agriculture Organization of the United Nations estimated that Madagascar had 10.3 million cattle, 1.7 million sheep and goats, and 21 million chickens.

Mauritius has 30,000 acres of sugarcane plantations that account for 65 percent of the economy. The plantations had one of the highest sugarcane and sugar yields in the world. Seychelles has a total land area of only 72 square miles (187 sq. km.), of which only 3,000 acres are cultivated. This 3 percent of the land area accounts for only 4 percent of the island nation's economy. The Comoros' agriculture is heavily weighted toward rice, which is the staple food of the populace.

Seychelles
Page 963

Dana P. McDermott

FOR FURTHER STUDY

Dickerman, Carol W., and Peter C. Bloch. *Land Tenure and Agricultural Productivity in Malawi.* Madison: University of Wisconsin-Madison, Land Tenure Center, 1991.

Gibbon, Peter, Kjieli J. Havnevik, and Kenneth Harmele. *A Blighted Harvest: The World Bank and African Agriculture in the 1980's.* Trenton, N.J.: Africa World Press, 1993.

Gleave, M. B., ed. *Tropical African Development.* New York: John Wiley & Sons, 1992.

Grove, A. T. *The Changing Geography of Africa.* 2d ed. Oxford, England: Oxford University Press, 1993.

Mortimore, Michael. *Roots in the African Dust: Sustaining the Sub-Saharan Drylands.* New York: Cambridge University Press, 1998.

Rached, Eglal, Eva Rathgeber, and David B. eds. *Water Management in Africa and the Middle East.* Ottawa, Canada: IDRC, 1996.

Ruskin, F. R., ed. *Lost Crops of Africa: Grains.* Diane Publishing, 1999.

INFORMATION ON THE WORLD WIDE WEB

A good site for detailed African agricultural information is that of the United Nations' Food and Agriculture Organization (FAO), which features a searchable database organized by individual country. (www.fao.org)

INDUSTRIES

While many people write off Africa as the continent of despair, other enterprising individuals and organizations have recognized its huge, untapped potential. Some development has occurred on the North African coast and in Southern Africa. Typically, the development has been of oil resources and relatively rare minerals or metals such as diamonds, gold, and chromium. Chemical industries and oil refineries exist in some countries, as do some textile plants and modest paper and pulp production. A typical African country's industrial employment is no more than a few percent, if that, of the country's population. Because of Africa's colonial past, much of Africa's exports goes to Europe.

CHEMICAL INDUSTRY. A handful of countries in Africa have significant chemical industries: Algeria, Morocco, Libya, Tunisia, Egypt, Nigeria, and South Africa. The Algerian chemicals industry is based in the industrial and refining centers of Skikda, Arzew, and Annaba, which include the Arzew refinery and the Skikda refinery. The refinery at Skikda has an aromatics complex that supplies benzene, toluene, xylenes, and paraxylenes. A large petrochemical complex at Skikda produces ethylene, chlorine and caustic soda, hydrochloric acid, vinyl chloride monomer, polyvinyl chloride (PVC), low-density polyethylene (LDPE), and high-density polyethylene (HDPE). The petrochemical center at Arzew produces petrochemicals and fertilizers, including methanol, phenol resin, melamine resin, and urea resins. Algeria produces nitrogenous and phosphatic fertilizers, mainly for the do-

mestic market, for which the demand is great.

Morocco's chemical industry, like that of Tunisia, is dominated by phosphate chemicals. Morocco has about two-thirds of the world's reserves of phosphate rock. The main products manufactured are phosphoric acids and phosphate-based fertilizers. These plants are located at Safi and Jorf Lasfar.

Tunisia is the world's fourth-largest producer of calcium phosphates and the world's third-largest fertilizer exporter. The state-owned industry produces a large volume of phosphoric acid, triple superphosphate (TSP), diammonium phosphate, nitrogen-phosphate-potash ammonium nitrate, and mono-ammonium phosphate. Paint, glue, and detergents also are manufactured in Tunisia.

Marsa El-Brega is Libya's main center for the manufacture of petrochemicals, producing methanol, ammonia, and urea. The National Petrochemical Company operates the Marsa El-Brega complex. The petrochemical complex at Abu Kammash produces ethylene dichloride and vinyl chloride monomer and PVC.

Egypt annually produces nitrogenous fertilizers, ammonia, urea, and ammonium nitrate at complexes at Talkha, Dikheila, Alexandria, and Suez. A petrochemical complex at Amerya produces ethylene, paraxylene, purified terephthalic acid (TPA), linear alkyl benzene, chlorine/caustic soda, vinyl chloride monomer, PVC, and low and high-density polyethylene. The salt extraction and processing plant at Lake Qaran produces sodium sulfate. A plant in

Port Harcourt oil refinery. (American Stock Photography)

in the Delta State has downstream petrochemical plants that produce polypropylene and carbon black.

South Africa's chemical industry is of substantial economic significance, contributing around 5 percent of the country's gross domestic product. The industry is the largest of its kind in Africa and produces a great range of products. There are base chemicals such as benzene, methanol, and toluene; inorganic chemicals such as caustic soda, sulfuric acid, and chlorine; intermediate chemicals such as ammonia, phenols, and plastics; and end-products such as paints, explosives, and fertilizers.

PULP AND PAPER. South Africa is the only African producer of pulp and paper other than neighboring Swaziland, which has a modest production controlled by a South African company. South Africa annually produces mechanical wood pulp, chemical wood pulp, newsprint, printing and writing paper, and large amounts of other paper and cardboard.

NORTHERN REGION. This region comprises Morocco, Algeria, Tunisia, Libya, and Egypt. Algeria is one of the major producers of oil and gas in Africa. Libya is North Africa's biggest oil producer and Europe's biggest North African oil supplier. Despite oil sanctions by the United Nations and the United States, the oil industry in Libya has remained active. In 1994 production of crude oil was 49.2 million tons. Most of this oil goes to Europe,

Alexandria supplies sodium carbonate to the local industry for the manufacture of glass, aluminum, and industrial cleaners.

Nigeria produces nitrogenous fertilizers and phosphatic fertilizers. A large plant at Onne, near Port Harcourt, produces urea and mixed fertilizers (nitrogen/phosphate/potassium). The Kaduna refinery in northern Nigeria produces linear alkyl benzene, benzene, and kerosene solvents. The refinery located at Warri with Italy being a key buyer. Libya had three oil refineries in the late 1990's. Tunisia's crude oil production in 1994 was 4.4 million tons.

Morocco has oil refineries at Sidi Kacem and at Mohammedia, near Casablanca. The two refineries have a capacity of seven million tons but produce about four million tons per year. The Maghreb-Europe gas pipeline began operating in 1996 and supplies 350 billion cubic feet (9.9 billion cubic meters) of gas per year to Spain and Portugal. Morocco is the world's largest exporter of phosphate rock. Phosphate reserves are estimated to be close to 60 billion tons.

Algeria has major deposits of phosphates and iron ore, and smaller deposits of coal, lead, and zinc. These are mined, as are some mercury and copper. A bonanza of high-grade gold has been found in the Ahaggar Desert hills of southern Algeria. Five vast geological provinces, each about 400 miles (600 km.) long, have been identified. Exploratory drilling at two deposits has produced yields graded at 0.89 ounce (25 grams) of gold per ton of ore and 0.58 ounce (16.5 grams) per ton of ore. In South Africa's declining gold industry, 0.23 ounce (6.4 grams) per ton is considered good.

Phosphate rock is mined in Egypt. In 1989 a new phosphate mine was brought into production at West Sabaeya to supply feedstock to the Abu-Zabaal Fertilizer and Chemical Company. Egypt also produces iron ore at Bahariya Oasis. There has been drilling to determine the feasibility of gold mining just west of the Gulf of Suez. Egypt also has eight oil refineries.

SUDANO-SAHELIAN REGION. This region comprises Mauritania, the Western Sahara, Senegal, Mali, Burkina Faso, Niger, Chad, and the Sudan. Since 1992, Mali has become Africa's third-largest

gold producer, after Ghana and South Africa.

Mauritania has become the major African supplier of iron ore to European steelmakers, providing 8 percent of 1994 European imports. A mine near Akjoujit was scheduled to open in late 1999 and produce 366,000 tons of copper, 802,000 ounces (22,720 kilograms) of gold, and 2,100 tons of cobalt in its lifetime. Senegal has phosphate mines. Burkina Faso produces two tons of gold per year. There is some mining of nickel and manganese. Niger is the world's second-largest supplier of uranium, producing 3,000 tons per year. Salt and sodium carbonate are also mined. Some companies are currently prospecting for gold.

Chad has oil reserves estimated at 650 million barrels of crude. Production from the fields at Kome, Miandoum, Bolobo, and Sedigui is expected to yield 150,000 barrels per day. Chad has deposits of sodium carbonate and alluvial diamonds, both of which are mined. The Sudan's oil reserves are currently estimated at 300 million barrels; its gas reserves have been estimated at 774 billion cubic feet (22 billion cubic meters). Gold, chromite, manganese, and mica are mined. The Western Sahara has little or no industry.

GULF OF GUINEA. This region comprises Guinea-Bissau, Cape Verde, Gambia, Guinea, Liberia, Sierra Leone, Côte d'Ivoire, Togo, Ghana, Benin, and Nigeria. Benin is believed to have 100 million barrels of crude oil. Production in 1994 was 275,000 tons of crude oil. Côte d'Ivoire's (Ivory Coast's) oil reserves have been estimated at 25 million barrels and recoverable gas reserves at 812 billion cubic feet (23 billion cubic meters) or more. Its offshore Espoir and Pelier oil fields began production in the late 1970's and peaked at 28,000 barrels of oil per day in 1986. Production from these fields has

*Oil refinery
Page 1025*

since tapered off to less than 4,000 barrels per day. Côte d'Ivoire also produces gold and about 15,000 carats of diamonds per year. Reserves of cobalt and nickel ore (which are found together) have begun to be mined.

Liberia has iron ore, gold, and diamond mining, which have been largely inactive since a civil war began in 1989. The country's iron ore reserves are in the billions of tons. Guinea has nearly half of the world's bauxite reserves, iron ore reserves in excess of 3 billion tons, and gold reserves of 1,000 tons of metal. All three are being mined. Ghana is now Africa's second-largest gold producer, and the world's eleventh-largest. Gold accounted for 45 percent of Ghana's export earnings in 1994.

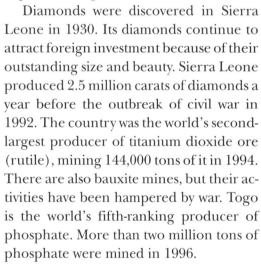

Diamond miners Page 1097

Diamonds were discovered in Sierra Leone in 1930. Its diamonds continue to attract foreign investment because of their outstanding size and beauty. Sierra Leone produced 2.5 million carats of diamonds a year before the outbreak of civil war in 1992. The country was the world's second-largest producer of titanium dioxide ore (rutile), mining 144,000 tons of it in 1994. There are also bauxite mines, but their activities have been hampered by war. Togo is the world's fifth-ranking producer of phosphate. More than two million tons of phosphate were mined in 1996.

Nigeria is the tenth-largest oil producer in the world, the third-largest in Africa, and the most prolific oil producer in sub-Saharan Africa. It currently produces 90 million tons of crude oil per year (2 million barrels per day), most of which it sells to international traders. The oil industry provides more than 90 percent of Nigeria's exports and 82 percent of the government's revenues. This industry and the country's four oil refineries are under national control. Gold, coal, tin, columbite (an oxide of iron and niobium), and a small amount of iron ore are mined.

Guinea-Bissau, Cape Verde, and Gambia have few industries.

CENTRAL REGION. This region comprises the Central African Republic, Congo-Brazzaville, Congo-Kinshasa, Cameroon, Gabon, Equatorial Guinea, São Tomé and Príncipe, Rwanda, and Burundi. Congo-Kinshasa has great reserves of copper and half the world reserves of cobalt. Both of these minerals are mined extensively. The country also has reserves of zinc and lead (which often occur together), gold, tantalum, beryllium, germanium, and lithium. Congo-Brazzaville has estimated oil reserves of 1.29 million barrels, with oil production of 215,000 barrels per day. The oil industry is predominantly run by foreign companies and is centered on the coastal city of Pointe Noire.

Cameroon produces 6.24 million tons of crude oil per year, which is 2 percent of the continent's oil production. Alucam (Societe Camerounnaise d'Aluminum) is Cameroon's major company and operates an aluminum smelter at Edea but uses alumina (aluminum oxide) from Guinea. This Central African republic produces more than a half million carats of diamonds per year. Gold is also mined.

Gabon produces 350,000 barrels of crude oil per day and has a 15,000-barrel-per-day oil refinery at Port Gentil. Manganese is produced from the Mouana deposits near Moanda and uranium from the Okla mine. Phosphate, niobium, and iron ore are also plentiful. Gabon may soon produce 15 percent of the world's supply of niobium.

In 1994 Equatorial Guinea's oil production was 6,000 barrels per day of crude oil and 27 million cubic feet (765,000 cubic meters) of natural gas. Oil reserves are estimated at 44 million tons.

Burundi, Rwanda, and São Tomé and Príncipe have little or no industry.

Continued on page 1105

MAJOR URBAN CENTERS IN AFRICA

Gibraltar
Algiers
Tunis
Oran
Sfax
Casablanca
Fez
Tripoli
Rabat
Benghazi
Alexandria
Cairo

Mediterranean Sea

Nouakchott
Zaria
Khartoum
Asmara
Dakar
Banjul
Niamey
Bamako
Djibouti
Bissau
Ouagadougou
Ief
Kano
N'Djamena
Conakry
Sokoto
Freetown
Abuja
Kumasi
Lome
Ibadan
Addis Ababa
Monrovia
Lagos
Bangui
Abidjan
Accra
Porto
Novo
Douala
Yaounde
Bata
Mogadishu
Libreville
Mbandaka
Kampala
Nairobi
Indian Ocean
Brazzaville
Kigali
Kinshasa
Bujumbura
Tanga
Mombasa
Matadi
Dodoma
Dar es Salaam
Luanda
Likasi
Atlantic Ocean
Huambo
Lubumbashi
Lilongwe
Lusaka
Harare
Antananarivo
Bulawayo
Windhoek
Walvis Bay
Gaborone
Pretoria
Maputo
Johannesburg
Mbabane
Maseru
Bloemfontein
Durban
Cape Town

Nigerian market. West Africans have long had a proclivity for trade and most of its towns and cities arose as marketing centers. (American Stock Photography)

Ait Ben Haddou, part of the urbanized northwestern part of Africa known as the Maghreb (place of the west) of the Arab world. (Corbis)

Garbage piles up in a residential neighborhood of Lagos, Nigeria's largest city, in 1999. Despite the country's large oil revenues, its government—like those of many other African countries—was unable to provide basic services and maintain the infrastructures of its cities. (AP/Worldwide Photos)

Sierra Leoneans lining up to vote in the capital city, Freetown, during the country's 1996 elections. Although postcolonial Africa has had a history of coups, military governments, and dictatorships most countries have strong democratic undercurrents. (AP/Wide World Photos)

Ghanaian president Jerry Rawlings (left) introduces U.S. president Bill Clinton and his wife, Hillary Rodham Clinton, to a crowd of more than 200,000 people assembled in Accra's Independence Square in March, 1998. In an effort to promote democracy, Clinton visited six nations on a tour of Africa. (AP/Wide World Photos)

In November, 2000—a quarter century after deposed Ethiopian emperor Haile Selassie mysteriously died—his remains were interred in a great public funeral in Addis Ababa. Haile Selassie was overthrown by a Marxist regime which was itself overthrown in 1991. (AP/Wide World Photos)

SELECTED AGRICULTURAL PRODUCTS OF AFRICA

Fortified granary in Tunisia—a relic of earlier times when protection of a community's agricultural produce was vital to the community's survival. (Corbis)

Tobacco plant. Tobacco is an important cash crop in many parts of Africa, and Zimbabwe is the world's third-largest producer of tobacco—after the United States and Brazil, both of which are twenty times bigger countries. (PhotoDisc)

Berber farms in the mountain slopes near Morocco's Mediterranean coast. The agricultural products of this region are those typical of the Mediterranean, steppe, and desert regions: wheat, barley, olives, grapes, citrus fruits, some vegetables, dates, sheep, and goats. (American Stock Photography)

Diamond mine workers sift through mud at the Colbert mine in central Sierra Leone, one of Africa's major diamond-producing countries. (AP/Wide World Photos)

A firestoker shovels a furnace in a Mozambique cashew nut factory, using the shells of the very nuts he is roasting as the fuel. (AP/Wide World Photos)

Among the engineering wonders of antiquity are Egypt's pyramids and the Great Sphinx, which was built around 2500 B.C.E. The Sphinx is sixty-nine feet (twenty-one meters) high and 243 feet (74 meters) in length. After being buried in sand for most of four millennia, the Sphinx is now threatened by air pollution. (PhotoDisc)

Alexandria, Egypt, seen from low-earth orbit in 1990. Dams have so reduced the amount of sediment that the Nile River pours into the Mediterranean Sea in its nearby delta that the coastline by Alexandria now exposes offshore shoals that were once buried in mud.
(Corbis)

The Great Sphinx by the pyramids is merely the largest of thousands of sphinx figures, such as this one at Alexandria, left by the early Egyptians.
(Corbis)

Satellite view of the Strait of Gibraltar, where Africa and Europe nearly meet. In 1998 Morocco and Spain signed an agreement to explore a route for a tunnel beneath the strait that would connect the two continents by rail. However, the only practical route for such a tunnel would require a project bigger and more expensive than the tunnel that connects Great Britain and France. (Corbis)

Cargo ship moving through the Suez Canal from the Gulf of Suez to the Mediterranean Sea. (AP/Wide World Photos)

During much of the year, Southern Africa's Limpopo River is an unimposing stream. However, like many African rivers, it can grow into a dangerous torrent during the rainy season. (R. Kent Rasmussen)

Residents of Mozambique's capital city, Maputo, walk through the floodwaters of the Limpopo River in early 2000. One of the African countries hardest-hit by flooding, Mozambique is also the site of some of the continent's most ambitious dam projects. (AP/Wide World Photos)

Train on South Africa's "Garden Route," along its southern coast. South Africa has a more fully developed network of railroads than other Africa countries, most of which have only lines from the coasts to inland cities or mining areas. (American Stock Photography)

In rain forest regions, such as the Congo Basin, road conditions can make surface transportation nearly impossible. (Jorge M. Garcia/Mercury Press)

Somali stevedores carrying bulk cargo by hand from lighters unloading a ship in a reef-protected harbor north of Mogadishu. The scarcity of natural harbors in Africa is one of many conditions that retard the continent's economic development. (AP/Wide World Photos)

Schoolchildren in Lesotho. The poverty of most African nations is an almost insuperable barrier to their schools having access to modern technological advances in communications. (American Stock Photography)

Vendors selling several different newspapers on the streets of Dakar, the capital of Senegal, in March, 2000. The papers report on the election of Abdoulaye Wade to the presidency and the ouster of the party that had been in power since independence. (AP/Wide World Photos)

EASTERN REGION. This region comprises Eritrea, Djibouti, Ethiopia, Somalia, Kenya, Tanzania, and Uganda. Kenya produces 350,000 tons of sodium carbonate per year, along with fluorspar (calcium fluoride) and small quantities of gold, iron ore, garnets, and limestone. Diamonds are mined in Eritrea. Gold, manganese, and platinum are mined in Ethiopia.

In Tanzania, gold and diamonds are mined. Uganda has mined copper, tin, tungsten, columbine-tantalite, beryl, bismuth, phosphate, limestone, and glasssand. Mining declined in the mid-1970's as a result of the poor political climate in the country and the economic policies in place at the time.

Djibouti and Somalia lack industries.

SOUTHERN REGION. This region comprises Angola, Zambia, Zimbabwe, Mozambique, Malawi, Botswana, Namibia, Lesotho, Swaziland, and South Africa. South Africa has 45 percent of the world's vanadium reserves, 90 percent of the world's platinum-group metal reserves, 68 percent of world's chrome ore reserves, 81 percent of the world's manganese, around 40 percent of the world's gold reserves, and 37 percent of the world's andalusite (a form of aluminum ore) reserves. It also has substantial reserves of other industrially important metals and minerals, including antimony, asbestos, diamonds, coal, fluorspar, phosphates, iron ore, lead, zinc, uranium, vermiculite, and zirconium. South Africa is the world's largest producer of gold, platinum-group metals, vanadium, and alumino-silicates, and one of the world's top producers of antimony, chromite, diamonds, ferrochrome, ferromanganese, fluorspar, manganese, titanium, vermiculite, and zirconium. The country is also a major producer and exporter of bituminous coal, cobalt, nickel, and granite.

Zambia is the world's fourth-largest copper-producing nation and the largest producer of cobalt, producing 20 percent of the world's total. Gold, coal, and emeralds are also being mined in Zambia. Zimbabwe is Africa's fourth-largest gold producer, after South Africa, Ghana, and Mali. Other principal metals and minerals produced are coal, diamonds, ferroalloys, nickel, asbestos, iron and steel, copper, tin, and graphite. Zambia has one oil refinery, located in Ndola. It is run by the Zambian Oil Company and provides most of the petroleum products required by the local market and for export.

Angola is one of Africa's major oil producing countries. After Nigeria, it is the most significant oil producer in Sub-Saharan Africa, with a production total of 650,000 barrels per day. The country's known recoverable reserves are estimated to total almost four billion barrels. Angola produces some 400,000 barrels of oil per day offshore from its enclave of Cabinda. The remainder of the 650,000-barrel-per-day total comes from Angola both on- and offshore. The petroleum industry is the sole economic mainstay of the Angolan government, and oil accounts for 40 percent of Angola's gross domestic product and for 90 percent of total exports. Several foreign companies have invested more than $8 billion in Angola. The state-owned company, Sonangol, which also owns the country's sole refinery at Luanda, controls refining and distribution of petroleum products. Mining in Angola is currently limited to diamond mining in the Lunda Norte Province, ornamental stones in the Huila and Namibe areas, and salt.

Namibia has become one of the world's leading producers of gem-quality diamonds, contributing 30 percent of the world's output. About 98 percent of the diamonds mined in Namibia are of gem quality, and since mining started near Luderitz in 1908, more than 100 million carats have been mined. In 1996 diamond production was 1,486 million carats, mostly gem quality. Onshore diamond deposits are becoming exhausted, but offshore diamond mining in Namibia soared during the 1990's, growing from 29,000 carats in 1990 to 650,00 carats in 1997. The potential for gem diamonds off Namibia's shores has been estimated at 1.5 billion to 3 billion carats, of which 95 percent are expected to be gem quality.

Namibia has the world's largest uranium mine, at Rossing, near Swakopmund. The mine produces low-grade uranium oxide. Production in the late 1990's, was close to its full capacity of 4,000 tons per year. The Haib copper mine, situated just north of the South African border near the town of Noordoewer, will be the seventh-largest producer of copper in the world, producing 85,000 tons a year of copper, over a 25-year span. This mine is also expected to produce 7,000 ounces (200 kilograms) of gold and 800,000 pounds (363,000 kilograms) of molybdenum concentrate.

Botswana is Africa's third-largest mining producer, after South Africa and Congo-Kinshasa. Diamonds, copper-nickel, soda ash, coal, and gold are mined. Botswana is Africa's largest, and the world's third-largest, producer of diamonds and second-largest producer of gem diamonds. Malawi has several million tons of coal reserves, which are beginning to be exploited.

There has been some mining of gold, bauxite, graphite, and marble in Mozambique. Swaziland has 200 million tons of coal reserves, asbestos, and diamonds, which are being mined.

INDIAN OCEAN ISLANDS. This region comprises Madagascar (the Malagasy Republic), Mauritius, Comoros, and the Seychelles. Madagascar may have promising reserves of heavy crude oil. At the end of the twentieth century, the island nation was producing a modest 37,000 tons of crude oil and 2,500 tons of natural gas per year. It is the world's tenth-largest producer of chrome and also produces graphite. Small-scale gold mining produces 100,000 ounces (2,830 kilograms) per year. Mauritius, the Comoros, and the Seychelles have little in the way of nonagricultural industries.

Dana P. McDermott

FOR FURTHER STUDY

Chipeta, Mapopa, ed. *Rural Industries in Malawi.* Harare, Zimbabwe: Southern Africa Printing and Publishing House, 1993.

Coughlin, Peter, and Gerrishon K. Ikiara, eds. *Kenya's Industrialization Dilemma.* Nairobi, Kenya: East African Educational Publishing, 1991.

Gleave, M. B., ed. *Tropical African Development.* New York: John Wiley & Sons, 1992.

Jourdan, Philip Paul, ed. *The Mining Sector in Southern Africa.* Harare, Zimbabwe: Southern Africa Printing and Publishing House, 1995.

Kesse, G. C. *Mineral and Rock Resources of Ghana.* Brookfield, Vt.: Ashgate, 1985.

Karekezi, Stephen, and Timothy Ranja. *Renewable Energy Technologies in Africa.* New York: St. Martin's Press, 1997.

United Nations. *Natural Resources Development in the Sahel: The Role of the United Nations Systems.* New York: United Nations, 1986.

INFORMATION ON THE
WORLD WIDE WEB

Mbendi, a Web site devoted to African business opportunities, features current news articles on African industry. (www.mbendi.co.za)

ENGINEERING PROJECTS

Most major engineering achievements in Africa relate to water management—for irrigation, consumption, and hydroelectric power—mineral and other extractive industries, and the means of moving mineral resources to ports and international markets. The general situation reflects basic geographical, economic, and historical facts about Africa: fairly low population densities in many areas (although they are increasing rapidly), extreme variability of rainfall in different seasons, a growing but comparatively modest consumption base, and surviving economic patterns of the recent colonial past.

Africa's rivers have the potential to generate more hydroelectric power than all the rest of the world's rivers combined. Indeed, the rivers of the Congo Basin alone could produce one-sixth of the world total, according to some estimates. However, African rivers can also be extremely destructive. With the exception of the Congo system (which is fed by rainy seasons in both hemispheres at different times of the year and thus has a fairly stable rate of flow), major river systems can carry devastating annual floods. Therefore, enormous effort has been applied to controlling these river systems and realizing their power potential.

DAMS: THE NILE WATERSHED. The capabilities of the Nile have shaped Egyptian history since ancient times. Shortly after the British occupied Egypt in 1882 (and soon after that, the whole Nile watershed except for Ethiopia), engineers began to try to regulate the Nile system. By 1900 there were flood control barrages in the

Nile Delta, and in 1907, the first Aswan Dam was completed to regulate the rate of annual flooding downstream.

When the British first occupied Egypt, the country was in the throes of rapid population growth and economic expansion. By early in the twentieth century, it was possible to anticipate that demand for water in the Nile watershed could outstrip supply in the short run. British engineers developed plans to turn the entire watershed into a storage and management area. By 1950 this project—actually a group of projects—came to be known as Century Storage. The idea was to store and manage water in such a way that, by the end of the twentieth century, sufficient water would be available in Nile reservoirs to overcome a five-year drought. Dams were completed in Sudan on both branches of the Nile before World War II, as centerpieces of the giant Gezira irrigation scheme.

The first postwar project was the Owen Falls Dam in Uganda, completed in 1954. Because Lake Victoria functions as a great natural reservoir for the dam, Owen Falls technically is the largest storage dam in the world, with a capacity of more than 205 billion cubic meters of water. The objective was to raise the level of Lake Victoria and thus provide a more reliable long-term water reserve. Turbines at the dam also generate hydroelectric power, although the equipment has had to be upgraded many times to meet demand. The logistics of such large projects are difficult in remote areas. Outflow from the spillways, for example, frequently is more than double what engineers anticipated,

Egyptian antiquities Pages 1098, 1099

Flooding Pages 971, 1101

A close view of the Pyramid of Cheops reveals the immense scale of the blocks used to build the pyramids. (Corbis)

leading to fears for the durability of the structure.

In the early 1950's, the new republican government in Egypt revived an old British recommendation for a huge storage dam just upstream from the original Aswan Dam, which came to be known as the High Dam project. The undertaking became a celebrated part of the Cold War

Silting
Page 1099

economic and ideological contest, when Western financiers backed away from the project and were replaced by funding and expertise from the Soviet Union. Dedicated in 1971, the High Dam at the time was the world's largest rock-fill construction dam. Standing 365 feet (111 meters) high with a crest of 12,566 feet (3,830 meters), the dam can impound 6 trillion cubic feet (170 billion cubic meters) of water in a reservoir 200 miles (320 km.) in length. Its hydroelectric turbines revolutionized the energy situation in Egypt, and the reservoir allowed hundreds of thousands of hectares to be opened to cultivation for the first time.

The High Dam became controversial as a case study in environmental upheaval. For example, because the fertile silt that had been deposited each year on their fields was trapped behind the dam, Egyptian farmers had to rely on a new chemical

---

THE EARLIEST ENGINEERS

The most impressive engineering feat in Africa remains the Great Pyramid, built around 2500 B.C.E. That human-made mountain is constructed of more than 3.2 million blocks laid out with a precision that continues to mystify archaeologists. The scale of the Great Pyramid foreshadows the gargantuan dimensions of more recent undertakings and those likely to be attempted in Africa's future.

fertilizer industry. The loss of the Nile's outflow to the sea brought about ecological change in the eastern Mediterranean of far greater magnitude than engineers foresaw, including the collapse of the sardine fishing industry and destruction of habitat and agriculture by invading seawater.

THE ZAMBEZI WATERSHED. In Southern Africa, British engineers completed the impressive Kariba Dam on the Zambezi River in 1959. At 180 billion cubic meters, its storage capacity is second in the world after Owen Falls. Kariba is a concrete arch structure approximately 425 feet (130 meters) high and carries a two-lane highway linking Zambia and Zimbabwe. It supplies nearly all the electricity requirements of both countries.

Shortly after achieving independence in 1975, Mozambique began the gigantic Cabora Bassa Dam project farther downstream on the Zambezi, a 560-foot-high (170-meter) structure that impounded a reservoir more than 78 miles (240 km.) in length. Completed in the late 1970's, this dam had the potential to usher in a new era of industrialization and power utilization in the whole region of Southern Africa, as well as provide irrigation and flood control for much of central Mozambique. Mozambique itself needed only about 10 percent of the dam's hydroelectric output.

Cabora Bassa received financing from the European Development Bank, largely because of its great regional potential, but political unrest prevented the region from realizing the full benefit of the project. Civil war broke out in Mozambique in 1979 and lasted for nearly two decades, destroying 80 percent of the power distribution grid. Reconstruction began in 1995 with the hope of restoring the system by 2000.

Restoration of Cabora Bassa was to make possible a regional power grid covering Mozambique, South Africa, Zambia, and Zimbabwe, with plans to reach farther west to Namibia and Angola and northward to the Katanga region of the Congo, tying in many smaller hydroelectric sites as well as those on the Zambezi. This sort of energy interdependence is regarded as a key not only to the economic development of the region but also to its political stability.

THE CONGO WATERSHED. The largest hydroelectric power potential in Africa, and perhaps in the world, lies at Inga Falls on the Congo River, about 25 miles (40 km.) upstream from the Atlantic river port of Matadi. Here the river falls nearly 330 feet (100 meters) in just 8.7 miles (14 km.), at a flow rate of about 43,000 cubic meters per second. Construction at Inga has been in phases: Inga I was completed in 1972 and provided electricity for a uranium enrichment plant nearby.

Inga II, completed in 1982, provided much needed power for the capital of Kinshasa and the mining industries in Katanga. These two projects brought the total generating capacity at Inga to 1,700 megawatts, an impressive figure but only a tiny fraction of the staggering estimated potential of 43,000 megawatts. Later stages will require not just power stations but a massive storage dam. In terms of both engineering and cost obstacles, as well as potential capacity, Inga is too large for the Congo and perhaps too large for Central Africa. The site requires an international market for electricity. As in the case of Cabora Bassa, chronic political and military unrest have stood in the way of such a development.

In 1999 the government of Congo-Kinshasa (formerly Zaire) announced ambitious plans to proceed with the next stages at Inga, designed to bring the project to maximum generating capacity by 2010. Conservatively estimated to cost $7.5 bil-

Inga Falls hydroelectric dam. (AP/Wide World Photos)

lion, expansion at Inga will include doubled transmission lines to Katanga and links to the regional power grid in Southern Africa largely for the benefit of South Africa, where power demands threaten to outstrip capacity. Transmission lines may also reach the huge market in Nigeria. Egypt may contract for as much as 12,000 megawatts. Should all these plans materialize, they will create an almost continental power grid and a totally new economic and political environment in Africa.

WEST AFRICAN DAMS. The largest storage dam and hydroelectric project in West Africa is at Akosombo in Ghana. Begun in 1961 and completed in 1965, Akosombo is a rock-fill structure of modest cost, just over 425 feet (130 meters) high with a crest of 2,200 feet (671 meters). The enormous storage reservoir inundated almost 4 percent of the total area of Ghana. The government built Akosombo in partnership with the Kaiser Corporation, which

contracted to ship bauxite from Jamaica and Guyana to the aluminum smelter facility at Tema. The smelter originally consumed most of the hydroelectric power, but additional generating capacity installed later enables the dam to supply most of the country's electricity needs and even export some to neighbors. A new fishing industry developed on the sprawling reservoir, and Lake Volta provides a useful transportation artery to the less-developed northern region of Ghana.

Another purpose of Akosombo was over-year storage of water for flood control and irrigation, as the Volta River is extremely variable in annual discharge. However, drought in the early 1980's was so severe that in 1983, the hydroelectric turbines had to be shut down for two years, with devastating economic consequences for the country. Neighboring Côte d'Ivoire has a smaller storage and hydroelectric facility on the Bandama River at Koussou, and several smaller dams are in place along the Niger.

IRRIGATION. Seasonal variability of water supply in much of Africa, as well as desert environments in the north and extreme south, have made irrigation and water pipelines as much of a concern on a continental scale as dams and power. Many of these schemes have been conceived on a vast scale, and the origins of some hark to colonial times. The French built an irrigation barrage on the Niger River at Sansanding in 1946 in hopes of revolutionizing irrigated agriculture in what is now Mali.

In the late 1940's, the British tried to turn much of what is now central Tanzania into a scientifically operated peanut complex through irrigation. These and other projects failed miserably, in part because of infertile soils, and in part because the engineers who planned the systems did not understand that successful irrigation schemes are dependent more on micromanagement by thousands of users than they are on just constructing a dam or main feeder channels. Later projects, which relied more on local planning and were more modest in anticipated outcome, have done better, but even these are often fairly ambitious engineering projects. For example, the Niono Project in central Mali diverts a large portion of the flow of the Niger through irrigation canals 20 miles (32 km.) long.

Many irrigation projects in Africa have been modeled on the very successful Gezira Project in Sudan. Conceived in the colonial period, the Gezira scheme placed several million hectares into cotton production in the region south of the confluence of the White and Blue Niles, by damming both rivers close by. As was often the case with major development in colonial times, the Gezira scheme also was designed to foster a separate Sudanese political consciousness and compete with cotton production in Egypt. Consequently, the scheme greatly accelerated water consumption on the upper reaches of the Nile watershed to the dismay of the Egyptians.

WATER SUPPLY. As African populations and living standards grow, demand for fresh water is increasing enormously in arid regions. In the Nile watershed, for example, there is demand for every drop available. The Jonglei scheme in deep southern Sudan, begun in the 1980's, was designed to canalize the flow of the Nile through this vast, swampy region, where the Nile loses an estimated 10 cubic kilometers of water annually to evaporation. Unrest interrupted the project in the late 1980's, as southern Sudan slipped into a chronic secessionist war.

In South Africa, the Orange-Fish Tunnel, 51 miles (82.5 km.) in length and nearly 18 feet (5.5 meters) in diameter, diverts water from the Hendrik Verwoerd Dam on the Orange River to irrigation projects and to cities on the South African coast. A much larger project to draw additional water from the uplands to supply

LARGEST STORAGE DAMS IN THE WORLD

Four of the five largest storage dams in the world are located on the African continent.

Storage Dam	Country	Volume, in Millions of Cubic Meters
Owen Falls	Uganda	204,800
Kariba	Zambia/Zimbabwe	180,600
Bratsk	Russia	169,270
High Aswan	Egypt	168,900
Akosombo	Ghana	148,000

major South African cities, the Lesotho Highlands Water Project, has engendered protests from environmentalists and other activists. Designed to move up to 80,000 cubic meters of water daily into South Africa, Lesotho Highlands will not be complete until 2020 at the earliest.

The largest water transmission project in Africa is the Great Man Made River in Libya. In the process of intensive exploration of Libya for oil and gas, geologists discovered enormous quantities of water locked in sandstone and limestone aquifers in the southern two-thirds of the country. Originally, the government hoped to develop agriculture in the middle of the Sahara by utilizing this water, as in the case of the Kufrah agricultural project in the late 1970's, but the strategy changed to bringing these enormous supplies by pipelines to the coast.

Suez Canal Page 1100

A 1,180-mile-long (1,900-kilometer) gravity pipeline, 13 feet (4 meters) in diameter, runs to a great holding reservoir south of Benghazi. Phase 2 of the project will focus on western Libya and provide drinking and irrigation water for the Tripoli area. These enormous pipelines were manufactured in Libya in sections of steel and concrete laminate, and laid in sections using specially constructed cranes. Completion of the project is scheduled for 2007.

TRANSPORT. Africa traditionally has had enormous transport problems. River transport is hampered by variable flows, only partly addressed so far by dams. The huge continental coastline has few natural indentations; consequently, harbors must be artificial. In general, these are of moderate size and in places choked with traffic. Many railroads date to colonial times, with a bewildering variety of gauges; modern railroads usually directly serve mine-to-port traffic. During the colonial period, development of a Cape-to-Cairo railroad, run-

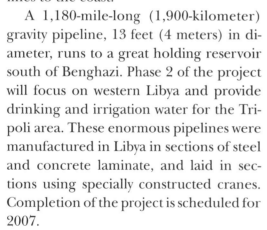

Oil drilling Page 1025

ning entirely through British-controlled territory the length of Africa, nearly became a reality, although not through much purposeful planning. In any case, local unrest and political jealousies among states have long since interrupted the route in many places. International airports are relatively numerous in Africa, but none classifies as a notable project. Except in South Africa and a few other isolated locations, the road system is only marginal.

The first subway in Africa opened in Cairo in 1983, and in 1998, a second, three-mile (five-kilometer) route, running under the Nile River from Cairo to Giza, began operation.

Among the major transport engineering feats in Africa is the Suez Canal. Archaeologists have shown that several Mediterranean-Red Sea canals, usually running through the Nile Delta, existed in earlier periods, but the present canal opened in 1869. Approximately 121 miles (195 km.) in length, the canal is a sea-level project that did not require complex locks. Constant dredging is required to keep the canal open, and since 1982, the waterway has been deepened to allow passage by ever-larger vessels. For security reasons, two highway tunnels have been drilled underneath the canal to connect the Sinai Peninsula with the rest of the country. The world's longest movable steel bridge, 2,100 feet (640 meters) in length, spans the canal at Al-Firdan.

MINERAL EXTRACTION. Oil-producing areas of Africa, such as Libya and southern Nigeria, are webbed with the familiar drilling, storage, pipeline, and refinery structures characteristic of the petroleum industry. Offshore drilling has provided serious engineering challenges, owing to the narrow continental shelf typical of most of Africa.

The mining industries of Southern Africa exploit some of the richest and most strategically important mineral deposits in the world. Mining of gold and diamonds, in particular, presents immense engineering challenges because of the great depth at which they often occur and, in the case of gold, volatile prices that demand ever more production efficiency. At South Africa's East Dreifontein gold mine, some shafts are nearly 6.5 miles (4 km.) deep. At such depths, atmospheric pressure is nearly double that on the surface.

Radioactivity and heat from the earth's core raise the temperature to as much as 122 degrees Fahrenheit (50 degrees Celsius). Free oxygen rarely exists so far underground, and must be pumped, pressurized, into the shafts, along with jets of water to keep the temperatures down. Not surprisingly, gold mining in South Africa ranks among the world's most dangerous professions.

THE FUTURE. Africa seems to encourage huge projects, some of which have not materialized but may do so in the future. For example, for more than eighty years there has been talk of a railroad across the Sahara, to link West African economies with the north. In 1998 Morocco and Spain signed an agreement to explore a route for a tunnel across the Strait of Gibraltar, which might connect with both a trans-Saharan and a trans-North African railroad system. Where the Strait of Gibraltar is narrowest, the water is far too deep to permit a tunnel, and it would have to follow a route to the west some 28 miles (45 km.) in length. Should this project be undertaken, it would be considerably more expensive and ambitious than the tunnel under the English Channel, and there are serious doubts whether Africa, as yet, is ready for it.

Some proposals for future irrigation and power schemes are comparably ambitious. Egypt has long dreamed of constructing a tunnel from the Mediterra-

nean to the Qattara Depression, a vast, subsea-level region in the northwest of the country. Inrushing water from the Mediterranean would take decades to fill the depression and generate hydroelectric power in the process. Another proposal would turn great areas of the Sahara into a global heat sink for climatic control.

Even if these future dreams do not all come to pass, given political stability, Africa in the year 2000 stood on the brink of a huge potential economic breakthrough that could accelerate markedly the progress of engineering on the continent. This could direct efforts to critical areas such as transport and communications and lead to the creation of a critical mass of engineering expertise in areas such as Egypt and South Africa.

William T. Walker

FOR FURTHER STUDY

Arnold, Guy, and Ruth Weiss. *Strategic Highways of Africa.* New York: St. Martin's Press, 1977.

Davis, Kingsley, and Dale Whittington. "International Management of the Nile: Stage Three." *Geographical Review* 71 (1981): 17-32.

Due, John. "The Problems of Railroad Transport in Tropical Africa." *Journal of Developing Areas* 13 (1979): 375-393.

Gleave, M. B., ed. *Tropical African Development.* New York: John Wiley & Sons, 1992.

Moore, Henry Clement. *Images of Development: Egyptian Engineers in Search of Industry.* Cambridge, Massachusetts: MIT Press, 1980.

Waterbury, John. *Hydropolitics of the Nile Valley.* Syracuse: Syracuse University Press, 1979.

Zymelman, Manuel. *Assessing Engineering Education in Sub-Saharan Africa.* New York: World Bank, 1993.

Gibraltar Page 1100

TRANSPORTATION

Unlike transportation in the United States, with its excellent connections of interstate road and rail transportation, numerous airports, and urban transit systems, transportation in Africa is problematic. Intercountry networks are poorly developed, connections within countries are similarly limited, and the quality of the system—state of repair, availability, efficiency—varies significantly among countries. Even when reliable transportation infrastructure exists, political conflicts such as civil war sometimes make it unusable.

HISTORICAL BACKGROUND. Transportation of goods and people has never been easy in Africa. The rivers, land, animals, and disease frequently presented major obstacles to transport. Before the Europeans arrived, transportation was primarily on foot, and most goods were carried on the head or back because the tsetse fly prevented the use of animals for lading and hauling. With a markedly seasonal flow, shifting channels, and many cataracts and falls, river transport was a major challenge for dugout canoes.

Coasts devoid of natural shelter and exposed to heavy surf required expensive breakwaters and harbors. In the rain forest, falling trees that blocked roads, washed-out roads, and broken bridges were always a challenge. Nevertheless, highly developed transport networks emerged in many parts of Africa during precolonial times, based primarily on paths beaten out of the bush by human feet. The major twentieth century thoroughfares are based on these paths.

During the colonial era that followed, these networks were restructured to penetrate into the interior from the seaports and railroads that were established, primarily to serve the commercial and administrative needs of the colonial powers. In the early phase, roads were built cheaply and of simple design, reflecting the low traffic densities of the time. Consequently, running speeds were low, vehicle life was relatively short, and large sections of the network were closed for varying periods during the rainy season. The seasonal nature of the road network remains an important feature of the system today—the dry season network is several times more extensive than the all-weather network.

After independence, the most intensively used links in the system were upgraded. Gravel or laterite surfaces have been replaced, sometimes by two-lane bitumen surfaces. Few motorways exist in the region; the Lagos-Ibadan Expressway and the Accra-Tema motorway are good examples of those that do. Bridges have replaced ferries, and roads have been realigned to take out sharp bends and steep gradients. Nevertheless, road densities vary significantly among locations, depending on population density, topography, proximity to urban centers, economic activity, and competing forms of transport.

ROAD TRANSPORTATION. Roads in African countries are generally of three classes: primary, secondary, and tertiary or rural roads. Primary and secondary roads are main arterial highways of relatively high standards, connecting major population centers and provincial capitals. Rural roads, which are usually in a poor state of repair, include penetration roads that provide access to potential development areas, provincial roads connecting small districts or communities, and feeder roads that link agricultural areas to market centers directly or by main arterial roads.

Rural travel is filled with difficulties. Roads and seasonal tracks are rarely maintained, and people walk along treacherous paths and footbridges to obtain water and firewood and to reach markets, schools, and clinics. These same tracks, paths, and footbridges are used to transport export crops and food destined for urban populations. In rural Africa most people walk, carrying their burdens, and women frequently carry the bulk of the burden. Other than walking, nonmotorized vehicles—bicycles, wheelbarrows, donkeys, and carts, both hand-pulled and animal-drawn—are the primary means of transport.

Seasonal inaccessibility is a perpetual problem that plagues rural transportation. Even during the dry season, when roads are generally drivable with little difficulty, transportation is rarely available. In some villages no car passes for days, while in others, a taxi arrives once a day. The rainy season compounds the unavailability problem. Road conditions deteriorate so much that in some places, access is frequently only by walking along muddy paths and sometimes wading through water. Other problems include broken bridges, flooded roads, washed-out paths, and overgrown tracks that provide good hiding places for poisonous snakes.

URBAN TRANSPORT. Urban transport consists of three main types of transit:

European exploration of Africa tended to follow rivers because of the comparative ease of transportation on water. (Leo Frobenius, *The Voice of Africa*, 1913)

THE HIGHWAY OF DEATH

During the late twentieth century, the deadly human immunodeficiency virus (HIV) and acquired immunodeficiency syndrome (AIDS) spread throughout Africa along major transportation routes, causing social havoc. Nowhere was it as visible as in East Africa. Its journey typically began in Djibouti, at the mouth of the Red Sea. From there it moved south to Mozambique and into Ethiopia. Truckers themselves were major HIV carriers, and every truck stop along their routes was a potential regional epicenter for the disease, as the truckers engaged in paid sex with local women. From Nairobi, Kenya, the trucking routes split, south to Tanzania and west to Uganda. Along the way, HIV devastated whole villages, causing fleeing residents to carry it to their new locations. No major city in its path emerged unscathed, no country remained untouched. The truck route from Malawi to Durban, South Africa, became known as the Highway of Death. During the late 1990's, an estimated 92 percent of truck drivers visiting Durban along that route were infected with HIV, primarily from sexual activity at their truck stops.

---

government-operated bus systems; privately owned and operated minibuses known as poda-podas (Sierra Leone), trotros (Ghana), or matatus (Kenya); and taxis. Government-operated buses are generally overloaded and unreliable and require users to wait at unsheltered terminals, and passenger loading is often disorderly and unorganized, particularly during peak periods. Most trips require multiple transfers, and the buses move slowly, frequently going only 5 to 8 miles (8-12 km.) per hour because of the ever-present extreme congestion or deterioration along the few available roads. Street trading along the main routes and failure to enforce regulations against on-street parking contribute to the congestion.

For most poor people in urban areas, transport is time-consuming, costly, and often unsafe. On average, 50 percent of transport in African cities is by walking or bicycling, but people who take some form of motorized transport can spend a high percentage of household income (up to 30 percent in Dar es Salaam, for example) on mobility. About 66 percent of urban traffic fatalities in Sub-Saharan Africa (which are much higher per capita than in developed countries) occur among pedestrians, with half of those fatalities being children.

THE PLANNED PAN-AFRICAN HIGHWAY. Progress in road building in Africa during the 1990's was spectacular. World Bank loans, supplementing by national budgets, financed the building and improvement of road networks in many African countries. African countries have been spending, on the average, about a quarter of the total financial provision of their national plans on transport development. More than 60 percent of this has been allocated to road construction, improvement, and maintenance. For example, Gabon has invested a substantial portion of its oil revenues in constructing all-weather roads and a railway into the interior. Nevertheless, the road network in Africa in the year 2000 was still inadequate, and only about one-third of the African road system was up to the standard of all-weather roads.

Action on highway networks in North Africa was initiated by the Economic Commission for Africa (ECA) in 1962 and is aimed at a trans-Saharan route that would link North Africa with West Africa and an East-West route—from Cairo passing through Tripoli, Tunis, Algiers, and Rabat—to link the countries of the Mediterranean coast. The East-West route virtually exists and the North-West highway is being built with international assistance.

In 1967 the Economic Commission for Africa established two long roads as priorities for the improvement of the West African road network: one coastal road of 3,356 miles (5,400 km.) running through Lagos to Dakar, and one of about 4,220 miles (6,800 km.) in the hinterland, roughly following the twelfth parallel and linking Nouakchott in Mauritania and Fort Lamy in Chad. International assistance to support these projects is well under way. With help from bilateral donor agencies, the Entente States (Côte d'Ivoire, Togo, Dahomey, Upper Volta, and Niger) are filling in other details of a West African network.

EAST AFRICA. In East Africa, links already exist among Kenya, Uganda, and Tanzania. Others are being developed between Zambia and Botswana, between Ethiopia and Kenya, and between Ethiopia and the Sudan with a possible extension to Egypt. These are the arteries of the Trans-East African Highway, the most important link of all. When fully completed, it should be about 4,000 miles (6,400 km.) in length and will link Mombasa in Kenya with Lagos in Nigeria, passing through Uganda, Zaire, the Central African Republic, and the United Republic of Cameroon.

The projected highway is also of interest to eleven neighboring states: Burundi, Chad, Congo, Ethiopia, Gabon, Niger, Rwanda, Somalia, Sudan, Tanzania, and Zambia. These four highways would be the backbone of the Pan-African road system and would be connected by feeder roads

to complete, stage by stage, the arterial highway system on the continent. Once the improvements of these four major highways are completed, it will be possible to travel from Algiers on the Mediterranean Sea to Mombasa on the Indian Ocean, thence to Dakar on the Atlantic Ocean and from Cairo to Gaberones in Botswana.

Once roads are constructed, regular maintenance is critical. Delayed or neglected maintenance inevitably produces costly repairs. The 220 miles (350 km.) of road from Kinshasa to the port of Matadi, which previously took about five hours to cover, had so badly deteriorated by the mid-1990's that trucks needed five days to complete the trip. In the year 2000, there was no paved road linking Brazzaville, the national capital of Congo-Brazzaville, with Pointe Noire, its major seaport.

RAILWAYS. In Africa, as in Europe and North America, the major period of railway development extended from the end of the nineteenth century to the end of World War I. This expansion, however, was not coordinated. Railways were built as common carriers, usually under government ownership, between 1895 and 1914, primarily to stimulate cash production of export crops, facilitate mineral development, and demonstrate colonial occupancy.

Most railways were single-line, used light track and simple signaling systems, and avoided embankments and cutting tunnels wherever possible. The result was sharp curves, steep gradients, and circuitous routes, and consequently, low running speeds. Moreover, track gauges varied between countries as did the braking and coupling systems. Thus, the colonizing powers left a difficult and costly legacy for independent African countries who wanted to link their rail services. As with roads, rail networks have been improved

An Angolan carries firewood alongside signs marking a minefield in central Angola in mid-2000. (AP/Wide World Photos)

LAND MINES

Besides diverting expenditure from maintenance and much-needed new construction, political instability, whether from civil war or ethnic conflicts, disrupts transportation systems. Even after the conflicts are over, roads and railways may remain unused for a long time because of the fear of land mines left over from civil wars. In 2000 most of Angola's roads were known, or suspected, to be mined. Supplies and people had to be flown in to many places, but because some airports were also mined, it was a risky operation. Large tracts of land in Mozambique were also extensively mined. Land mines on many major roads severely disrupted trade and exchange. Mining of roads and insecurity resulting from civil conflicts forced Zimbabwe, Zambia, and other land-locked states to reroute much of their freight through South Africa.

considerably since the 1960's, leading to lower transport costs. Recent improvements typically include realignment and strengthening of the track, signaling system improvements, and extension of the original network either to fill in missing links or to connect new, previously unserved locations.

The early railways were constructed partly to facilitate the administration of interior regions and to bring supplies from ports to central consumption or distribution points and partly—especially in the south—to enable valuable minerals or commodities to reach the coast for export. Railways are much more important than rivers in the transport structure of West Africa but are few and widely spaced. Instead of forming a network, the rail pattern comprises a series of individual fingers that extend inland from various ports but which seldom connect with other railway lines.

Many railway lines are not properly connected, limiting their utility. For example, Cameroon's seaport of Douala is connected to the inland capital, Yaoundé, by rail. Apart from a few rail fingers reaching inland from seaports, the region is devoid of railways, and roads only serve areas poorly. Isolation and poor transport are major obstacles to development in this region. Similarly, mineral production in the Shaba province of Congo-Kinshasa has no railroad outlet northward. Mineral exports routed through Angola to Lobito or Beira in Mozambique have been disrupted by local wars. Consequently, most exports take the long, expensive route through Zambia and Zimbabwe to South African ports.

The most productive parts of East Africa are linked by a connected system of railways leading inland from the seaports of Mombasa in Kenya, and Dar es Salaam and Tanga in Tanzania. Mombasa, the most important seaport in East Africa, has two ports—a picturesque old harbor used primarily by small vessels, and a modern deep-water harbor with facilities for handling large vessels. From Mombasa, the main line of the Kenya-Uganda railway leads into Nairobi, Kenya's capital, and continues westward to Kampala. Dar es Salaam has rail connections to Lake Tanganyika, Lake Victoria, and Zambia.

WEST AFRICA RAILWAYS. In French-speaking West Africa, a major railway line links the Senegal River port of St. Louis with Dakar and extends to Bamako. The railway line linking Abidjan through Bobo Dioulasso to Ouagadougou in Burkina Faso was completed in 1955. Guinea's railway line links the national capital, Conakry, with Kankan in the interior. In Togo, the rail line connects Lomé, the capital, with Blitta in the interior. In neighboring Benin, the railway line links Cotonou with Parakou, and a short coastal line linking Porto Novo, the capital, was completed in 1930.

Ghana's railway lines are centered in the southern one-third of the country and link Sekondi and Takoradi in the Western Region through mining and forested regions to Kumasi in the Ashanti Region and Accra, the national capital. Another line links Accra with Takoradi in the west, producing what has been called locally the Golden Triangle, reflecting the relative economic development of the region. Nigeria is served by nearly 2,000 miles (3,218 km.) of rail that cover the economically important regions of the country. The major links include Lagos-Ibadan-Kano via Ilorin and Zaria. The Port Harcourt-Enugu line now connects the Lagos-Ibabdan-Kaduna line. Liberia's only railroad links Monrovia, the capital and leading port, with the vast iron ore deposits of the nearby Bomi Hills 45 miles (72 km.) away.

CENTRAL AFRICAN RAILWAYS. A chain of railways links the Atlantic Ocean with Lake Tanganyika and avoids the series of rapids and falls that peaks in Stanley Falls. The Congo-Ocean railway links the Congo River with the Atlantic Ocean at Pointe Noire, providing efficient passage for passengers and freight, including minerals. The Benguela railway runs almost horizontally along the width of Angola, connecting to the Bulawayo–Port Francqui line at Tenke. The railway line from Kigoma connects the Indian Ocean at Dar es Salaam with branch lines from Tabora to Mwanza on the southern shore of Lake Victoria in Tanzania; the Tanzam Railway, built by Tanzania with Chinese assistance, links Dar es Salaam to Zambia.

EAST AFRICAN RAILWAYS. The Kenya-Uganda line, almost 600 miles (970 km.) long, links Mombasa with Kisumu on the shores of Lake Victoria. This line has been extended to link Kasese, which has become a major shipping point for copper from the Kilembe mines in the foothills of the Ruwenzori Mountains. Sudan Railways, more than 2,000 miles (3,200 km.) long, provides bypasses along the cataract-ridden section of the Nile between Khartoum and the Egyptian border, giving Khartoum direct access to Port Sudan on the Red Sea and several large towns in the country. The Somalia-Ethiopia line weaves through wadis and ravines to link Djibouti in the Gulf of Aden with Addis Ababa. The Eritrean railway is a narrow-gauge line linking the Red Sea port of Massawa with Asmara, the capital of Eritrea, and with Keren and Agordat.

SOUTHERN AFRICAN RAILWAYS. South Africa is probably the most well-served region in terms of railways. One line links Port Elizabeth with Windhoek, the capital of Namibia, and Walvis Bay on the Atlantic Ocean. Another links Cape Town with Pretoria through Bloemfontein and connects to the Bulawayo line.

A single system links Bulawayo in Zimbabwe with Livingstone to the northwest, Harare to the northeast, and Beira, the Mozambican port on the Indian Ocean. This same system also runs south to Gaborone, capital of Botswana, where it connects the South African system, and also southeast to Maputo.

AIR TRANSPORT. Well suited to Africa's geographic vastness, air transportation has become the primary means of international, and sometimes national, travel in Africa. During the late 1940's and the

South African railroad Page 1102

Congo River Pages 962, 1103

1950's, as great advances were made in the extension and improvement of rail and road services, a new transport factor emerged in the introduction of internal and international scheduled air services.

The rapid development of air transport increased the movement of goods and people, and began to open up the hitherto largely closed interior of the continent. Transport became much quicker and usually cheaper. Since then, internal air services have steadily increased, and intercontinental air transport, especially of passengers, has developed greatly. The largest international airports are at Casablanca, Morocco; Las Palmas, Canary Islands; Cairo, Egypt; Dakar, Senegal; Abidjan, Côte d'Ivoire; Lagos, Nigeria; Douala, Cameroon; Addis Ababa, Ethiopia; Nairobi, Kenya; and Johannesburg, South Africa.

WATER TRANSPORTATION. Historically, throughout the vast interior between the Sahara and the Zambezi River, people or goods have been transported by canoe or boat on the great river systems of the Nile, Senegal, Niger, Congo, Ubangi, and Zambezi Rivers and on the few but large lakes. Where conditions were suitable, engine-powered craft later supplemented or displaced canoes, but further development of water transport has been slight. Also notable were the construction of lake ports and the installation of rail ferries across Lake Victoria. Meanwhile, on the coasts, artificial harbors have been developed. New berths have been added to established port facilities, and several ports have been constructed. In planning new ports, the choice of site, probable costs, and the possibilities of using containers or other unitized loads have been taken into consideration.

The Congo River is the largest watershed in terms of drainage and discharge in Sub-Saharan Africa. The Congo flows across a relatively flat basin that lies more than 1,000 feet (300 meters) above sea level, meandering extensively through the rain forest. Entry from the Atlantic Ocean is precluded by a series of falls and rapids that make the Congo River only partially navigable. Nevertheless, the Congo River has been the major corridor of travel within Congo-Brazzaville and Congo-Kinshasa (formerly Zaire). Heavily laden barges ferry people and cargo between Kinshasa and Kinsangani and to Brazzaville on the opposite bank of the river. Navigation on the Zambezi is limited because of strong rapids, the basis for the Kariba Dam on the border of Zambia and Zimbabwe as well as the Cabora Bassa in Mozambique.

River transport is more important in the Congo River basin than elsewhere in Sub-Saharan Africa. In Congo-Kinshasa, river transport is an important part of the integrated transport system. This system consists of the Matadi to Kinshasa railway, river services from Kinshasa to Kinsangani, the rail link from Kinsangani to Ukundi, and river services onward from Lualaba to Kindu and then a rail link to Shaba. The other national axis consists of river services from Kinshasa to Ibbo on the Kasai River and a rail link onward to Shaba. Transshipments on both routes are numerous, and transit times are long. This increases costs and makes freight vulnerable to damage and pilfering. The Congo and Oubangoui Rivers provide a vital link both for Congo-Brazzaville, particularly its northern parts, and for the Central African Republic where Bangui, the capital, is an important river port that also serves neighboring Chad.

On the Niger River, seasonal navigation is possible from the railhead at Kouroussa

Canoe on Southern Africa's Chobe River. (Corbis)

to Bamako, from Koulikro to Ansongo, and from Niamey to Yelwa. In the lower reaches, the river is navigable from the Niger Delta to Lokoja all year, and seasonally to Baro and Jebba. On the Benue, the open season is June to November to Makurdi, and shortens to six to eight weeks in August and September at Garoua. The Senegal and Gambia Rivers, the White Nile from Juba to Khartoum, and the East African lakes, particularly Victoria and Tanganyika, are also used as links in the transport network.

HARBORS. Good natural harbors are scarce in West Africa because of the abun-

Lake Tanganyika Page 1165

dance of offshore sandbars and silt-choked river mouths. This necessitates the transfer of goods from ships to shore by small boats and the associated large expenses. Inland, frequent rapids and annual seasonal fluctuations in water level limit the utility of rivers for transport. The rivers that carry major traffic include the Niger and its tributary, the Benue; the Senegal; the Gambia; and to a smaller extent, the Volta in Ghana.

Navigation is not well coordinated with the other transport systems in the region. For example, while the extensive navigable waterways of the Congo River system are used primarily for inland transport, they lack a direct outlet to the sea. The railways on either bank linking Kinshasa and Brazzaville are narrow-gauge, limited in capacity, and unconnected to each other.

Other problems with inland waterways for modern transport include the following: Most rivers are characterized by alternating sections of low gradients and rapids, few rivers are navigable any distance from their mouths, which often have difficult access; unreliable rainfall patterns mean that the rivers may be closed to navigation for part of the year; they often flow through areas of low transport demand; and the location of political boundaries frequently reduces traffic.

Joseph R. Oppong

FOR FURTHER STUDY

Addus, A. Abdussalam. "Road Transportation in Africa." *Transportation Quarterly* 43, no. 3 (1989): 421-433.

Banjo, Adegboyega G. "Deregulation of Urban Public Transport Services: Some Realities for Policy Makers in African Cities." *Third World Planning Review,* 16(4): 411-428.

Grove, A. T. *The Changing Geography of Africa.* 2d ed. Oxford, England: Oxford University Press, 1993.

Hodder, B. W., and M. B. Gleave. "Transport, Trade and Development in Tropical Africa." In *Tropical African Development,* edited by M. B. Gleave. New York: John Wiley & Sons, 1992.

Kimble, George H. T. *Tropical Africa.* New York: Twentieth Century Fund, 1960.

Quaye, Kwei, and Daniel Badoe. "Delivery of Urban Transport in Sub-Saharan Africa. Case Study of Accra, Ghana." *Journal of Advanced Transportation* Vol. 30, no. 1 (Spring, 1986): 75-94.

COMMUNICATIONS

Although some countries in Africa have modern technology and take part in the revolution in commerce and communications that has been sparked by the World Wide Web, at the end of the twentieth century, most Africans did not have access to the Internet or to most modern modes of communication. Many cultural and political changes are needed before Africans can have the same access to modern communication systems available in other parts of the world. Africa's poverty and health-related problems could be partly overcome if communication systems were better developed on that continent. On the other hand, communication systems undoubtedly would be improved if Africa's nations were not so poor and if there were more money for both education and other development.

BROADCASTING. Television and radio broadcasting in Africa lags far behind the standards of the United States, Canada, Japan, and members of the European Union. Only South Africa, the most modern country in Africa, had broadcast media availability that was similar to that found in those countries. In 1997 South Africa had 556 television broadcast stations, 164 FM radio stations, and 15 AM radio stations available to its 43.5 million citizens. It also had 144 network repeaters and one shortwave station. In 1999 South Africans owned 7.5 million radios and about the same number of television sets. Few other African nations had such access to the broadcast media.

For example, Algeria, whose 1997 population of 31.1 million was almost three-fourths that of South Africa, had only 18 television broadcast stations, 23 AM radio stations, 1 FM station, and 8 shortwave stations. Algeria had only 2 million television sets and about 3.5 million radios in 1999, about 1 television for every fifteen people and one radio for every ten.

Another relatively well-developed country, Nigeria, had 82 AM radio stations, 32 FM stations, and 10 shortwave stations in 1997. In that year Egypt, which covers an area about three times that of New Mexico, had 42 of its own broadcast stations. In the parts of Egypt closest to Europe, various European television channels could be received. In all of Egypt, in 1997, there were 57 AM radio stations, 14 fourteen FM stations, and 3 shortwave stations. In 1998 there were approximately 5 million television sets in Egypt and 16.5 million radios.

Many African nations' citizens had far less access to modern media than did the citizens of Algeria, Nigeria, and Egypt. In 1999 Eritrea had only 1 broadcast television station, a government-controlled station that disseminated government-approved information to the country's four million citizens. In 1997 Eritrea had 2 AM radio stations and 1 shortwave station.

The situation was worse in Somalia, with a population of 7 million. In 1997 Somalia had 5 shortwave stations, but no television stations and no FM or AM radio stations. In contrast, West Virginia, with a population of 1.2 million, had 20 broadcast television stations.

TELECOMMUNICATIONS. In Africa, the telecommunications system is no better

Lesotho school Page 1104

developed than the broadcasting capability. Use of telecommunications is hampered by outmoded, inadequate cable, and by the fact that the countries generally must buy equipment abroad since, with the exception of South Africa, no African nation manufactures telephone equipment.

As in the broadcast media, South Africa leads the African continent in telecommunications development and use. In 1997 South Africa had adequate carrier-equipped open wire lines, coaxial cables, microwave relay links, and radio communications stations. It also had one subma-

Residents of Dakar gather to listen to radio on a Senegalese election in early 2000. As in other parts of the developing world, many Africans depend on radio to get most of their news. (AP/Wide World Photos)

COMMUNICATIONS IN BOTSWANA

In 1999 the 1.5 million citizens of the Southern African nation of Botswana communicated with each other in the country's official language, English, as well as in the local language, Setswana. They did not communicate often over the telephone, however, since there were only nineteen thousand telephones. Few people could receive information over broadcast television, since there were no broadcast stations in the country and only thirteen thousand television sets in the entire country. In this situation, much information must be passed orally. However, Botswana had a relatively high literacy rate of about 70 percent in the late 1990's, and several newspapers were available for citizens to read, including *The Botswana Gazette*, which could be accessed over the Internet for those few people who had Internet access.

rine cable and three Intelsat satellite earth stations. Internet access over telephone lines was readily available to those who could afford it. There were approximately 4.2 million phones in South Africa—about one for every ten people.

Although Egypt had an adequate number of telephones in the late 1990's, it did not have lines and services available to meet the demands created by those phones and their users. There were 3.1 million phones in Egypt in 1997, including more than 75,000 cellular phones. Egypt had five coaxial submarine lines available for carrying customers' calls and four satellite earth stations for relaying them.

At the end of the twentieth century, people in some African nations had little possibility of speaking by telephone to people in other parts of the world. Somalia's 7.5 million people had only 9,000 telephones. Civil war had completely destroyed public telecommunications. Relief agencies working there depended on their own private telecommunications systems. Local cellular service was available only in Mogadishu, and only in Mogadishu could international calls be made using available satellites. At the end of the twentieth century, persons in Mogadishu could call out of the country only from telephones at local hotels.

In Nigeria, there were only about 405,000 phones in 1995. Intercity phone traffic was carried by coaxial cable, microwave radio relay, and twenty earth stations. International calls were made possible by three Intelsat stations and by one coaxial submarine cable. While the telephone system there suffered from extremely poor maintenance at the end of the twentieth century, a major expansion project was in process.

In 1999 Eritrea had about four phones for each one hundred families. Burkina Faso had a similar rate, with a total of about twenty-one thousand phones for its 11.5 million citizens. By comparison, an average American town of ten thousand residents has more than twenty thousand phones.

In Algeria, there were 1.3 million phones available for use by its more than 31 million people in 1997. Of these, 5,200 were cellular phones. Cellular service was good in the northern part of the country, but poor in the south. Algeria had a domestic satellite system with twelve earth stations, five submarine cables, microwave relay to Italy, France, Spain, Morocco, and Tunisia, and coaxial cable to Morocco and Tunisia. Algeria hosted two Intelsat stations, one Intersputnik station, and one Arabsat station.

NEWSPAPERS. In many areas of Africa, particularly in West Africa and in Central Africa, the adult illiteracy rate was more than 50 percent in 1999. In Benin, this rate was 75 percent for women and 51 percent for men; in Burkina Faso, it was 91 percent for men and 71 percent for women. Even with high illiteracy rates, most African nations have newspapers available for those who can read. A few newspapers are available on the World Wide Web.

South Africa, where the literacy rate is about 82 percent for both men and women, has twenty-three newspapers available over the Internet. These include newspapers in German as well as in English. Johannesburg's well-known *Mail and Guardian* can be found on the Internet, as can *The Asian*, the German newspaper *Die Burger*, and the *Johannesburg Star.* South Africa also has many local papers, available to its citizens but not on the Internet.

In 1999 nine Kenyan newspapers could be accessed over the World Wide Web, including *Economic Review.* Even Mozambique, where the illiteracy rate was 75 percent for women and 42 percent for men in 1999, had several local and national newspapers, including the French-language *Noticias de Mozambique*, that could be accessed over the Internet. Senegal and Benin also had French-language newspapers on the World Wide Web, *Le Jour* in Senegal and *La Nation* in Benin. Both *The Botswana Gazette* and Nairobi's *East African* are English-language newspapers available over the Internet.

Senegalese newspapers
Page 1104

THE WORLD WIDE WEB. Few citizens of Africa could access the World Wide Web by the end of the twentieth century, for several reasons. First, African nations do not have the sophisticated telephone connections that exist in other parts of the world. Fiber-optic cable is less common in Africa than in the United States, Europe, or Japan. There is also less access to satellite communications in Africa. The equipment needed for Internet access is expensive and beyond the means of the average African, and little of it is manufactured in Africa. Furthermore, use of computers and the Internet requires well-developed literacy skills. Many Africans are illiterate in their own languages, and few Africans have the knowledge of English that is necessary to use many of the interfaces that support the Internet. African universities have not been actively involved in research in Internet use or in the development of technology to help Africans to use the Internet.

Realizing the need for continent-wide planning in order to improve communications and to bring the Internet within the reach of all Africans, in the late 1990's, seventeen African nations worked together to create a network for their domestic television data and telephony needs. As a result of those efforts, the first Afrocentric Rascom satellite, Intelsat 804, was built, followed by Intelsat 805. Such efforts have increased the likelihood that the average African will have Internet access, but in the year 2000 this modern form of communication was available only to a small minority of Africans.

INTERNATIONAL COOPERATION. In 1997 several African ministers met in Cairo, Egypt, to consider a United Nations' report on transportation and communications in Africa. The ministers present at this meeting agreed that African nations, working together, must build efficient transport and communication systems so that twenty-first century Africa could offer its citizens the economic hope that the Internet has brought to the rest of the world. The meeting determined that Africa must pursue and deepen ongoing economic reforms in general, along with specific reforms in transportation and communications systems. The ministers agreed that Africa needs critical human, institutional, and entrepreneurial capacities in communication areas. They also noted that rapid development of communications and transportation sections must be reconciled with the need for a balanced environment and that special attention must be paid to human security and safety issues.

Africa faces political and cultural issues that mitigate against Africans using the Internet as extensively as do citizens in other parts of the world. Technical personnel do not cooperate fully across countries' borders, and while there is some conferencing among technicians from various countries, more needs to take place. Problems between cultural groups sometimes have made this sort of association difficult. In many African nations, telecommunications and media are controlled by the central governments. There is little economic incentive within countries to improve communication systems overall, or increase Internet accessibility or availability.

Africa has a wide variety of languages and cultures. Technology developers cannot provide interfaces in all possible languages or in modes specific to all cultural groups. Varying levels of education on the part of users make it difficult for technologists to train people to use the Internet. Technology teachers must consider the literacy levels of students and the knowledge that students possess about technology itself.

COMMUNICATION STANDARDS AND INTERNET ACCESS. African leaders realize that continental communications systems must be improved for the citizens of Africa to share in the economic hope that much of the rest of the world enjoys through the development of a global economy. Many Africans agree that there should be a continental communications network. Such a network, supported by modern technology and maintained by highly trained technicians, would help local people to publish information and make it available on the Internet. The network would also be responsible for training local people to use the Internet as a tool for education and financial gain. It also is generally accepted that every African nation must develop a communications plan that will take into account the needs and cultural practices of the individual countries. Such plans would include provisions for developing Internet access within various locales.

Providing African universities with access to all new technologies would improve communications systems in Africa. Universities, as centers of knowledge, have a responsibility for improving technology and creating new uses for it, and making sure that Africa's citizens understand technology and communications systems. With adequate access to technology, universities can research the creation of Internet interfaces in many languages and can conduct forums to discuss the use of the Internet by various language and cultural groups.

EFFECTS OF POOR COMMUNICATIONS. Several African leaders have attempted to develop modern technology, and there are examples of Internet commerce and the use of the World Wide Web and commercial broadcasting for communication. In most areas of Africa, however, particularly in Southern Africa, only the elite

University of Dar es Salaam Page 1153

members of society have access to these modes of communication. No other continent lags so far behind in the development of communication systems as does Africa. The average African does not have access to a telephone or a television broadcast. This lack of communication creates a negative cycle: Africa does not have well-developed communication systems because its people are poor and poorly educated; but one reason Africans are so poor and poorly educated is because the continent has poorly developed communications systems.

At the World Education Conference in Dakar, Senegal, in May, 2000, delegates from 180 countries listened as World Bank president James D. Wolfenshon lamented the fact that 115 million children around the world, most of them from Africa and South Asia, had no access to primary education. While educational radio and television broadcasts provide educational opportunities for some public school children in Africa, further development of educational broadcasting capabilities would make it more likely that children in remote areas of Africa could be educated.

Only about 15 percent of the money that industrialized countries contribute to Africa is allocated for education; most goes for the development of infrastructure. Such contributions fuel another vicious cycle: Africa needs infrastructure development, but its citizens cannot plan or utilize such development if they are not educated. Better communications systems and the education of students to use new technology would make it more likely that donations from industrialized countries would be most effectively used in developing infrastructure.

At the beginning of the twenty-first century, Africa was in the grip of an acquired immunodeficiency syndrome (AIDS) epidemic. In Zimbabwe, more than 25 percent of adults were infected with the AIDS virus; in Malawi, the rate was 15 percent. All across Africa, particularly in the sub-Saharan region, millions of people had AIDS; yet communication systems were so poor that few of these people knew that their condition made them part of an epidemic. The effects of this epidemic could have been ameliorated if Africans had better access to communications systems and education. Few who knew that they had the disease knew how to treat it or how they had contracted it. Education and communication were so poor that myths related to the disease increased the likelihood that infected people would infect others. Cultural taboos prevented some people who were stricken with the disease from getting medical help.

Better communication and education could help lessen the number of cases of AIDS in Africa. This was proven by the efforts of Ugandan President Yoweri Museveni. In 1997 the percentage of Ugandan adults infected with the AIDS virus stood at 30 percent. Museveni launched a media and education campaign to help Ugandans understand AIDS. By the year 2000 the percentage of AIDS-infected Ugandan adults had fallen to 9 percent.

Annita Marie Ward

FOR FURTHER STUDY

Eribo, Festus, and Jong Ebot, eds. *Press Freedom and Communication in Africa.* Trenton, N.J.: Africa World Press, 1994.

Gleave, M. B., ed. *Tropical African Development.* New York: John Wiley & Sons, 1992.

Grove, A. T. *The Changing Geography of Africa.* 2d ed. Oxford, England: Oxford University Press, 1993.

Mshomba, Richard E. *Africa in the Global*

Economy. Boulder, Colo.: Lynne Rienner, 2000.

Noam, Eli M., ed. *Telecommunications in Africa.* New York: Oxford University Press, 1999.

Ritts, Herb. *Africa.* New York: Bullfinch Press, 1994.

Ukadike, Nwachukwu Frank. *Black African Cinema.* Berkeley: University of California Press, 1994.

GAZETTEER

Places whose names are printed in SMALL CAPS *are subjects of their own entries in this gazetteer.*

Aba. Important trade center in eastern NIGERIA (West Africa); an Ibo town, part of the Imo state. Population in 1992 was 270,500. It grew in the early twentieth century, when the British established a military base nearby. In 1929 the site of the Aba Riot, a women's revolt against the high taxes imposed by the British administration. Approximately fifty women died in the conflict.

Abidjan. Largest city in CÔTE D'IVOIRE and its capital until 1983. Located on the Atlantic coast of West Africa; population was 1,850,000 in 1984. Côte d'Ivoire's center of commerce and manufacturing; often referred to as the "Paris of Africa" because of its beauty.

Abuja. Capital of NIGERIA since 1991. Total area of 2,824 square miles (7,315 sq. km.) with a 1990 population of 300,000. Located 300 miles (480 km.) inland.

Accra. Capital and largest city in GHANA. Located on the Gulf of GUINEA; population in 1998 was 945,100. First settled by the Ga ethnic group in 1482, and further developed by the British during colonial rule. Ghana's major international airport is located here.

Adamawa Plateau. An upland area of volcanic origin in West Africa. Extends from central CAMEROON into southeastern NIGERIA and the western part of CENTRAL AFRICAN REPUBLIC. Average elevation is about 3,300 feet (1,000 meters). Savanna vegetation dominates this sparsely populated region. The chief occupation is raising cattle.

Addis Ababa. Capital, economic and manufacturing center, educational center, and largest city of ETHIOPIA. Population was 3 million in 1992. Located on a plateau 8,000 feet (2,440 meters) above sea level, in an area with many streams. Founded in 1887 by the Ethiopian emperor Menelik II; became the national capital two years later. Textiles, food processing, metals, cement, and plywood are its chief industries. Connected by railroad to the port of DJIBOUTI. The name means "new flower" in Amharic.

Adrar Temar. Region running from MOROCCO in NORTH AFRICA to SENEGAL in West Africa. Covering almost 28,000 square miles (73,000 sq. km.) of barren land, oases, and sparse forests in the highland, the region supports nomadic herding. *Adrar* is a Berber word for "plateau" or "mountain."

Afar Depression. V-shaped depressed block that cuts about 360 miles (600 km.) through ETHIOPIA, southward from the Red Sea.

Agadir. Sixteenth century city on the Atlantic coast in southern part of MOROCCO. Destroyed in 1960 by a devastating earthquake and almost completely rebuilt, it is among Morocco's most modern cities. Has an international seaport and attracts many winter tourists.

Agulhas Current. Warm, swift ocean current moving south along East Africa's coast. Part moves between Africa and MADAGASCAR to form the Mozambique Current. The warm water of the Agulhas Current increases the average temperatures in the eastern part of South Africa.

Ahaggar Mountains. Mountain range in southeastern ALGERIA. Peaks rise to 9,652 feet (3,001 meters) at Mount TAHAT, the highest point in Algeria, and 8,054 feet (2,455 meters) at DJEBEL TELERTHEBA. Tamanrasset and Tazrouk are located among the range's jagged peaks. The tropic of CANCER runs through the area, making it hot in sum-

*Abidjan
Page 1158*

*Addis
Ababa
Page 1093*

mer. The area is dry, and much of the wood that has grown at the higher altitudes has been harvested, leaving the mountains quite bare.

Akosombo Dam. Earth-filled dam in West Africa on the VOLTA RIVER in GHANA; similar to the KAINJI DAM in NIGERIA. Is 2,100 feet (640 meters) long and 243 feet (74 meters) above water level. Opened in 1966 at a cost of $228 million, after almost five years of construction. Supplies hydroelectric power to the ACCRA-Tema region of Ghana; has a capacity of 912 megawatts. Also called Volta Dam.

al-Qayrawan. See KAIROUAN.

Alexandria Pages 1039, 1099

Albert, Lake. Lake in Central Africa, located in northeast CONGO-KINSHASA along the border with UGANDA. It is 100 miles (160 km.) long and 25 miles (40 km.) wide, covering about 2,065 square miles (5,350 sq. km.), at an altitude of 2,030 feet (620 meters). Northernmost of the great central African lakes. The SEMLIKI RIVER empties into it from the southwest; the Victoria Nile River in the northeast is its outlet. Discovered in 1864 by Samuel Baker and named after Queen Victoria's consort, Prince Albert. Called Lake Mobutu from 1973 to 1998.

Alexandria. Second-largest city in EGYPT. Founded in 332 B.C.E. by Alexander the

Alexandria, Egypt. (PhotoDisc)

Great, the city's namesake. Population was 2.9 million in 1996. Located on the MEDITERRANEAN SEA, at the western extreme of the NILE delta, in the narrow coastal strip of Egypt that has around 8 inches (200 millimeters) of precipitation per year. It had one of the seven wonders of the ancient world, a massive lighthouse known as the Pharos of Alexandria. From the fourth century B.C.E. to the seventh century C.E., it was the academic center for the Mediterranean world. Its legendary library had nearly a half million volumes at its pinnacle in the third century C.E. As Egypt's main port, nearly 80 percent of imports and exports pass through Alexandria. Its diversified manufacturing base includes oil refining, paper, plastics, food processing, and textiles.

Algeria. Largest country in NORTH AFRICA and second-largest in Africa. Bounded by the MEDITERRANEAN SEA on the north, MOROCCO on the west, MAURITANIA and MALI on the southwest, NIGER to the east southeast, and LIBYA and TUNISIA on the east. Covers 2,381,741 square miles (919,595 square meters); population in 1990 was about 23 million. Its chief cities are its capital, ALGIERS, and ORAN, CONSTANTINE, and Annaba, all in the north. Most of the southern part of the country is sparsely populated desert.

Algiers. Largest city and capital of ALGERIA. Situated midway along the coast of the MEDITERRANEAN SEA between MOROCCO and TUNISIA. Has been a thriving community and important port for more than three thousand years. Its population exceeds 1,500,000. The city was controlled by Turkey, then France, until Algeria gained its independence in 1962.

Angola. Republic previously known as Portuguese West Africa, located south of CONGO-KINSHASA and north of NAMIBIA. Total area of 481,354 square miles (1.2 million sq. km.) with a 1990's population of 10 million. Capital is LUANDA. Most of the country is known as the ANGOLAN PLATEAU. Divided into three major regions: from west to east, the coastal plain, a transition zone, and a vast inland plateau. The low-lying coastal plain varies from about 30 to 90 miles (50-150 km.) in width. The transition zone, which consists of a series of terraces or escarpments, is about 90 miles (150 km.) wide in the north, but diminishes to about 19 miles (30 km.) in the center and south. Has a basically tropical climate, although cooler ocean currents make temperatures along the coast fairly temperate. Rich in natural resources, producing diamonds, copper, iron, and uranium. Vegetation ranges from rain forest to dry savanna. After the Portuguese decolonized the area in 1875, a civil war drove out most Portuguese settlers.

Algeria
Page 1025

Angolan Plateau. Vast plateau covering about two-thirds of ANGOLA. Has an average elevation of 3,000 to 5,000 feet (1,000 to 1,520 meters); highest point is Mount Moco (8,597 feet/2,620 meters). Angola's main rivers, the Caunza and the Cunene, flow from these mountains to the Atlantic Ocean.

Annobón. Tiny volcanic island off Africa in the Gulf of GUINEA, part of EQUATORIAL GUINEA. Located at 1°25′ south latitude, longitude 5°37′ east. The island's highest elevation is 2,727 feet (831 meters). It has an area of 7 square miles (18 sq. km.); its population was 2,360 in 1989. Has a high annual rainfall—about 117 inches (2,972 millimeters)—as a result of its closeness to the equator, and is covered with dense equatorial forest. Discovered by Portuguese navigators around the 1470's.

Angola
Page 1153

Antanana-rivo
Page 1154

Antananarivo. Capital and largest city of MADAGASCAR, founded about 1625. Located in a central province of the same name, it was the major settlement of the Merina, the island's most organized people. The population in 1993 was about 675,700.

Ascension Island. Barren island in the ATLANTIC OCEAN. Located about 500 miles (800 km.) south of the equator at 7°57' south latitude, longitude 14°22' minutes west. Ascension became a dependency of ST. HELENA in 1922 and was a refueling point for British planes and ships during the war with Argentina over the Falkland Islands in 1982. Ascension's highest elevation is 2,817 feet (859 meters). It has an area of 34 square miles (88 sq. km.); its population was about 1,100 in 1999.

Asmera. Capital, primary port, and largest city of ERITREA. Had a 1990's population of 400,000. Located near gold and copper mines; local manufacturing includes food processing, textiles, perfumes, glass, cement, bricks, lumber, and leather.

Aswan. A major city on the Upper NILE RIVER in EGYPT, known for the Aswan High Dam, a major source of hydroelectricity for the country. Construction of the dam created Lake NASSER, the largest body of water in Egypt and SUDAN. Population was 220,000 in 1992.

Asyut. City in central EGYPT, on the NILE RIVER. Located just south of the Al Ibrahimiyah Canal, which furnishes water to several western Nile Valley locales and feeds the Al Fayyum depression, more than 180 miles (300 km.) from Asyut. Dates, sugarcane, and grains are produced in the region. A center for the ancient sect of Coptic Christians and a stronghold for fundamentalist Islam. Population was 321,000 in 1992.

Atlas Mountains. Mountain range in NORTH AFRICA. The RIF and Middle Atlas Mountains run across northern MOROCCO into parts of western ALGERIA and down the center of Morocco. The High Atlas Mountains run through the center of Morocco to the south, where they meet with the Anti-Atlas Mountains that extend toward WESTERN SAHARA.

Badagry. Small coastal city in NIGERIA, near the Republic of BENIN. Mostly populated by the Yoruba people. A major slave port on the Bight of BENIN between 1711 and 1810. Its beautiful beaches welcome tourists.

Bamako. Capital, largest city, and financial and industrial center of MALI. The city straddles the NIGER RIVER, which is a major mode of transportation. Population was 646,000 in 1987.

Bandaka. Capital of EQUATOR PROVINCE in northwest CONGO-KINSHASA. Located on the left bank of the CONGO RIVER, about 370 miles (595 km.) north northeast of KINSHASA, the nation's capital. A commercial and river communications center. Founded by Henry Morton Stanley in 1883; called Coquilhatville until 1966.

Bandundu. Province in southwest CONGO-KINSHASA. It covers 100,254 square miles (259,958 sq. km.). Population was 5.2 million in 1995. Drained by the CONGO, KASAI, and Kwango Rivers. Commercial center of agricultural products, including palm oil, manioc, and peanuts, mainly for KINSHASA. Population was 74,945 in 1995. Called Banningville until 1966.

Bangui. Capital and main commercial center of the CENTRAL AFRICAN REPUBLIC. Located in the southwest of the country, on the west bank of the UBANGI RIVER near the country's border with CONGO-KINSHASA. Population was 553,000 in 1995. Most of the country's industries are located there.

Banjul. Capital and largest, most-developed city of GAMBIA. Founded by the British in 1816 as a port and a base for suppressing the slave trade. Originally called Bathurst, renamed Banjul in 1973. Population was 44,200 in 1994.

Barrage Vert. Long rows of Aleppo pine trees the Algerian government planted along the SAHARAN ATLAS ridge from MOROCCO to the Tunisian border, a distance of 1,500 miles (2,400 km.), to prevent the SAHARA from encroaching on the fertile agricultural areas to its north. This succeeded in containing the desert which, if left alone, might gradually extend all the way to the MEDITERRANEAN SEA, making ALGERIA and other parts of NORTH AFRICA a wasteland. French phrase for "green barrier."

Bas-Congo. Province in southwest CONGO-KINSHASA. Covers 20,818 square miles (53,980 sq. km.). Population was 2,835,000 in 1995. Bordered on the south by ANGOLA, on the west by the Atlantic Ocean and the Angolan enclave of CABINDA, on the north by CONGO-BRAZZAVILLE.

Basutoland. Colonial-era name for LESOTHO.

Bechuanaland. Colonial-era name for BOTSWANA.

Beida. Small town on the MEDITERRANEAN SEA about 120 miles (190 km.) east of Benghazi which once was LIBYA's summer capital. The government has expanded and modernized the city.

Belgian Congo. See CONGO-KINSHASA.

Benguela Current. Northward-flowing current along the western coast of Southern AFRICA.

Benin. Small West African nation, formerly a French colony. Total area of 43,475 square miles (112,600 sq. km.) with a population of 6 million in 1998. Capital is PORTO-NOVO, but the port city of COTONOU is the commercial and political capital. Called DAHOMEY until 1975. French is the official language but Yoruba, Fon, and Adja are also spoken. Considered to be the birthplace of West Indian voodoo and black magic. Administered within the federation of FRENCH WEST AFRICA during the era of colonial rule.

Benin, Bight of. Part of the Gulf of GUINEA in West Africa. Extends approximately 450 miles (720 km.) from the mouth of the VOLTA RIVER to the NIGER RIVER. Fed by the Ogun, Benin, Mono, and Oueme Rivers. Its principal ports include ACCRA, GHANA; PORTO-NOVO and COTONOU, BENIN; LOMÉ, TOGO; and LAGOS, NIGERIA. Was known as the Slave Coast throughout the eighteenth century.

Benin Kingdom. Historic kingdom of the Edo-speaking people in southwestern NIGERIA. Not related to the independent Republic of BENIN to the west.

Benue River. Longest tributary of NIGER RIVER. It rises in the northern part of CAMEROON and flows west across east central NIGERIA. It is about 673 miles (1,083 km.) long. The Benue and Niger Rivers divide northern Nigeria from southern Nigeria.

Bette Peak. Highest mountain in LIBYA. Located in the TIBESTI MOUNTAINS near the CHAD border, it is 7,500 feet (2,290 meters) high, slightly more than half the height of MOROCCO's Jebel TOUBKAL.

Biafra, Bight of. Part of the Gulf of GUINEA in West Africa. Extends approximately 400 miles (640 km.) from the mouth of the NIGER RIVER in NIGERIA to Cape Lopez in GABON. Fed by the Cross, Niger, and the Sanaga Rivers. Its

Benguela Current Page 969

Benin Page 1154

principal ports include MALABO, EQUA-
TORIAL GUINEA; PORT HARCOURT and
CALABAR, Nigeria; and DOUALA, CAM-
EROON.

Bight of Benin. See BENIN, BIGHT OF.

Bight of Biafra. See BIAFRA, BIGHT OF.

Bioko. Large island in the Gulf of GUINEA,
part of the nation of EQUATORIAL
GUINEA and site of its capital, MALABO.
Located about 25 miles (40 km.) off the
coast of Africa. The island's highest
point, at 9,866 feet (3,007 meters), is
Santa Isabel, a volcano that erupted in
1923. The climate is tropical wet. Formerly known as Fernando Po in honor
of one of its Portuguese discoverers, the
island eventually became part of Spanish Guinea, which gained its independence in 1968. The island was subsequently renamed Bioko in honor of an
early king. It covers an area of 779
square miles (2,018 sq. km.) and had a
population of 57,200 in 1983.

Bizerte. Northernmost city in TUNISIA,
with a population of just under
100,000. Once a French naval base; a
port for iron ore and the center of the
commercial fishing industry on the
coast. When German and Italian forces
invaded Tunisia by air from Sicily in
World War II, it was the site of their
most bloody battles against the Allies.
Blockaded by Tunisian troops in 1961,
the base was evacuated by the French,
who departed from it entirely in 1963.

Bloemfontein. Judicial capital of SOUTH
AFRICA and administrative capital of
the FREE STATE Province. Most of the
region is on the interior plateau, generally level, with an average altitude of
4,480 feet (1,400 meters). Because of
low rainfall, there are few rivers and
streams. Summers are warm to hot and
winters are cold with some snow and
frost. Produces maize, wheat, and beef
cattle. Founded in 1846 by Afrikaans-

speaking farmers who arrived in the
1830's and 1840's and later established
a settlement in the area. The name
means "fountain of flowers."

Bo. Administrative center for the southern province of SIERRA LEONE; the capital of the Protectorate of the Sierra Leone from 1930 until 1961. It is the
leading commercial and educational
center for the nation's interior. Population was 269,000 in 1994.

Bongor. Capital of Mayo-Kebbi Prefecture
(province) in southwestern CHAD. Located about 149 miles (240 km.) from
N'DJAMENA, Chad's capital. Its economy is based on rice, cotton, and fishing. A center of resistance for the southern Christians and Animists against the
Muslims in the north. Population was
195,000 in 1993.

Botswana. Republic in Southern Africa.
Total area of 231,800 square miles
(600,370 sq. km.) with a 1990's population of 1.4 million. Capital is Gaborone,
which has a population of only about
60,000. The KALAHARI DESERT covers
much of the country, and the rest is
largely savanna. The economy is largely
agricultural, but diamond deposits
were discovered in the late twentieth
century. Created as the British protectorate of BECHUANALAND in the nineteenth century.

Brazzaville. Capital of CONGO-BRAZZA-
VILLE and the country's largest commercial, industrial, and administrative
center, and major river port. Located in
the southeast of the country on the
right bank of the CONGO RIVER, opposite KINSHASA. Terminus of the railroad
from POINTE-NOIRE on the Atlantic
Ocean, and of navigation on the CONGO
and UBANGI RIVER systems. Founded
in 1880 by French explorer Pierre
Savorgnan de Brazza and named after
him. Population was 938,000 in 1997.

*Botswana
Page 974*

Bujumbura. Capital and largest city of BU-RUNDI. Located on the northeastern tip of Lake TANGANYIKA, with a 1987 population of 215,000. The lake gives Burundi access to the Tanzanian railroad that connects the lake to the INDIAN OCEAN port of DAR ES SALAAM. Fishing, food processing, cotton textiles, handcrafts, hides, beer, and cement are major local industries.

Bukavu. Capital of South KIVU province in east CONGO-KINSHASA. A commercial and industrial center and port. Located on the southwest shore of Lake KIVU at an altitude of 4,768 feet (1,453 meters). Tourism is a principal activity. Population was 201,570 in 1994. Called Costermansville until 1966.

Burkina Faso. Poor, landlocked country in West Africa; formerly called UPPER VOLTA. Total area of 105,946 square miles (274,378 sq. km.) with a population of 10.9 million in 1997. OUAGADOUGOU is the capital and largest city. French is the official language, but Mossi and other indigenous languages are used. This military-ruled republic has depended on economic aid from France.

Burundi. Landlocked country in Africa. With an area of 10,747 square miles (27,834 sq. km.), slightly larger than Vermont, and a population of more than 5.5 million, it is one of the most densely populated regions on the continent. Capital is BUJUMBURA. Savanna is the typical natural vegetation. Around 43 percent of the land is arable; about 12 percent is forest, most of which is located in nature preserves. The climate is tropical, but its effects are ameliorated by altitude, as most of the country is a hilly plateau, averaging between about 4,600 and 5,900 feet (1,400 and 1,800 meters) above sea level. Ethnic violence between the em-powered minority Tutsis and the Hutus, who make up 85 percent of the population, has been a recurring problem. Burundi's social structure and economy also have been disrupted by its high rate of AIDS infection.

Cabinda. Province of ANGOLA separated from the rest of the country by the narrow strip of CONGO-KINSHASA along the lower reaches of the CONGO RIVER. The oil-rich coastal enclave has had a simmering independence movement since the 1960's.

Cairo. Capital of EGYPT and the most populous city in Africa. Its metropolitan area officially has 10.7 million people, but most late 1990's estimates put the number closer to 16 million. Long a center for education; Al Azhar University, founded in 988, is the oldest Islamic university in the world and the oldest continually operated university on the planet. The primary publishing center for the Arabic-speaking world; the home of museums, theater, and opera; and the region's financial center. It has been the political capital of Egypt since its founding in 969 by the Fatimids, although the land it sits upon has been settled for 6,000 years. Located just south of the beginning of the NILE Delta, on both banks of the river. Its diversified manufacturing base includes cotton textiles, food processing, automobile assembly, aircraft assembly, chemicals, iron, and steel.

Calabar. Capital of Cross River State in the southeastern part of NIGERIA. Located on an estuary of the Gulf of GUINEA on the left bank of the Calabar River. Population in 1992 was 157,800, the majority of whom belonged to the Efik minority group. A market center for the surrounding area, with trade in palm oil, rubber, and timber.

Cairo
Page 1155

Burundi
Page 1165

Caldera de Taburiente, La. The world's largest volcanic crater, approximately a mile deep, located on the CANARY ISLAND of La Palma. Site of a Spanish national park since 1954.

Cameroon. Country in west Central Africa, bounded by NIGERIA to the northwest, CHAD to the northeast, the CENTRAL AFRICAN REPUBLIC to the east, CONGO-BRAZZAVILLE to the southeast, GABON and EQUATORIAL GUINEA to the south, and the Atlantic Ocean to the southwest. Covers 179,714 square miles (466,000 sq. km.), with a population of 15 million in 1998. Capital is YAOUNDÉ. Natural resources include timber, oil, bauxite, iron ore, and rubber. In the late twentieth century, petroleum became the main export and source of income. Originally created as Kamerun by Germany during the late nineteenth century; after World War I the country was taken away from Germany by the new League of Nations, which divided its administration between Great Britain and France. In 1960 both British and French territories became independent. They united in 1961.

Cameroon Mountain. Active volcano and the highest mountain in West Africa; elevation of 13,435 feet (4,095 meters). Located in southwestern CAMEROON near the Gulf of GUINEA. The rich soils of the mountain slope make it ideal for agriculture.

Canal des Pangalanes. Natural channel running about half the length of the east coast of MADAGASCAR. Separated from the INDIAN OCEAN by river silt and sand deposited by ocean currents, it is used for navigation.

Canary Islands Page 1155

Canary Islands. Group of seven major and six minor volcanic islands located in the North ATLANTIC OCEAN off southern MOROCCO, which is 67 miles (108 km.) from the nearest island. The islands nearest the African coast have a desert climate; the rest are subtropical, although water must be conserved for agriculture. When European explorers arrived in the early fifteenth century, they called the indigenous people the Guanches. The Canaries constitute two provinces of the European nation Spain. Because of their pleasant climate and often luxuriant plant life, much of it introduced, the Canaries are popular with tourists. The islands cover 2,808 square miles (7,273 sq. km.), and their highest point is the volcano PICO de Teide. The population was 1,493,000 in 1991. The islands take their name from the latin word for "dog," not from the name of a bird.

Cancer, Tropic of. The parallel of latitude that runs 23°27′ minutes north of the equator. It runs through the arid deserts of WESTERN SAHARA, southern ALGERIA, and southern LIBYA, making these areas exceptionally hot in summer, even at the higher elevations.

Cap Bon. Large outcropping of land that juts into the Gulf of TUNIS and the MEDITERRANEAN SEA on TUNISIA's northeast coast. The area around it is relatively undeveloped, with none of the large communities that exist west of the Gulf of Tunis.

Cape Agulhas. The true southern tip of the African continent, located in the southwestern part of SOUTH AFRICA. Generally considered to be the dividing line between the INDIAN and the Atlantic Oceans.

Cape Coast. Capital of the Central Region in southern GHANA. Population was 85,200 in 1994. First settled by the Portuguese in 1610; was the capital of the British GOLD COAST until the 1870's, when the capital was moved to ACCRA. Its main products include coconuts, cocoa, corn, cassava, and frozen fish.

Cape of Good Hope. Promontory in southwestern SOUTH AFRICA that is generally viewed as the southernmost point in Africa, although CAPE AGULHAS is somewhat farther south. Rises 840 feet (256 meters) above the sea. Its main city is CAPE TOWN, one of South Africa's main cities and the jumping-off point for travel to Antarctica. The first European to visit it was the Portuguese captain Bartolomeu Dias in 1488.

Cape Peninsula. Long, rocky peninsula on the southwestern side of SOUTH AFRICA that separates the Atlantic Ocean from the INDIAN OCEAN's False Bay. Extending south of CAPE TOWN, the cape is a scenic and popular tourist destination.

Cape Point. Southernmost tip of SOUTH AFRICA's CAPE PENINSULA.

Cape Town. Legislative capital and one of the main cities in SOUTH AFRICA. Cape Town is located in the western Cape, with a 1990's population of 1.9 million. Has a Mediterranean climate, with warm, dry summers and cool, wet winters. The main rivers in the area—the Black, the Diep and the Liesbeek—have been turned into canals. TABLE MOUNTAIN is a great tourist attraction. TABLE BAY is South Africa's second-largest port and the main departure

Cape of Good Hope Page 1156

Cape Point Page 1157

Cape Town Page 962

Central Cape Town, with Table Mountain in the rear. (Corbis)

Carthage in the late nineteenth century. (Arkent Archive)

point for those visiting Antarctica by ship. The harbor offers safe anchorage and fresh supplies to visiting ships. Fishing is an important industry. The cold BENGUELA CURRENT on the west coast is famous for crayfish and lobster. The city has a mixed economy, originally based on agriculture, but based on industries such as chemicals and food processing.

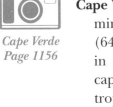

Cape Verde Page 1156

Cape Verde. Nation of ten major and five minor islands lying about 400 miles (640 km.) off the coast of WEST AFRICA in the North ATLANTIC OCEAN. The capital is PRAIA. The islands have a subtropical desert climate, and the lack of fresh water and other resources has encouraged emigration. Once a Portuguese colony, Cape Verde became independent in 1975. Cape Verde comprises 1,560 square miles (4,040 sq. km.), and

its highest point, the active volcano Cano Peak on the island of Fogo, reaches 9,300 feet (2,835 meters). There were about 406,000 inhabitants in 1997.

Capricorn, Tropic of. The parallel of latitude that runs 23°27′ minutes south of the equator.

Caprivi Strip. Narrow panhandle of NAMIBIA, stretching about 300 miles (485 km.) east from the northeastern corner of the main part of the country to touch the ZAMBEZI RIVER, where ZAMBIA, ZIMBABWE, and BOTSWANA all nearly touch each other. The strip is a historic anomaly created when Germany pressured Great Britain into allowing it to extend its Southwest Africa territory to the Zambezi.

Carthage. Ancient city that was destroyed by the Romans in 146 B.C.E. They laced its fertile fields with salt so that nothing could be grown in them. Renamed TU-NIS, it later became TUNISIA's capital. A modern, fashionable residential community named Carthage stands on the site of the ancient city 9 miles (14 km.) east of Tunis, dotted with the lavish villas of high-ranking government officials and foreign diplomats.

Casablanca. The largest city in NORTH AF-RICA, and the commercial capital of MOROCCO. Located on the Atlantic Ocean about a third of the way south from TANGIER to WESTERN SAHARA,

with a population of about 3,250,000. Most international flights into Morocco land there.

Central African Republic. Landlocked country in Central Africa bounded on the south by CONGO-KINSHASA, east by SUDAN, north by CHAD, west by CAMEROON, and southwest by CONGO-BRAZZAVILLE. Covers an area of 238,220 square miles (617,700 sq. km.), with a population of 3.5 million in 1999. Capital is BANGUI. Natural resources include diamonds, uranium, and timber. Coffee, cotton, peanuts, and food crops are

Hassan II Mosque in Casablanca, Morocco. (Corbis)

grown. Industries include timber, textiles, soap, cigarettes, processed food, and diamond mining. Became independent from France in 1960.

Ceuta. City on the Tangier Peninsula in northernmost SPANISH MOROCCO, across the Straits of Gibraltar from the British colony of GIBRALTAR on the Iberian Peninsula. Its Jebel Musa is one of the two so-called PILLARS OF HERCULES.

Chad. Independent west-central African republic; main borders are with LIBYA on the north, SUDAN on the east, NIGER on the west, and the CENTRAL AFRICAN REPUBLIC on the south. Total area of 495,752 square miles (793,200 sq. km.), with a population of about 7.5 million in 1998. Largely a desert country, its official languages are French and Arabic. Its rivers flow north, emptying into Lake CHAD. Administered within FRENCH EQUATORIAL AFRICA during the colonial era, which ended in 1960. Capital is N'DJAMENA.

Chad, Lake. The fourth-largest lake in Africa. Located in west central Africa in CAMEROON, CHAD, NIGERIA, and NIGER. It is 13 to 23 feet (4 to 7 meters) deep in the south where it is navigable, and about 13 feet (4 meters) deep in the northwest. Has an average area of approximately 9,400 square miles (24,300 sq. km.).

Chagos Archipelago. Tiny group of atolls in the INDIAN OCEAN. The islands are shared by the United Kingdom and the United States for defense purposes, but are claimed by MAURITIUS. The archipelago covers 23 square miles (60 sq. km.); the sole inhabitants are American and British military personnel.

Chelia, Mount. Highest mountain in the northern half of ALGERIA, at 7,648 feet (2,330 meters). Located in the eastern reaches of the ATLAS MOUNTAINS, in the section known as Kabylia.

Cheliff River. River in the coastal plains of ALGERIA. Although not navigable, it provides water for agricultural irrigation in the fertile coastal areas. Receives runoff from the ATLAS MOUNTAINS.

Chott Djerid. The largest lake in TUNISIA. Located on the edge of the SAHARA, close to the Algerian border and 62.5 miles (about 100 meters) from DJEBEL CHAMBI, Tunisia's highest point. Formed by a 70-mile-deep (113 km.) depression in the ground; often dry. Also known as Shatt al-Jarid.

Comoros. Archipelago of four volcanic islands, located in the northern MOZAMBIQUE CHANNEL. Three of the islands make up the independent nation of Comoros; the fourth island, MAYOTTE, remains a French colony. The islands have a tropical monsoonal climate and frequently experience violent cyclones. After gaining independence from France in 1975, Comoros had a long period of political instability and was invaded by mercenaries several times. Comoros' highest elevation is 7,746 feet (2,361 meters) at Mont Kartala, a volcano that erupted in 1977 and 1991. The area of the nation of Comoros is estimated at between 719 and 838 square miles (1,862 and 2,170 sq. km.); its population was about 540,000 in 1996.

Conakry. National capital and largest city in GUINEA. Has one of the best natural deepwater harbors on the coast of West Africa. Connected by rail to Kankan, Guinea's second-largest city, which provides access to the NIGER RIVER. Population was 763,000 in 1980.

Congo, Democratic Republic of. See CONGO-KINSHASA.

Congo, Republic of. See CONGO-BRAZZAVILLE.

Congo-Brazzaville. Country in west Central Africa; officially known as the Republic of the Congo. Total area of

132,047 square miles (342,002 sq. km.) with a population of 2.7 million in 1998. Bounded on the west by the Atlantic Ocean, the south by ANGOLA, on the southeast and east by CONGO-KINSHASA, on the northeast by the CENTRAL AFRICAN REPUBLIC, on the northwest by CAMEROON, and on the west and southwest by GABON. BRAZZAVILLE is the capital and most-developed city. Had the first communist government in Africa, but rejected communism in the early 1990's. French is the official language. Administered within FRENCH Equatorial Africa during the colonial era, which ended in 1960.

Congo Free State. Private colonial empire in Central Africa created by Belgium's King Leopold II during the 1880's. His regime's ruthless exploitation of the country led the Belgian government to take it away from him and transform it into the BELGIAN CONGO in 1908. This colony became independent in 1960 as the Democratic Republic of the Congo, later better known as CONGO-KINSHASA.

Congo-Kinshasa. Central African nation officially known as the Democratic Republic of the Congo. Straddles the equator between 5 degrees north and 12 degrees south latitude. Total area of 905,354 square miles (2,347,583 sq. km.)—one-quarter the size of the United States—makes it Africa's third-largest nation. Has only 25 miles (40 km.) of coastline, on the Atlantic Ocean. Bordered on the west by CONGO-BRAZZAVILLE and the Angolan enclave of CABINDA; on the north by the CENTRAL AFRICAN REPUBLIC and the SUDAN; on the east by UGANDA, RWANDA, BURUNDI, and TANZANIA; on the southeast by ZAMBIA; and on the southwest by ANGOLA. Population in 1998 was about 49 million. French is

the official language. Rich in natural and mineral resources, including vast deposits of industrial diamonds, cobalt, and copper. Has the largest forest reserves and the largest hydroelectric potential in Africa. Originally created as the CONGO FREE STATE during the 1880's; became the Belgian Congo in 1908. Secessionist movements have beset the country since independence in 1960. In 1996 the three-decade regime of Mobutu Sese Seko was overthrown by Laurence Kabila with the help of Uganda and Rwanda. Mobutu renamed the country ZAIRE in 1970; Kabila restored its original name in 1997. Capital is KINSHASA.

Congo River. Main river in Central Africa. Starts from KATANGA province at an altitude of 4,650 feet (1,415 meters) in southeast CONGO-KINSHASA, near the border with ZAMBIA. Flows northward to KISANGANI, bends westward, and later flows southwest from around BANDAKA to reach the Atlantic Ocean. From where it is joined by the UBANGI RIVER, it forms the border between Congo-Kinshasa and CONGO-BRAZZAVILLE. One of the world's longest rivers, about 2,900 miles (4,670 km.), second in Africa only to the NILE RIVER. Its drainage basin of about 1.34. million square miles (3.46 million sq. km.) receives an average of 60 inches (1,525 millimeters) of rain annually. Its rate of flow at its mouth is about 1,450,00 cubic feet per second, making it second in the world only to the Amazon River. The first European to find its mouth was the Portuguese navigator Diego Cao, in 1482. Navigability is limited because of several cataracts. At one time known as the Zaire River. The upper course is also called the Lualaba River.

Constantine. Ancient city in NORTH AFRICA, now ALGERIA's third-largest city.

Congo River Pages 962, 1158

*Dakar
Page 1104*

Located 50 miles (80 km.) south of the MEDITERRANEAN SEA, perched high on chalk cliffs. A deep gorge runs through the center of the dramatic, beautiful city; numerous bridges connect the two parts of the town that are separated by the river. Originally called Cirta; named Constantine by the Roman conquerors after the Roman emperor Constantine. Was the Turkish capital in eastern Algeria.

Corisco Island. Part of EQUATORIAL GUINEA in West Africa. Located at the mouth of Corisco Bay off the coast of West Africa. Has an area of 5 square miles (14 sq. km.). Initially claimed by Portugal in 1472; taken over by Spain from 1858 to 1968. Agriculture and fishing are the major industries.

*Côte
d'Ivoire
Pages
1036,
1158, 1168*

Côte d'Ivoire. Former French colony in West Africa. Total area of 124,518 square miles (322,501 sq. km.) with a population of 15 million in 1997. Capital was moved from the coastal city of ABIDJAN to YAMOUSSOUKRO, farther inland, in 1983. After achieving independence in 1960, the country enjoyed rapid economic growth and multiparty democracy until December, 1999, when the military took over. French is the official language. The English name is Ivory Coast. Administered within the federation of FRENCH WEST AFRICA during the era of colonial rule.

*Dar es
Salaam
Page 1153*

Cotonou. Largest city, and the financial and commercial center in the Republic of BENIN. Located on the Gulf of GUINEA, its business activities attract traders from neighboring countries, such as NIGERIA and TOGO. Population in the 1990's was 180,000.

Cyrenaica. Region of LIBYA that extends from the MEDITERRANEAN SEA to CHAD, in which 51 percent of Libyans live. Coast curves away from the SURT DESERT to the Mediterranean Sea. Its

130-mile (210-kilometer) arch connects the cities of Benghazi and DERNA.

Dahomey. Historic kingdom in West Africa that gave its name to the French colony of Dahomey, which later changed its name to Republic of BENIN.

Dakar. Capital of SENEGAL. Has one of the best harbors on the Atlantic coast of Africa, which was the major supply port for the Allied Powers in Africa during World War II. Called the Gateway to Africa during French colonial rule, when it was the administrative capital of FRENCH WEST AFRICA. Population was 1 million in 1990.

Dakhla. North African port city two-thirds of the way down the coast of WESTERN SAHARA toward MAURITANIA. Located just north of the tropic of CANCER, it is one of the two population centers in this sparsely populated, largely desert region.

Dar es Salaam. Capital, leading port, financial and educational center, and largest city in TANZANIA. Founded in 1860 as a summer residence for the sultan of ZANZIBAR. During the German colonial period, which began in 1885, it was greatly expanded and became the capital of the German colonies in 1891. Population was 1.7 million in 1995. Its name means "haven of peace." During the 1990's, Tanzania's administrative capital was scheduled to be moved inland to Dodomo, to help develop the sparsely populated interior of the country.

Darnah. See DERNA.

Delagoa Bay. INDIAN OCEAN inlet near the southern tip of MOZAMBIQUE on which the capital city, MAPUTO, stands.

Derna. Small coastal town in LIBYA, located east of BEIDA, near the foot of Green Mountain. A quaint town, with abundant palm trees and jasmine, whose fragrance perfumes the air. Had

Dar es Salaam harbor in 1869. (Arkent Archive)

a large Italian population, from 1915 to 1970, which left Libya because of political pressures. Also known as Darnah.

Diego Garcia. Atoll in the CHAGOS ARCHIPELAGO, in the INDIAN OCEAN. Located at 7°20′ south latitude, longitude 72°25′ east, with an area of 11 square miles (28 sq. km.). Site of a United States naval base and space-tracking station.

Dire Dawa. City of eastern ETHIOPIA. Located about midway between ADDIS ABABA and its port, DJIBOUTI. Light manufacturing includes textiles, food processing, and cement production. Population was 164,850 in 1994.

Djanet Oasis. Large oasis in the SAHARA in southeastern ALGERIA, around which a

thriving town has developed. Mud and brick houses are built on terraces on the steep hills. Its water supply comes mostly from underground springs.

Djebel Chambi. Highest mountain in TUNISIA. Located in the west central part of the country, close to the Algerian border, it reaches a height of 5,066 feet (1,544 meters).

Djebel Telertheba. Peak in the AHAGGAR MOUNTAINS of southeastern ALGERIA, in NORTH AFRICA. It rises to 8,054 feet (2,455 meters) west of DJANET. Sometimes snow-capped in winter.

Djemila. Ancient Algerian city on the MEDITERRANEAN SEA. The stone arch, temple, and forum of a Roman city stand as mute testimony to the Roman occupation of the area in ancient times.

Djerba Island. Large island in the MEDITERRANEAN SEA off TUNISIA's east coast, across the Gulf of GABÈS from the city of GABÈS. Legend has it that this island and KERKENNA, 86 miles (138 km.) to the north, are the remains of the lost continent of Atlantis. Djerba Island is also thought by some to be the legendary isle of the Lotus-Eaters in Homer's *Odyssey*.

Djibouti. Country located on the Gulf of Aden, in northeastern Africa. Total area of 8,957 square miles (23,200 sq. km.), about the size of New Hampshire, with a population of 440,000 in 1998. Capital city is also called Djibouti, in which nearly 90 percent of the country's people live. The land consists primarily of arid plateaus, with mountainous terrain to the north. The country's wettest region receives 15 inches (380 millimeters) of rain per year. Land use centers on grazing, and only one-tenth of the land is even suited for this usage. Occasional oases produce some crops for local production. Many of the people are refugees from political unrest in SOMALIA and ETHIOPIA. Most of Djibouti's trade is centered upon shipping, as it is the main channel of shipping for its landlocked neighbor, Ethiopia.

Dodoma. City in the interior of TANZANIA. Located at the intersection of the railway connecting Lake TANGANYIKA to the coastal capital of DAR ES SALAAM and the central highway, which links southern Africa to EGYPT. A regional market for the agricultural district surrounding it. An administrative center for the region since its founding by the Germans in 1907. Scheduled to become the capital of Tanzania. The legislative branch moved there from Dar es Salaam, although the rest of the gov-

ernment has remained on the coast. Population was 203,000 in 1988.

Douala. Main maritime port and a major industrial center in southwest CAMEROON. Located 130 miles (210 km.) west of YAOUNDÉ; connected to the rest of the country by road-and-railroad networks. Capital of German Kamerun (1901-1916) and later of the French portion of CAMEROON (1940-1946). Population was about 1.2 million in 1991.

Drakensberg Mountains. Mountain range on the southeastern coast of Southern Africa, about 700 miles (1,125 km.) long. Among its peaks are Thabana Ntlenyana, the highest in SOUTH AFRICA, 11,425 feet (3,482 meters) above sea level. The second-highest is Mont-aux-Sources at 10,822 feet (3,299 meters), where South Africa's scenic Royal Natal National Park is located.

Durban. SOUTH AFRICA's third-largest city and its main INDIAN OCEAN seaport. Capital of KWAZULU/NATAL state. Had a 1990's population of 107,000. Summers are warm and wet, and winters are mild. The AGULHAS CURRENT warms the coastal waters, and vegetation is luxuriant. One large river, the Mgeni, flows into the sea there. Its harbor is the busiest in South Africa, and it is the center of KwaZulu-Natal's manufacturing industry. Portuguese navigator Vasco da Gama arrived there on December 25, 1487, and named the region Natal after the birth of Christ.

East London. Major port located in the eastern Cape Province of SOUTH AFRICA on the INDIAN OCEAN. Located at the mouth of the Buffalo River. Population was 100,000 in the 1990's; its primary economic activity is the export of agricultural products.

Eastern Province. Province in north and northeast CONGO-KINSHASA. Covers an area of 204,164 square miles (529,397 sq. km.). Bounded on the north by the CENTRAL AFRICAN REPUBLIC, the northeast by SUDAN, and the east by UGANDA and Lake ALBERT. Primarily equatorial rain forest; drained by the Uele-Kibali, Aruwimi-Ituri, and CONGO RIVERS. Produces palm oil, coffee, cocoa, rubber, quinine, and timber. KISANGANI is the provincial capital. Population was 5.6 million in 1995.

Edward, Lake. Lake in the GREAT RIFT VALLEY in east central Africa along the border between UGANDA and CONGO-KINSHASA. About 50 miles (80 km.) long, 26 miles (42 km.) wide, and 365 feet (110 meters) deep, covering 830 square miles (2,152 sq. km.). SEMLIKI RIVER is its outlet into Lake ALBERT to the north. Its western shore is within VIRUNGA NATIONAL PARK. Called Lake Idi Amin 1973-1979.

Egypt. Country in northeastern Africa. Total area of 385,227 square miles (997,740 sq. km.), about two-thirds the size of Alaska. Had a 1990's population of 66 million. Capital is CAIRO. Desert covers about 90 percent of the country; the rest includes the Nile Valley, scattered oases, and a narrow strip along the Mediterranean coast that receives 8 inches (200 millimeters) of rain during the winter months. Ninety-nine percent of Egypt's 66 million people live in the Nile Valley, one of the world's most densely populated areas. About 40 percent of the labor force is engaged in agriculture, on farms regulated by the government to be no larger than 20 hectares; 22 percent is employed in mining and manufacturing. Crude oil accounts for just under half of its exports, with cotton second. Tourism is another major industry.

El Aaiún. An international port in NORTH AFRICA and one of two cities in the dis-

puted territory of WESTERN SAHARA. Located just south of the disputed border with MOROCCO. Many of the area's approximately 165,000 inhabitants live there.

El Bahira. Salt lake in NORTH AFRICA, near TUNIS's harbor. Connected to the MEDITERRANEAN SEA by a 20-foot (6-meter) channel that has opened Tunis as a port.

El Borma. Small North African community in the southwest of TUNISIA near the Algerian border. Oil discovered there brought sudden, unexpected prosperity to this desert region.

Equator Province. Province in northwest CONGO-KINSHASA. Covers an area of 155,680 square miles (403,678 sq. km.). Capital is BANDAKA. The mean altitude is 1,200 feet (365 meters), and it is covered with dense equatorial forest. Has no railroads and is mostly agricultural.

Equatorial Guinea. Former Spanish colony in west equatorial Africa, astride the equator. Total area of 10,830 square miles (28,050 sq. km.) with a 1998 population of 443,000, most of whom are Roman Catholics. Capital is MALABO. The only African nation in which Spanish is the official language.

Equatorial Guinea Page 1159

Er Rachidia. Town in eastern MOROCCO, on the edge of the SAHARA. Its market does a brisk business with those who rove the Sahara, largely Bedouins who travel on camels seeking food, water, and grazing areas for their sheep.

Erfoud. Desert community in the far eastern part of MOROCCO, almost due east of ESSAOUIRA on the eastern side of the High ATLAS MOUNTAINS. As the last stop before the sand dunes of MERZOUGA begin, it is an important supply center for Bedouins and other nomads who travel the desert looking for food, water, and grazing areas for their sheep and camels.

Egypt Pages 1039, 1098-1099, 1160

Eritrea. Country in Africa, located on the RED SEA. Total area of 46,775 square miles (121,144 sq. km.), with a 1990's population of 3.8 million, 82 percent of whom live in rural areas. Capital is ASMARA. Plains are found along the coast and in the west; the center and southern regions are plateaus, giving way to mountains in the north. Most of the people are engaged in grazing or subsistence farming. Droughts and the war for independence from ETHIOPIA in the early 1990's have left the country impoverished.

Essaouira. Ancient Moroccan port city, located due west of MARRAKESH and north of AGADIR. A popular tourist destination for Moroccans, Europeans, and Americans.

Ethiopia Pages 1093, 1159

Ethiopia. Landlocked country in Africa. Total area of 437,598 square miles (1,133,380 sq. km.) with a population of more than 58 million in 1998. Capital is ADDIS ABABA. More than half of the land is on the Ethiopian Plateau, which ranges from 3,280 to 5,510 feet (1,000 to 1,680 meters) in elevation. Bisected by the GREAT RIFT VALLEY. To the north are mountains (Ras Dashen is the highest at 15,158 feet (4,620 meters), and to the west an encroaching desert. Maximum rainfall on the plateau is 71 inches (1,800 millimeters) per year. Roughly 86 percent of the population engages in agriculture, virtually all in subsistence enterprises. Ethiopia is among the world's poorest nations, subject to disastrous droughts and the expanding SAHARA, with little tax base to support the infrastructure necessary to begin intensive industrialization. Coffee comprises two-thirds of the country's export value.

Fès Page 1160

Fernando Po. See BIOKO.

Freetown Page 1092

Fès. Historic inland city in the northern part of MOROCCO, and the most ancient of Morocco's four imperial capitals. In the late eighth century, the indigenous Berber tribesmen there were subdued and converted to the Muslim faith. Fès soon became home to Muslim refugees fleeing from Spain and TUNISIA. Modern Fès is three cities: the ancient city, fifteen hundred years old; New Fès, which was built on higher ground near the old city when the population was exploding; and the town built by the French in the twentieth century some distance from the older towns. The combined towns have a population of more than one million. Also spelled "Fèz."

Fezzan. Desert in southwestern LIBYA. It is inhabited by nomads, who travel to find food, water, and grazing land for their flocks. Although it occupies 33 percent of Libya's land mass, it is home to less than 10 percent of the country's population. It contains some large oases in which small communities have flourished, notably SABHA, Murzug, Umm Al-Aranib, and Ghat.

Francophone states. Countries of the MAGHREB that have been most influenced by the French. Most notable are ALGERIA and MOROCCO, in which French is the second language and is used for many governmental affairs.

Free State. Province in central SOUTH AFRICA originally known as the ORANGE FREE STATE, which took its name from a nineteenth century Boer republic. Capital city is BLOEMFONTEIN. Main physical feature is the DRAKENSBERG MOUNTAINS. Primarily an agricultural area with a temperate climate, but there also are gold and diamond mines. The University of the Orange Free State is located in Bloemfontein. See also CONGO FREE STATE.

Freetown. Capital, chief port, and largest city in SIERRA LEONE. Located on the

Freetown in the late 1890's. (William Harvey Brown, *On the South African Frontier,* 1899)

rocky Sierra Leone Peninsula. Population was 469,780 in 1985. First settled by freed slaves in the late eighteenth century, including black slaves who fought on the side of the British during the American Revolution.

French Equatorial Africa. Created in the 1880's, a colonial administrative region that ceased to exist in 1960, when its component colonies became independent as the CENTRAL AFRICAN REPUBLIC, CHAD, CONGO-BRAZZAVILLE, and GABON.

French West Africa. Created in the 1880's, a colonial administrative region that ceased to exist in 1960, when its component colonies became independent as DAHOMEY (later renamed BENIN), Ivory Coast (later known as CÔTE D'IVOIRE), MALI, MAURITANIA, NIGER, SENEGAL, and UPPER VOLTA (later renamed BURKINA FASO). GUINEA left the federation in 1958.

Funchal. Capital and chief port of a Portuguese district also named Funchal, which consists of the MADEIRA archipelago off the coast of Africa. Founded in 1421, Funchal had a population of about 110,000 in the 1990's.

Gabès. Desert city established around a large North African oasis. Although on the Mediterranean coast, it is extremely dry, more a desert city than a coastal one. Also known as Qābes.

Gabès, Gulf of. Gulf formed by an indentation in the MEDITERRANEAN SEA, extending from SFAX to DJERBA ISLAND. Oil strikes there and in EL BORMA drastically changed TUNISIA's economy.

Gabon. Country in west Central Africa. Straddles the equator and is bounded by EQUATORIAL GUINEA and CAMEROON to the north, CONGO-BRAZZAVILLE to the east and south, and the Atlantic Ocean to the west. Total area of 103,350 square miles (267,987 sq. km.) with a

*Gibraltar
Page 1100*

*Giza
Pages
1098, 1160*

population of 1.2 million in 1998. Capital is LIBREVILLE. Dense equatorial rain forest covers three-fourths of the country. Natural resources include woods, minerals, and petroleum. One of the world's largest producers of manganese. Agriculture is a small part in the economy, and the transportation infrastructure is poor. Became independent from France in 1960. The island state of SÃO TOMÉ AND PRÍNCIPE is located offshore.

Gambia. Smallest nation in mainland Africa. Total area of 4,127 square miles (10,689 sq. km.) with a population of 1.25 million in 1997. Capital is BANJUL. Mandingo, Wolof, and English are spoken. Divided into two by the GAMBIA RIVER and, apart from a small Atlantic Ocean coastline, completely surrounded by SENEGAL. Gambia and Senegal are allied in foreign affairs and defense but their cultural differences prevent unification.

Gambia River. West African river, rising in the Fouta Jallon in GUINEA and flowing west through the nations of GAMBIA and SENEGAL. Enters the Atlantic Ocean near St. Mary's Island, BANJUL, the Gambian capital. It is about 700 miles (1,100 km.) long.

Garamba National Park. Park in northeast CONGO-KINSHASA, near the SUDAN border. Established in 1938; covers about 1,937 square miles (5,020 sq. km.). Covered with high-grass savanna with occasional forest galleries. Known for its wildlife, including the white rhinoceros, eland, and giraffe.

*Ghana
Pages
1040, 1093*

Ghana. County in West Africa, formerly called GOLD COAST by the British. Total area of 92,098 square miles (238,534 sq. km.) with a 1997 population of 18.2 million, more than half of whom are Ashanti, who speak Akan. Capital and largest city is ACCRA. English is the official language.

Gibraltar. Small British colony on the Iberian Peninsula 14 miles (22 km.) north of the North African coast. In legend, the Rock of Gibraltar is one of the PILLARS OF HERCULES, the other being the Jebel Musa at CEUTA in SPANISH MOROCCO.

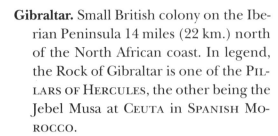

Giza. Home to EGYPT's great pyramids, and a suburb of CAIRO. Population was 2.14 million in 1996. The pyramids were built in the twenty-sixth century B.C.E.; the largest, that of Cheops, ranks among the seven wonders of the ancient world. Giza is an educational center, the seat of Cairo University and a number of other institutes, and a manufacturing and industrial center. Population was 2.14 million in 1996.

Gold Coast. Name of GHANA when it was a British colony.

Great Rift Valley. A continuous fault in the earth's crust that runs nearly 3,000 miles (4,830 km.) through East Africa and Southwest Asia. At its greatest width, it is more than 100 miles (160 km.) wide. Elevations vary from 6,000 feet (1,829 meters) above sea level in KENYA to 1,340 feet (408 meters) below sea level at the Dead Sea (between Israel and Jordan), the lowest point on earth. Contains a chain of lakes, stretching from Lake NYASA in south-central Africa to the Sea of Galilee in Israel.

Guinea. Republic in West Africa, and the first colony in FRENCH WEST AFRICA to gain independence (1958). Total area of 94,926 square miles (245,858 sq. km.) with a population of 7.4 million. Capital is CONAKRY. French is the official language. Called French Guinea before independence. West Africa's three major rivers—GAMBIA, NIGER, and SENEGAL—originate in the plateau region. Administered within the federation of FRENCH WEST AFRICA during the era of colonial rule.

Continued on page 1169

Tanzania's University of Dar es Salaam, a few years after it opened during the 1960's. Most African nations cannot afford to build and operate more than one modern university. (R. Kent Rasmussen)

Southern Angola's Quicama National Park. After decades of civil war, Angola had few remaining large animals. In the early twenty-first century, South Africa helped Angola to reintroduce wild animals in Quicama. (AP/Wide World Photos)

Antananarivo, the capital and largest city of Madagascar, was founded in about 1625 near the center of the island. Its population in 1993 was about 675,700. (American Stock Photography)

A young boy plays in a fishing boat by the town of Ganvie in Benin. Most of the West African town's twelve thousand residents live in houses built on stilts over Lake Nokoue. (AP/Wide World Photos)

Built astride the Nile River, Cairo is both Egypt's capital and Africa's most populous city. (PhotoDisc)

The Canary Islands, viewed from space in June, 1991. Dust clouds over the Sahara in Northwest Africa are visible to the right. (Corbis)

South Africa's Cape of Good Hope takes its name from the optimism that early Portuguese navigators felt when they rounded the point separating the Atlantic and Indian Oceans on their voyages to India. (Corbis)

Cape Verde fishermen drag a boat up a shore on São Vicente island. (AP/Wide World Photos)

Looking north from Cape Point—the position from which lines radiate in the metallic plaque in the foreground. The body of water in the background is False Bay—the western limit of the Indian Ocean. (R. Kent Rasmussen)

A young boy casts his fishing net into the Congo River near Kisangani, in Congo-Kinshasa. The livelihood of his community depends primarily on the fish they harvest from the river. (AP/Wide World Photos)

Côte d'Ivoire. In September, 2000, Ivorians took to the streets of Abidjan to demonstrate against the country's first military junta and to demand a return to constitutional government. (AP/Wide World Photos)

Residents of Equatorial Guinea paddling a small boat on the estuary of the Utamboni River, which runs along the country's border with Gabon. Many people in the tiny Central African nation are dependent on river transportation for contact with the outside world. (David Gala/Mercury Press)

A Coptic priest blesses pilgrims gathered at Entoto, Ethiopia. Ethiopia is one of the oldest Christian countries in the world. (AP/Wide World Photos)

Fès's Blue Gate and mosque. A northern Moroccan city, Fès contains some of the world's best-preserved medieval Islamic architecture. (Corbis)

Giza is home to Egypt's great pyramids, which were built in the twenty-sixth century B.C.E. Cheops, the largest, ranks among the seven wonders of the ancient world. (PhotoDisc)

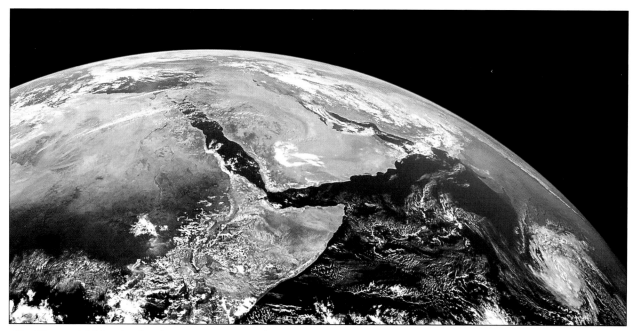

The Horn of Africa is clearly visible in this 1972 satellite image of the region. The aridity of the Middle East and Northeastern Africa makes this part of the world one of the best regions for satellite pictures of land masses. (Corbis)

Similar in many ways to a large American city, Johannesburg, South Africa, is probably Africa's most thoroughly modern major city. (PhotoDisc)

Sunset over Mount Kilimanjaro's Mawenzi Peak, on Africa's highest mountain. (AP/Wide World Photos)

Kenya's Masai Mara Game Reserve has one of the largest collections of big game on the continent. (American Stock Photography)

Niger is an arid country and is gradually being taken over by the Sahara Desert from the north. Here, a Tuareg man draws water from a well to irrigate crops on his small oasis plot north of Agadez. (AP/Wide World Photos)

A cataract on the upper reaches of the Nile River, near its source at Lake Victoria in Uganda. (AP/Wide World Photos)

Mombasa is the home to one of the most substantial reminders of the Portuguese era in East Africa—Fort Jesus, a massive structure at the entrance to Mombasa's harbor built in the late sixteenth century. (R. Kent Rasmussen)

Lake Tanganyika. Bujumbura workers unload Zambian sugar headed for a Burundi beer factory. Africa's second-largest lake, Tanganyika is 410 miles (660 km.) long and connects ports in Burundi, Congo-Kinshasa, Tanzania, and Zambia. (AP/Wide World Photos)

Victoria Falls. Located on the Zambezi River, which separates Zambia and Zimbabwe, where the river is a mile wide and falls about 400 feet (120 meters). (Corbis)

Canoers on Lake Victoria. (Corbis)

Windhoek, the capital and commercial and transportation center of Namibia, is built on a dry plateau in the central of the country. (Corbis)

The first president of the independent Côte d'Ivoire d'Ivoire, Felix Houphouet-Boigny, built this gigantic basilica in Yamoussoukro during the 1980's for no clear purpose. (AP/ Wide World Photos)

Zanzibar, a low-lying island off the coast of East Africa, was historically an important trading port before the colonial era. The old district of its capital city still retains the chaotic layout of its precolonial past. (R. Kent Rasmussen)

Guinea, Gulf of. An arm of the Atlantic Ocean, located in West Africa, between Cape Palmas at the southeastern edge of LIBERIA and Cape Lopez in GABON. Forms two bays: the Bight of BIAFRA and the Bight of BENIN.

Guinea-Bissau. Country located near the western tip of Africa, and the first Portuguese colony in Africa to gain independence (1974). Total area of 13,948 square miles (36,125 sq. km.) with a 1990's population of slightly over 1 million. Known by the name of its capital city, Bissau, to differentiate it from neighboring GUINEA. Portuguese is the official language. The offshore Bijago Archipelago is part of the country. The Fulani and the Balante make up the two largest ethnic groups. Called Portuguese Guinea before independence.

Harare. Capital and largest city of ZIMBABWE, with a population of about 1.2 million people during the early 1990's. Founded as Fort Salisbury (later Salisbury) by a British force occupying the northeast part of the country in 1890. The country's main commercial, financial, and transportation center.

Hoggar Mountains. See AHAGGAR MOUNTAINS.

Horn of Africa. Protrusion of northeast Africa extending into the INDIAN OCEAN, at the point where the Arabian Peninsula broke away from Africa. The tip of the Horn is part of SOMALIA.

Ibadan. Second-largest city in NIGERIA. A Yoruba city, it is the capital of Oyo State. Located about 100 miles (160 km.) inland from the Atlantic coast. A commercial city, well served by roads and air routes, and the first African city to have a television station (1959). Population was 1.2 million in 1990.

Indian Ocean. Third-largest body of water on the earth; forms the coastline of Southern Africa. A tropical ocean, little of which is north of the equator, and it has no inflow of cold water in its northern areas. It has a moderating effect on the southeastern coast of Africa. It is somewhat deeper than the Atlantic Ocean. The LIMPOPO and ZAMBEZI Rivers drain into it.

Inga Falls. Rapids in Central Africa, along the border between CONGO-KINSHASA and CONGO-BRAZZAVILLE. The site of thirty-two rapids where the CONGO RIVER falls 850 feet (260 meters) in about 220 miles (355 km.). One of the world's largest hydroelectric-dam projects is being built there, providing electricity to KINSHASA, Congo-Brazzaville, KATANGA, and ZAMBIA, more than 1,000 miles (1,600 km.) away.

Ivory Coast. See CÔTE D'IVOIRE.

Johannesburg. Largest city in SOUTH AFRICA and the hub of South Africa's commercial, financial, industrial, and mining undertakings; capital of Gauteng Province. Its 1990's population was 2.7 million. Located 5,707 feet (1,740 meters) above sea level, it has warm summers and cold to mild winters. In 1886 the discovery of gold triggered one of the biggest gold rushes in the history of the world. Also called Egoli, a Zulu name meaning "City of Gold."

Johannesburg Page 1161

Jos. Capital of the Plateau State in the middle belt of NIGERIA. Located on the Delimi River near the center of JOS PLATEAU, about 4,100 feet (1,250 meters) above sea level. Its average monthly temperature of 69 to 77 degrees Fahrenheit (21 to 25 degrees Celsius), cooler than any other city in Nigeria, attracts tourists. The center of the nation's tin mining industry. Population was 195,000 in 1995.

Horn of Africa Page 1161

Jos Plateau. Tropical highland in northern NIGERIA. It has an elevation of about 4,200 feet (1,300 meters) and

Indian Ocean Page 1157

covers an area of almost 3,000 square miles (7,800 sq. km.). Has a cooler temperature and more rainfall annually than the surrounding lowlands.

Kabompo River. River in Southern Africa that flows into the ZAMBEZI from the east. Drains the watershed between the Zambezi and CONGO RIVER systems. The Lunga River, which flows into it, is more important for internal navigation than the upper Kabompo.

Kainji Dam. One of the largest dams in the world, located in West Africa. Constructed on the NIGER RIVER in western NIGERIA at a cost of $209 million, it opened in 1968 after four years of construction. It extends about 6 miles (10 km.) and has twelve hydroelectric turbines capable of generating 960,000 kilowatts. Supplies electricity to most cities in Nigeria and some neighboring states.

Kainji Lake. Reservoir on the NIGER RIVER in western NIGERIA (West Africa) created by the KAINJI DAM. About 84 miles (135 km.) long and 20 miles (30 km.) wide. Several villages were moved for the creation of the reservoir. The lake supports fishing and irrigation.

Kairouan. City in NORTH AFRICA, on the MEDITERRANEAN SEA half-way down TUNISIA's eastern coast. Founded around 670 B.C.E. Its great mosque, completed in the ninth century C.E., is a major attraction. Tourists are also drawn there for the rugs hand-woven by the inhabitants. Also called al-Qayrawan.

Kalahari Desert. One of the world's major deserts, occupying parts of SOUTH AFRICA, BOTSWANA, and NAMIBIA. Covers 275,000 square miles (712,250 sq. km.). Its appearance is one of sandy, red soil except during the rainy season, when large mud flats appear.

Kalemie. Port on the west shore of Lake TANGANYIKA, south of the outlet of the LUKUGA RIVER, in Central Africa. Located in KATANGA province in southeast CONGO-KINSHASA. A commercial center and terminus of a railroad from LUBUMBASHI and KINDU. Commercial activities include fishing, textiles, and cement. Population was 101,300 in 1994. Called Albertville until 1966.

Kampala. Largest city, educational center, and political capital of UGANDA. Population was nearly 800,000 in 1991. Located near Lake VICTORIA, the largest body of water in this landlocked country, and connected by rail to its primary port, Port Bell. Access to Lake Victoria gives Kampala access to the INDIAN OCEAN port of DAR ES SALAAM, TANZANIA, via rail. Principal manufactured products are textiles, processed food, cement, and cigarettes. Built on the site of a fort founded by the British in 1890.

Kananga. Capital of KASAI OCCIDENTAL province in south central CONGO-KINSHASA. Main commercial and communication center in the region. Population was 393,000 in 1994. Known as Luluabourg until 1972. A mutiny of African troops in the CONGO FREE STATE took place there in 1895.

Kano. Commercial center and capital of Kano State in northern NIGERIA. Located about 500 miles (805 km.) northeast of LAGOS. Population was 700,000 in 1990, the majority of whom were Hausa Muslims. It has the largest mosque in Nigeria.

Kariba, Lake. Reservoir forming part of the border between ZAMBIA and ZIMBABWE, in Southern Africa. Created by Kariba Dam, which was built in the 1950's, it collects the waters of the ZAMBEZI RIVER. The lake is 175 miles (280 km.) long and fills Kariba Gorge; the concrete dam is 2,000 feet (610 meters) long and 420 feet (128 meters) high.

Karisimbi Mountain. Extinct volcano in east CONGO-KINSHASA. Highest peak (about 14,787 feet/4,507 meters) of the VIRUNGA range. Located near the border with RWANDA, just northwest of MIKENO Mountain, about 20 miles (32 km.) northeast of Goma. The mountain's top is occasionally covered with snow.

Kasai Occidental. Province in south central CONGO-KINSHASA. Covers 59,746 square miles (154,921 sq. km.) with a population of 3.3 million in 1995. Capital is KANANGA. The KASAI RIVER and its tributaries drain most of the province. The diamond mines of Tshikapa supply the international market with gems.

Kasai Oriental. Province in south central CONGO-KINSHASA. Covers 65,754 square miles (170,500 sq. km.) with a population of 3.8 million in 1995. Capital is MBUJI-MAYI. The diamond mines of Mbuji-Mayi supply the international market with the industrial diamonds.

Kasai River. One of the principal left tributaries of the CONGO RIVER, running mainly in CONGO-KINSHASA. Rises on the central plateau of ANGOLA and forms part of the border between Angola and Congo-Kinshasa in the south. Length is more than 1,338 miles (2,150 km.), of which about 250 miles (400 km.) is in Angola. Its lower course is called the Kwa. Navigable to about 475 miles (765 km.)) upstream. Diamonds are washed in the southern Congolese section.

Katanga. Province in southeast CONGO-KINSHASA. Covers 191,827 square miles (497,407 sq. km.). Population was 4.1 million in 1995. Capital is LUBUMBASHI. Katanga Plateau covers most of the region, with altitude varying between 3,000 and 6,000 feet (900 and 1,800 meters). The most industrialized region of the country, it was developed as a complex of mining and industrial towns as well as transportation and communications networks. Produces

Early Katanga copper mine. (Isaac F. Marcosson, *An African Adventure*, 1921)

Central Kenya's Sweetwaters Game Reserve is one of the few places in Africa that still harbors black rhinoceroses. (Corbis)

*Kenya
Pages 975,
971, 1162*

*Mt. Kili-
manjaro
Pages 965,
1162*

copper, tin, cobalt, manganese, zinc, and uranium. In the 1960's, it attempted to secede from the rest of the country.

Kenya. Country straddling the equator in East Africa. Covers 224,959 square miles (582,646 sq. km.), slightly smaller than Texas. In the 1990's, its population was 28 million in the 1990's, most of whom live in the south. Its capital city, NAIROBI, is also the financial capital of East Africa. Kenya has a narrow coastal plain that gives way to a series of plateaus and mountains. The highest region is in the center of the country, culminating in the extinct volcano Mount Kenya, Africa's second-highest peak at 17,060 feet (5,200 meters). The highlands are bisected by the Eastern RIFT VALLEY. The northern two-thirds of the country is either desert or steppe. Kenya is the most industrialized nation of East Africa. Its industry is dominated by food processing (especially tea and coffee) and textiles. Refined petroleum and cement are ex-

ported to other East African nations. Much of the labor force is employed in service industries, including tourism. However, many people are still engaged in subsistence agriculture.

Kerkenna Island. Large island off the coast of TUNISIA, across from SFAX on the east coast of the mainland. Legend has it that this and DJERBA ISLAND are the remains of the lost continent of Atlantis, which some people think was inundated by a huge tidal wave in ancient times.

Khartoum. Capital and transportation, economic, and educational center of SUDAN. Located at the heart of the Gezira, an enormous region of irrigation agriculture where the White and Blue Niles combine to form the NILE RIVER. Population was about 1 million in 1993. Industries include printing, food processing, textiles, and glass manufacturing. The area has had significant settlement for more than 6,000 years. Built in 1821 as an outpost for EGYPT's new southern empire, Khartoum became a British colony soon afterward.

Kigali. Largest city and political capital of RWANDA. Located on a highway that connects it to BURUNDI and UGANDA, its population was 233,000 in 1991. Textiles, processed foods, chemicals, and refined tin are produced there.

Kilimanjaro, Mount. Highest mountain in Africa, located in northeastern TANZANIA. A dormant volcano, with twin peaks situated nearly 6.8 miles (11 km.) apart, the higher at 19,340 feet (5,895 meters) above sea level, the lower at 16,894 feet (5,149 meters). Despite its tropical location, it is high enough to have a permanent snowcap. Its lower regions, owing to ancient lava flows, are quite fertile, producing coffee and plantains.

Kimberly. City in the northern Cape Province of SOUTH AFRICA. Diamonds were discovered there in 1871, and it is one of the largest sources of diamonds in the world. Population was 150,000 in the 1990's; its economy, while still based on diamond mining, includes iron mining and diamond finishing.

Kindu. River port and capital of MANIEMA province in east central CONGO-KINSHASA. Located on both banks of the CONGO RIVER, about 390 miles (630 km.) south of KISANGANI. The Congo River is navigable from Kindu to about 100 miles (160 km.) south of Kisangani. Kindu is also a terminus of railroads from LUBUMBASHI and KALEMIE and an important transshipment point. Population was 86,800 in 1994.

Kinshasa. Largest city in black Africa and the capital and commercial and industrial center of CONGO-KINSHASA, which takes its unofficial name from the city. Located in the southwest of the country, directly across the CONGO RIVER from BRAZZAVILLE, the capital of CONGO-BRAZZAVILLE. The terminus of navigation on the Congo River from KISANGANI, and the railroad terminus from MATADI. Population was 4.7 million in 1994, more than 30 percent of whom live in squatting zones. Founded in 1887 by Henry Morton Stanley. Called LÉOPOLDVILLE before 1966.

Kisangani. Capital of EASTERN PROVINCE in northeast CONGO-KINSHASA, and an important commercial and distribution center. Straddles the CONGO RIVER. The country's second major

river port, the terminus of the railroad from the south, and the head of steam navigation to KINSHASA. Population was 417,500 in 1994. Henry Morton Stanley first reached the area in 1877, and established the post five years later. City was called Stanleyville until 1966.

Kivu, Lake. Lake in east CONGO-KINSHASA, along the border with RWANDA. Highest lake (altitude 4,788 feet/1,460 meters) of the GREAT RIFT VALLEY. It is 60 miles (96 km.) long, 30 miles (48 km.) wide, and 1,600 feet (490 meters) deep, covering about 1,100 square miles (2,850 sq. km.). Contains a large volume of dissolved methane gases. Main ports are BUKAVU and Goma.

Kivu, South. Province in east CONGO-KINSHASA. It is bordered on the east by Lake KIVU and RWANDA. With altitudes varying from 3,000 to more than 10,000 feet (900 to 3,000 meters), the climate is mild and temperate, and vegetables can be grown. Rich in mineral resources, including gold and tin. Covers 25,123 square miles (65,145 sq. km.) with a population of 2.8 million in 1995.

Kolwezi. Industrial town in KATANGA province in southeast CONGO-KINSHASA. Population was 417,800 in 1994. Located on the Lubumbashi-Lobito railroad about 80 miles (130 km.) from LIKASI and 145 miles (230 km.) from LUBUMBASHI. Major producer of copper and cobalt.

Kumasi. Capital of the Ashanti region of GHANA. Located in central Ghana, in a dense forest belt. The commercial center for the rich cocoa-producing area. In 1951 Ghana's University of Science and Technology opened there. Population was 400,000 in 1990.

Kwando River. Largest tributary of the ZAMBEZI RIVER in Southern Africa. Flows in a generally straight course to the southeast. For much of its course, it flows through vast swamps dotted with islands. Also known as the Chobe or the Linyante River.

KwaZulu/Natal. South African state on the western side of the country on the INDIAN OCEAN. Capital is DURBAN; second major city is PIETERMARITZBURG, the site of the University of Natal. Climate is subtropical; the main agricultural product is sugarcane. The African population is mostly Zulu, and the dominant language is English.

Lagos
Page 1092

Lagos. Largest city and former national capital of NIGERIA. Located at the southwestern end of Nigeria's Atlantic coastline, it is the country's industrial and commercial center along the busiest seaport. The seat of the Lagos State government. Population was 2.1 million in 1994.

Las Palmas de Gran Canaria. Capital of Las Palmas province in the CANARY ISLANDS, located on the island of Gran Canaria. Its nearby port, Puerto de la Luz, is the most important in the Canary Islands. Founded in 1478, the city had a population of about 373,800 in 1995.

Léopoldville. Capital of the BELGIAN CONGO. Name was changed to KINSHASA in 1966. Named in honor of King Leopold II (1835-1910) of Belgium.

Lesotho
Page 1104

Lesotho. An independent kingdom completely surrounded by SOUTH AFRICA. Total area of 11,716 square miles (30,344 sq. km.) with a 1990's population of 1.9 million. Capital and only large city is Maseru. The DRAKENSBERG mountain range dominates it and is the source of two important rivers, the Orange and the Tugela. Economy is predominantly agricultural. A large portion of its population is migratory, as many workers travel to South Africa to find employment. Created as the Brit-

ish protectorate of BASUTOLAND during the 1860's.

Liberia. Oldest independent state in black Africa. Total area of 42,950 square miles (111,241 sq. km.) with a population of 2.6 million in 1997. Capital is MONROVIA. Founded by the American Colonization Society, who purchased land in 1822 to create an African homeland for freed American slaves. Has the world's largest merchant navy because of its low taxes and registration of many foreign-owned ships.

Libreville. Capital and commercial and educational center of GABON. Located on Gabon's northwest shore and an important seaport on the Gulf of GUINEA. A highly industrialized town, with sawmills, plywood and cloth-printing factories, brewing, and shipbuilding. Offshore oil was discovered north of the city in 1970's. Population was 419,000 in 1997. The capital of FRENCH EQUATORIAL AFRICA from 1888 to 1904. Name means "free town."

Libya. The fourth-largest country in Africa. Located in NORTH AFRICA, it covers 679,362 square miles (1,760,000 sq. km.), about two and a half times the size of Texas, with a 1990's population of 3.6 million. Bordered on the north by the MEDITERRANEAN SEA, on the west by ALGERIA and TUNISIA, on the east by EGYPT and SUDAN, and on the south by NIGER and CHAD. Ninety percent desert, with no rivers. Its population has grown rapidly as a result of its low death rate, high birth rate, and prosperity brought by the oil boom that began in the 1960's.

Likasi. Industrial town in KATANGA province in southeast CONGO-KINSHASA. Located on the Lubumbashi-Lobito railroad about 65 miles (105 km.) northwest of LUBUMBASHI. The country's leading center of copper and cobalt refining; also has chemical factories manufacturing sulfuric acid, hydrogen chloride, sodium chlorate, and glycerin. Founded in 1917. Population was 299,000 in 1994.

Lilongwe. Capital of MALAWI in Southern Africa. Had a 1990's population of 180,000. Founded in 1947; became a city in 1966, when the population was less than 20,000. Population increased as a result of an extensive government construction program. Located near the border of MOZAMBIQUE and ZAMBIA in the heart of Malawi's agricultural region on the Lilongwe River and is a market center for tobacco and other crops.

Limpopo River. River originating in northern SOUTH AFRICA that flows through, or forms borders of, South Africa, BOTSWANA, ZIMBABWE, and MOZAMBIQUE. Enters the INDIAN OCEAN at DELAGOA BAY. It is around 1,000 miles (1,610 km.) long.

Lomami River. Left tributary of CONGO RIVER in central CONGO-KINSHASA. Rises in the southeast of the country in KATANGA province, about 15 miles west of KAMINA, and flows north about 900 miles (1,500 km.) to join the Congo River about 70 miles (110 km.) west of KISANGANI. Navigable upstream for about 250 miles (400 km.).

Lomé. Largest city and major port of TOGO, on West Africa's Guinea Coast.

Lorenço Marques. See MAPUTO.

Lualaba River. See CONGO RIVER.

Luanda. Capital, largest city, and chief port of ANGOLA in Southern Africa. Had a population of about 1.2 million in the 1990's. Located on the west coast of Africa, along the Atlantic Ocean, it is one of the only cities along a stretch of more than 870 miles (1,400 km.) of Angolan coastline. Average temperatures range between 69.8 degrees Fahren-

heit (21 degrees Celsius) in January and 60.8 degrees Fahrenheit (16 degrees Celsius) in June. Has light industrial facilities such as foundries, sawmills, textile mills, cement, and food processing plants. Fishing is also important. Founded in 1576, it was the main center of Portuguese settlement in Angola.

Luapula River. River in southeast CONGO-KINSHASA along the border with ZAMBIA, in Central Africa. Originating from the south end of Lake Bangweulu, it flows south then north for 350 miles (560 km.), emptying into Lake MWERU. Considered the upper course of the LUVUA RIVER. Navigable upstream from Lake Mweru for more than 60 miles (96 km.).

Lubumbashi. Capital of KATANGA province in southeast CONGO-KINSHASA; the country's second-largest city and main commercial and industrial center. Located on a railroad near the border with ZAMBIA, at an altitude of 5,008 feet (1,526 meters). Population was 851,400 in 1994. Established by Belgium as a copper-mining settlement in 1910; called Elisabethville until 1966.

Lufira River. Right tributary of the CONGO RIVER in southeast CONGO-KINSHASA. Originates in the KATANGA highlands near the border of ZAMBIA, about 70 miles (110 km.) northwest of LUBUMBASHI; runs 300 miles (480 km.) northward to join the Lualaba River at Lake Kisale next to Lake UPEMBA. One of its many rapids is Mwadingusha Falls—the site of one of the largest hydroelectric plants in the country.

Lukuga River. Right tributary of the CONGO RIVER in southeast CONGO-KINSHASA, and the only outlet for Lake TANGANYIKA. Originates from the west shore of Lake Tanganyika at KALEMIE and runs about 200 miles (320 km.) to

Limpopo River Page 1100

empty its water in the Lualaba River.

Lusaka. Capital, chief administrative center, and the major financial, transportation, and manufacturing hub of ZAMBIA in Southern Africa. Had a population of 900,000 in the 1990's. Located on a high plateau in the south central region, at an altitude of 4,265 feet (1,300 meters). Established by European settlers in about 1905 as a small trading post.

Luvua River. Right tributary of the CONGO RIVER in southeast CONGO-KINSHASA. Originates from the north end of Lake MWERU and flows 215 miles (345 km.) northwest to join the Lualaba River. Navigable for shallow-draught boats for about 100 miles (160 km.) upstream. A hydroelectric plant was built at Piana-Mwanga, about 120 miles (195 km.) upstream.

*Mada-gascar
Page 1154*

Madagascar. Fourth-largest island in the world, an INDIAN OCEAN island nation officially known as the Malagasy Republic. Located about 200 miles (320 km.) across the MOZAMBIQUE CHANNEL from the coast of southeast Africa. MOZAMBIQUE is its closest mainland neighbor. The tropic of CAPRICORN cuts across its southern half. Plains lie along the east and west coasts, the latter of which has several natural harbors. A range of highlands closely parallels the east coast, while an unusual channel, the CANAL DES PANGALANES, runs along the same coast. In the north, a massif rises to Mount Tsaratanana, at 9,450 feet (2,880 meters) the island's highest point. The island is drained by several rivers. The home of several highly sophisticated kingdoms, Madagascar was colonized by the French but became independent again in 1960. Madagascar stretches 994 miles (1,600 km.) from north to south, covers 226,739 square miles (587,000 sq. km.), and had a population of 13,427,800 in

*Maghreb
Page 1091*

1994. The island's economy is basically agricultural, and it exports large amounts of extremely high-quality rice and timber. A favorite place for naturalists, as its isolation has resulted in the evolution of exotic species that are found nowhere else. During the colonial period, it was a French possession. Although geographically tied to the African continent, its culture is closer to those of France and Southeast Asia. Capital is ANTANANARIVO.

Madeira. Archipelago located about 350 miles (563 km.) from the African coast of MOROCCO. The group's largest island, also called Madeira, rises to an elevation of 6,106 feet (1,861 meters). The northern part of Madeira Island receives most of the rainfall, which is distributed throughout the island by a system of tunnels and canals. The archipelago was uninhabited when it was discovered in the early fifteenth century. The group constitutes the Portuguese province of FUNCHAL, and the province's capital is also known as Funchal. Madeira is noted for its wine production, especially the fortified wine known as Madeira, and is a favorite among tourists for its genial climate. It covers 308 square miles (798 sq. km.) and has a population of 257,000.

Maghreb. Area of NORTH AFRICA between the MEDITERRANEAN SEA on the north and the SAHARA on the south. It includes MOROCCO, ALGERIA, TUNISIA, and parts of LIBYA. Most of its inhabitants have a common history, but have not been organized into a cohesive social or political entity.

Maiko National Park. Protected area in eastern CONGO-KINSHASA, halfway between BUKAVU and KISANGANI. Covers about 4,180 square miles (10,840 sq. km.). The main vegetative cover is the dense equatorial forest. Animal species include gorillas, elephants, leopards, and okapi. The park is not open to tourism.

Majardah. River system in NORTH AFRICA that begins in ALGERIA and drains into the Gulf of TUNIS. The most important river system in Algeria and TUNISIA and the only river in these countries that has water year-round.

Malabo. Capital, largest city, and economic center of EQUATORIAL GUINEA. Located on the northern coast of BIOKO Island (formerly Fernando Po Island) near the equator. Founded in 1827 by the British as Port Clarence. Population was 37,000 in 1991.

Malagasy Republic. See MADAGASCAR.

Malawi. Republic in southeastern Africa. Total area of 45,747 square miles (118,485 sq. km.) with a 1990's population of 10.5 million. Capital is LILONGWE. Extends about 520 miles (835 km.) north to south and varies in width from about 50 to 100 miles (80 to 160 km.). Much of its surface is covered by Lake Malawi, the third-largest lake in Africa. Several plateaus lie to the east and west of Lake Malawi. Has a rainy season from November to April. Almost all of its wealth comes from agriculture. Formerly the British protectorate of Nyasaland.

Mali. Republic in West Africa. Total area of 478,767 square miles (1,240,006 sq. km.) with a population of 10 million in 1997. Capital is BAMAKO. French is the official language. Contains the fabled city of Timbuktu, once known as the center of Islamic learning and commerce. Administered within the federation of FRENCH WEST AFRICA during the era of colonial rule.

Maniema. Province in east central CONGO-KINSHASA. Covers 51,062 square miles (132,400 sq. km.), with a population of 1.3 million in 1995. Provincial capital is

KINDU. Drained by the CONGO RIVER, called the Lualaba River there. Was the main base for the slave trade in the nineteenth century.

Maputo. Capital and largest city of MOZAMBIQUE in Southern Africa. Had a population of 1,600,000 in the 1990's. Located on DELAGOA BAY, an inlet of the INDIAN OCEAN. Has an excellent harbor; a tourist industry has emerged in part because of the fine sand beaches. Lined with sand dunes and swamps. Climate is mainly tropical. Produces refined petroleum, building materials, clothing, and foods. Maputo received its current name after Mozambique achieved independence in 1975; known as Lorenço Marques in colonial times.

Maradi. A major commercial and transportation center in the southern part of NIGER. Efficient highways connect it to NIAMEY, Niger's capital, and the city of KANO in NIGERIA. Its chief products are cotton and groundnuts (peanuts). Population was 114,000 in 1990.

Marrakesh. Second-largest city in MOROCCO. Located inland toward the center of Morocco, west of the High ATLAS MOUNTAINS, with a 1990's population of more than 1.5 million. It began as a town of tents in an oasis during the eleventh century and has long been a trading center. It is considered the unofficial capital of the southern part of the country.

Mascarene Islands. Small group of islands in the INDIAN OCEAN east of MADAGASCAR that includes MAURITIUS, RODRIGUES, and RÉUNION. Named after Pedro Mascarenhas, a Portuguese visitor of the early sixteenth century.

Matadi. Capital of BAS-CONGO province in southwestern CONGO-KINSHASA; the country's major port and a major commercial center. Located about 100

Mali
Pages
1033, 1038

miles (160 km.) from the Atlantic port of Banana and is the farthest point reached by ocean ships. Also the head of the railroad to KINSHASA. Population was 172,700 in 1994. Founded in 1879 by Henry Morton Stanley.

Mauritania. Islamic republic in West Africa, heavily dependent on aid from France. Total area of 395,956 square miles (1,025,525 sq. km.) with a 1997 population of 2.4 million, most of whom are Moors and many of whom are nomads. Capital is Nouakchott. About 80 percent of the country is located in the SAHARA. Islam is the official religion and Arabic is the official language. Administered within the federation of FRENCH WEST AFRICA during the era of colonial rule. Located directly south and east of the disputed WESTERN SAHARA territory (formerly Spanish Sahara). To its east is the southern part of ALGERIA.

Mauritius. Nation of volcanic islands in the INDIAN OCEAN east of MADAGASCAR, part of the MASCARENE group. The nation's capital is PORT LOUIS. The nation of Mauritius includes Mauritius Island, RODRIGUES, the Agalega Islands, and the Cargados Carajos Shoals. Although the climate is tropical monsoonal, irrigation is necessary for organized agriculture. Mauritius was the home of the dodo, a large flightless bird slaughtered to extinction for its meat. It was a British colony until its independence in 1968. The islands' total area is 788 square miles (2,040 sq. km.), and the population was about 1,148,000 in 1997.

Mayotte. African island in the COMOROS chain. Because of the island's long association with France and its stronger economic base, its citizens chose to remain attached to France when the rest of the chain declared independence in 1975. Mayotte and several nearby islets cover an area of 144 square miles (374 sq. km.). In 1997 the population was about 131,300.

Mbuji-Mayi. Industrial town and capital of KASAI ORIENTAL province in south central CONGO-KINSHASA. Population was 806,500 in 1994. It became a mining town after the discovery of diamonds in the area in 1909, and the region produced up to 10 percent by weight of the world's industrial diamonds until 1990.

Mediterranean Sea. Large sea that separates NORTH AFRICA from EUROPE. It takes its name from Latin words meaning "in the middle of land"—a reference to its nearly land-locked nature. Covers about 969,100 square miles (2.5 million sq. km.) and extends 2,200 miles (3,540 km.) from west to east and about 1,000 miles (1,600 km.) from north to south at its widest. Its greatest depth is 16,897 feet (5,150 meters). Major African ports on the Mediterranean include ALGIERS, ALEXANDRIA, BIZERTE, Oran, Port Said, Sfax, Tripoli, and TUNIS.

Meknes. City in MOROCCO, located 50 miles (80 km.) directly inland from RABAT, with a 1990's population of more than 750,000. Renowned for the seventeenth century Bab el Mansour, one of the most elaborate and richly decorated of Morocco's city gates. Because of its excellent architecture, Meknes has been called the Versailles of Morocco. In its prime, Meknes had fifty palaces and sixteen miles of protective walls with twenty gates.

Melilla. A Spanish community on a cape extending from MOROCCO into the MEDITERRANEAN SEA close to the Algerian border. One of two Spanish possessions in NORTH AFRICA (the other being CEUTA), which are surrounded by Morocco and have been considered by Spain for autonomous status.

Merzouga. Desert outpost east of ERFOUD, in NORTH AFRICA, where the sand dunes of the SAHARA begin. There, sand drifts over the few roads that exist, much as snow drifts over roads in blizzard conditions in America's midwestern states.

Mikeno. Extinct volcano in east CONGO-KINSHASA. Second-highest peak (about 14,600 feet/4,450 meters) of the VIRUNGA range. Located near the RWANDA border, just northwest of KARISIMBI MOUNTAIN, in VIRUNGA NATIONAL PARK.

Mobutu, Lake. See Lake ALBERT.

Mogadishu. Capital and largest city of SOMALIA, Africa. Founded around 900 by Arab traders. Until the outbreak of civil war and the ensuing anarchy that paralyzed the country in the 1990's, it was the chief economic center for the nation. Population was more than 900,000 in 1990.

Mombasa. Second-largest city and the primary port of KENYA. Population was more than 600,000 in 1991. The most significant port of East Africa, with rail connections to Lake VICTORIA and DAR ES SALAAM, and roads to most other INDIAN OCEAN ports of the region. Primary ocean port for landlocked UGANDA and RWANDA. Founded in the eighth century by Moslem traders.

Monrovia. Capital, chief port, and most developed city in LIBERIA. Founded in 1822 and named after U.S. president James Monroe. Located at the entrance of the Mesurado River on the Atlantic coast. The city's population reached a quarter million people during the 1980's; however, it was devastated by civil war during the 1990's.

Morocco. A kingdom in NORTH AFRICA; part of the MAGHREB. Total area of 177,117 square miles (460,500 sq. km.),

including the disputed WESTERN SAHARA (nearly 100,000 square miles). Had a 1990's population of about 25 million, including 165,000 in Western Sahara. Capital is RABAT; largest city is CASABLANCA. Bordered on the north by the MEDITERRANEAN SEA and the Atlantic Ocean, on the west by the Atlantic Ocean, on the east by ALGERIA, and on the south by Western Sahara. The closest North African country to Europe, being just 14 miles (22 km.) from GIBRALTAR. Rabat and Casablanca are on the Atlantic Ocean; other important communities—FÈS, MARRAKESH, MEKNES, and QUARZAZATE—are inland. The ATLAS MOUNTAINS run down the center of Morocco, and the RIF MOUNTAINS run east-west in the north.

Moroni. Capital of the African island nation of COMOROS, on Njazidja (also known as Grande Comore) Island. It has been an important regional trading center for centuries. Its population is about 30,000.

Mozambique. Southern African republic, directly to the northeast of SOUTH AFRICA. Total area of 309,500 square miles (801,600 sq. km.), with a 1990's population of 15 million. Capital is MAPUTO. Most of the country is coastal lowland with plateaus inland that rise to nearly 8,000 feet (2,436 meters), which is the height of Mount Binga near the western border. Its main river is the ZAMBEZI RIVER, which is dammed behind the Cabora Bassa Dam. The Rovuma, Save, and LIMPOPO Rivers are also important. Became independent from Portugal in 1975.

Mozambique Channel. Channel of the INDIAN OCEAN stretching between MADAGASCAR and the coast of southeast Africa, near COMOROS. It is 300 kilometers (186 miles) wide at its narrowest point. Several live coelacanths, primitive fish

Mombasa Page 1165

Mozambique Page 1101

Morocco Pages 973, 975, 1096, 1160

Nairobi, Kenya. (Corbis)

thought to have been extinct for seventy million years, have been caught in this channel.

Mwanza. A major port city on Lake VICTORIA in TANZANIA. Population was 233,000 in 1988. Products are shipped there from neighboring landlocked UGANDA and BURUNDI for rail transport to DAR ES SALAAM on the INDIAN OCEAN. Major manufacturing industries are cotton textiles, meat packing, and fishing.

Mweru, Lake. Lake in southeast CONGO-KINSHASA, along the border with ZAMBIA. It is about 70 miles (110 km.) long, 30 miles (50 km.) wide, and 30-50 feet (9-15 meters) deep, covering about 173 square miles (450 sq. km.). Receives water from the LUAPULA RIVER from the south. Its outlet is the LUVUA RIVER, which drains into the CONGO RIVER. Navigable by small steamboats and barges. Its main ports in the Democratic Republic of Congo are Kilwa and Pweto.

Naftah. See NEFTA.

Nairobi. Capital and largest city of KENYA, Africa, and the dominant commercial and financial city of East Africa. Population was more than 2 million in 1991. Founded in 1899 by the British and quickly became the colonial administrative center. Located 5,495 feet (1,675 meters) above sea level, it has a relatively cool climate, ample water reserves, and a well-developed infrastructure. Tourism, manufacturing, textile and food processing, and several export industries fuel its economy. Its downtown area is the most modern of any East African city. Economic disparities are evident in the economic segregation of traditional neighborhoods and the existence of shantytowns.

Nakuru. A major transportation center in the GREAT RIFT VALLEY, in the highland region of west central KENYA, Africa, near Lake Nakuru. A center for food processing and textiles. Population was 150,000 in 1991.

Namibia. Republic on the Atlantic side of Southern Africa. Total area of 318,252 square miles (824,268 sq. km.) with a 1990's population of 1.5 million. Capital is WINDHOEK. Shares a long border with SOUTH AFRICA, which has long tried to dominate it. Climate is arid; the country includes the forbidding KALAHARI DESERT. Rich in mineral resources; diamonds and other gems are its main exports. Formerly German Southwest Africa.

Nasser, Lake. Reservoir in Africa, 298 miles (480 km.) long, created by the building of the Aswan High Dam. Many significant sites disappeared under the water; however, the temples of Abu Simbel—constructed by Rameses II in the thirteenth century B.C.E.—were saved.

This was a magnificent technological achievement, as the massive structures were disassembled, moved, and reassembled on higher ground. Named for the leader of EGYPT when the project was undertaken, Gamal Abdel Nasser.

Namibia
Page 1167

Temple of Abu Simbel, which had to be moved to escape the rising waters of artificial Lake Nasser. (PhotoDisc)

N'Djamena. Capital and largest city of CHAD, with a population of about 688,000 during the early 1990's. Located on the Chari River, at the country's border with northeastern NIGERIA, near Lake CHAD.

Nefta. One of the largest oases in TUNISIA. Located in the southwestern part of the country on the shores of SHATT AL-JARID, Tunisia's largest lake, which is often dry because of lack of rain and desert conditions. Nefta is 25 miles (38 km.) from another large oasis, TOZEUR, and is just slightly farther than that from the Algerian border. Also called Naftah.

Nile River Pages 1099, 1155, 1164

Niamey. Capital of NIGER. Located in the southwestern part of the country on the banks of the NIGER RIVER. Construction of the Kennedy Bridge in 1970 led to the expansion of the city. Population was 400,000 in 1983.

Niger Page 1163

Niger. Country in West Africa, named after the famous river that flows through part of the country. Total area of 489,200 square miles (1,267,028 sq. km.) with a 1997 population of 9.4 million, most of whom are black Muslims. Capital is NIAMEY. Official language is French. Administered within the federation of FRENCH WEST AFRICA during the era of colonial rule.

Niger River. Third-longest river in Africa—2,600 miles (4,183 km.). Rising in the GUINEA highlands near the SIERRA LEONE border, it flows first northeast, then east, and finally southeast across NIGERIA into the Gulf of GUINEA. A critical source of water for MALI and NIGER. BAMAKO, capital of Mali, and NIAMEY, capital of Niger, are located on its banks.

Nigeria Pages 1090, 1092

Nigeria. Most populous black nation in the world; located in West Africa. Total area of 356,669 square miles (923,772 sq. km.) with a population of 107 million in 1997. Capital is ABUJA. English is the official language, but there are 11 major indigenous languages in 240 dialects. The three major ethnic groups are the Yoruba in the west, the Ibo in the east, and the Hausa-Fulani in the north. A major exporter of petroleum and a member of the Organization of Petroleum Exporting Countries (OPEC). After achieving independence in 1960, was the country largely ruled by the military until late 1999, when a civilian government was elected.

Nile River. The longest river in the world, the Nile has two main branches. The White Nile, its major branch, begins in Lake VICTORIA, travels through UGANDA, SUDAN, and EGYPT to the MEDITERRANEAN SEA, a distance of about 4,160 miles (6,700 km.). Near KHARTOUM it is joined by the Blue Nile, which rises in ETHIOPIA's Lake Tana. Much of the Nile's course takes it through the eastern SAHARA, bringing life to an otherwise inhospitable land. Prosperity in Egypt and northern Sudan is possible only because of this river, which has made both countries major agricultural producers. From the city of Edfu in Upper Egypt ("upper" refers to southern Egypt, up the Nile River) to the beginning of the delta, the river valley averages 14 miles (23 km.) in width. The delta itself is 150 miles (250 km.) wide at the sea. Until the erection of twentieth century dams, the Nile flooded this region annually. Flood cycles reinvigorated the soils with silt, brought fish beyond its banks, and provided enough excess water to be stored for use later in the agricultural year. The damming of the Nile interrupted the flow of water. The Nile was also the prime transportation route for traders and people who lived along its banks. The cataracts, or rock waterfalls, that appear in the river helped insulate early Egyptians from invasion from the south.

North Africa. The area lying south of the MEDITERRANEAN SEA, east of the Atlantic Ocean, north of the SAHARA, and west of EGYPT and SUDAN. It comprises four independent nations, MOROCCO, ALGERIA, TUNISIA, and LIBYA, and the disputed region of WESTERN SAHARA. Its countries are a mixture of Islamic and Western cultures, although the majority religion in the area is Islamic.

Northern Rhodesia. Colonial-era name of ZAMBIA.

Nyamlagira. Active volcano of the VIRUNGA MOUNTAINS in east CONGO-KINSHASA. Located about 20 miles (32 km.) north of Lake KIVU in the southern part of VIRUNGA NATIONAL PARK. More than 10,000 feet (3,000 meters) high.

Nyasa, Lake. One of the chain of lakes in the GREAT RIFT VALLEY. Bordered by MOZAMBIQUE, ZAMBIA, and TANZANIA, it covers 8,683 square miles (22,490 sq. km.).

Nyasaland. See MALAWI.

Nyiragongo. Active volcano of the VIRUNGA MOUNTAINS in east CONGO-KINSHASA. Located near the RWANDA border, northeast of Lake KIVU, about 12 miles (20 km.) north of the town of Goma. About 11,400 feet (3,475 meters) high.

Okavango. Southern African river that flows through NAMIBIA and BOTSWANA. About 1,120 miles (1,700 km.) long. It originates in upper ANGOLA and eventually merges with the Cuito River. In the lowlands, it forms the Okavango Delta, which is basically a swamp and home to a number of unique plants. Named after the Okavango people, who inhabit Namibia.

Olduvai Gorge. Region of the GREAT RIFT VALLEY in northern TANZANIA, which has been one of the two most productive sites for uncovering early hominid life on earth. (The other is Lake TURKANA, also in Africa.) It is about 50 miles (80 km.) long, nearly 300 feet (91 meters) deep.

Omdurman. Largest city in SUDAN. Population was 1.3 million in 1993. Situated on the NILE RIVER, just north of the confluence of the Blue Nile and White Nile Rivers. Located within the Gezira, the major irrigated agricultural region of SUDAN, it shares its metropolitan area with the capital, KHARTOUM.

Oran. Second-largest city in ALGERIA, located 225 miles (360 km.) west of ALGIERS, on high cliff plateaus that plunge to the MEDITERRANEAN SEA. Has more European influence than other Algerian cities. More Christian than Muslim, it once had more cathedrals than mosques.

Orange Free State. Former name of SOUTH AFRICA's FREE STATE province.

Ouagadougou (Wagadugu). Capital and largest city in BURKINA FASO. Founded in the fifteenth century as the capital of the Mossi Kingdom. Known for its prestigious national museum, major craft centers, and textiles. Population was 360,000 in 1985.

Pemba. East African offshore island located a few miles north of ZANZIBAR, from which it was historically ruled.

Philippeville. See SKIKDA.

Pico de Teide. Volcano on Tenerife in Spain's CANARY ISLANDS that erupted in 1909. At 12,162 feet (3,707 meters) it is the highest point in Spain and in the ATLANTIC OCEAN. By contrast, California's Mount McKinley, the highest peak in North America, rises to 20,320 feet (6,194 meters).

Pietermaritzburg. City in KWAZULU/NA-

TAL in SOUTH AFRICA. Located on the Umzunduzi River near DURBAN. Had a 1990's population of 100,000 and is the site of the University of Natal. Founded in 1839 by Boers fleeing British domination in the Cape Colony.

Pillars of Hercules. Name given to GIBRALTAR on the Iberian Peninsula and Jebel Musa in CEUTA, the northernmost reach of MOROCCO. According to classical mythology, Hercules formed them when he tore a mountain apart to get to Cádiz on Spain's southwest coast.

Pointe-Noire. Main maritime port in southwest Republic of the CONGO. Located about 250 miles west of BRAZZAVILLE. A commercial and industrial center and the terminus of the railroad from Brazzaville. It has a refinery, which processes offshore petroleum. Population was 567,200 in 1992. Capital of FRENCH EQUATORIAL AFRICA 1950-1958.

Port Elizabeth. Major South African port on the INDIAN OCEAN. Located on the southeastern coast of the country, equally close to CAPE TOWN in the south and DURBAN. Also a major rail, airline, and manufacturing center. Has an extensive tourist industry and is close to the Addo Elephant National Park. Named after Elizabeth Donkin, the wife of Rufane Donkin, the governor of the Cape Colony in the 1820's.

Port Harcourt. Capital of Rivers State in the southeast of NIGERIA. Located on the Bonny River in the Niger delta. A major industrial center, with exports including petroleum and palm products. Population was 371,000 in 1992. In 1915 the British established a port in the city that served eastern and parts of northern Nigeria.

Port Louis. Capital and largest city of MAURITIUS, in the INDIAN OCEAN. Founded in 1735, it has long been an

important regional trading center. It had a population of 146,000 in 1997.

Port Said. Resort and fueling station for ships, situated at the juncture of the SUEZ CANAL and the MEDITERRANEAN SEA. Population was 469,500 in 1996. Founded in 1859 as the canal was being constructed. Also a manufacturing center, producing chemicals, processed food, cotton, and cigarettes.

Port Sudan. The only RED SEA port in SUDAN. Population was 300,000 in 1993. It exports cotton, sheep, cattle, and gum arabic.

Porto-Novo. Capital and second-largest city of BENIN. Its busy port is located on a lagoon that connects to the Gulf of GUINEA. Population was 101,000 in 1994.

Portuguese East Africa. See MOZAMBIQUE.

Portuguese Guinea. See GUINEA-BISSAU.

Praia. Capital and largest city of CAPE VERDE, built on cliffs overlooking a small natural harbor on the southern coast of the island of São Tiago. A popular vacation spot, it has attracted tourists with historical museums and sites such as the old slave quarters where slaves were housed before being shipped to the Americas. The population was 95,000 in 1998.

Pretoria. Administrative capital, transportation and manufacturing center, and fourth-largest city in SOUTH AFRICA; capital of TRANSVAAL Province. Located northeast of JOHANNESBURG. South Africa's two largest universities, the University of Pretoria and the University of South Africa, are located there. Founded in 1855 by Marthinus Pretorius, the first president of South Africa, who named it for his father, Andries Pretorius, a Boer military leader.

Príncipe. Small African island, part of the nation of SÃO TOMÉ AND PRÍNCIPE. Located in the Gulf of GUINEA at 1°37′ north latitude, longitude 7°25′ east. It has an area of 45 square miles (117 sq. km.) and a population of about 5,500 in 1991.

Qābes. See GABÈS.

Quarzazate. North African desert outpost. Located inland from AGADIR and ESSAOUIRA in MOROCCO, between the high ATLAS MOUNTAINS and the SAHARA. Many desert motion pictures have been filmed there. Although somewhat isolated, it is a trading center for Bedouins who wander the Sahara.

Rabat. Capital of MOROCCO and administrative center of government when the French controlled Morocco. Located on the Atlantic Ocean between CASABLANCA to the south and TANGIER to the north. Many of its 1.5 million inhabitants are employed in government positions.

Ras Lanuf. Small city on the southwest shore of the Gulf of SIDRA, in NORTH AFRICA, with an oil refinery capable of producing 220,000 barrels of oil a day. Also called Ra's al Unuf.

Red Sea. Body of water separating Northeastern Africa from the Arabian Peninsula. An extension of the GREAT RIFT VALLEY, formed when the plate on which the Arabian Peninsula is situated tore loose from Africa. It is 157 miles (2,253 km.) long, and up to 220 miles (354 km.) wide. An important conduit for oil tankers moving from the Arabian Peninsula and PERSIAN GULF destined for Europe via the SUEZ CANAL, which connects the Red Sea to the MEDITERRANEAN SEA.

Réunion. Island in the INDIAN OCEAN east of MADAGASCAR, part of the MASCARENE group. Its capital is SAINT-DENIS. Its highest elevation is 10,069 feet (3,069 meters). Piton de la Fournaise, at a slightly lower elevation, is an active volcano. Réunion is an overseas department of France. Its area is 968 square miles (2,507 sq. km.), and its population was 697,600 in 1998.

Rhodesia. See ZIMBABWE.

Rhumel River. North African river that runs through CONSTANTINE, in ALGE-

Late nineteenth century view of the Rhumel River gorge in Constantine, Algeria. (Arkent Archive)

ria's northeastern area near TUNISIA, 50 miles (80 km.) inland from the MEDITERRANEAN SEA. It has created deep gorges below the chalky cliffs that it has carved out through the centuries.

Rif Mountains. North African mountains running along the coast of the MEDITERRANEAN SEA north of the ATLAS MOUNTAIN chain. They rise steeply and dramatically from the sea in the northwestern extreme of MOROCCO, reaching heights of 6,000 feet (1,830 meters).

Rift Valley. See GREAT RIFT VALLEY.

Rodrigues. Island surrounded by a coral reef in the INDIAN OCEAN, part of the nation of MAURITIUS. Its highest elevation is about 1,289 feet (393 meters), and it has an area of 46 square miles (119 sq. km.).

Ruwenzori Mountains. Nonvolcanic mountain range in Central Africa. Located between Lakes EDWARD and ALBERT, along the border between UGANDA and CONGO-KINSHASA. About 40 miles (65 km.) wide, it extends north-south for 80 miles (130 km.). Its highest point is 16,795 feet (5,120 meters). Snow cover can be found from 14,000 feet (4,270 meters). The entire base has dense equatorial forests with several vegetation zones succeeding each other in altitude. The western side of the range is in Ruwenzori National Park.

Ruzizi River. River in Central Africa along the borders of CONGO-KINSHASA, RWANDA, and BURUNDI. The outlet of Lake KIVU into Lake TANGANYIKA. About 100 miles (160 km.) long, with many rapids in its upper course. A hydroelectric power plant near Lake Kivu supplies electricity to BUKAVU and the surrounding region.

Rwanda. Landlocked country in Africa. Total area of 10,169 square miles (26,338 sq. km.), with a population of nearly 8 million in 1998. Capital is KIGALI. The western VIRUNGA MOUNTAINS—with their highest peak, the extinct volcano KARISIMBI, at 14,787 feet (4,507 meters)—slope into a hilly plateau in the center of the country, in which most of the people live. Ninety-four percent of the population is rural, virtually all engaging in subsistence agriculture. Like its neighbor BURUNDI, Rwanda has one of the highest rates of AIDS infection in the world, and has had ethnic strife between the minority Tutsis (9 percent of the population) and the more numerous Hutus (90 percent).

Sabha. Largest oasis in LIBYA, with a permanent population of nearly twenty thousand. Located in the SAHARA, it grew rapidly in the 1960's, when large deposits of oil were discovered in the desert. Irrigation canals were built to bring in water to sustain the workers needed for economic growth. New schools, hospitals, roads, and an airport were also built.

Sahara. Largest desert in the world. Covers 3.5 million square miles (9 million sq. km.)—almost the same area covered by the entire United States—and it continues to grow. The desert extends about 3,000 miles (4,830 km.) from the RED SEA to the Atlantic Ocean, and about 745 miles (1,200 km.) from the coast of the MEDITERRANEAN SEA south to the SAHEL, a dry steppe region across West and Central Africa. The desert has three distinct divisions: the Libyan Desert (also known to Egyptians as the Western Desert) extends from the west bank of the NILE RIVER into eastern LIBYA; the Arabian Desert (also known to the Egyptians as the Eastern Desert) runs from the east bank of the Nile River to the Red Sea, roughly to the bor-

Sahara
Page 965

der of SUDAN; the Nubian Desert lies to the south of the region, encompassing most of northern Sudan. The effect of high-pressure systems keeps out almost all rain; most of the region receives less than 5 inches (127 millimeters) of rain per year. Aside from the Nile, only occasional oases provide water in the region. Wadis (seasonal river beds) are found near coastal areas where rainfall occurs. The Sahara is among the world's hottest places. The world's highest recorded temperature of 136.4 degrees Fahrenheit (58 degrees Celsius) was recorded in the shade at Azizia, Libya, in 1922.

Saharan Atlas Mountains. One of two mountain ranges in NORTH AFRICA that divide ALGERIA into three physical regions. Runs from Colom-Bechar in the west to Annaba in the east.

Sahel. Region in West Africa that is a transition zone between the dry SAHARA in the north and the wet tropical areas in the south. Annual rainfall ranges between 4 and 8 inches (102 and 203 millimeters). Most of the rain falls between June and September. Peanuts and millet are common crops in this region; there is also nomadic herding.

Sahil. A stretch of the coastline of TUNISIA that makes an S-curve to the south, running from the Gulf of TUNIS past CAPE BON. There are two busy harbors in this area. Sahil comes from the same Arabic word for "coast" that gave East Africa's Swahili language its name.

St. Helena. Island in the South ATLANTIC OCEAN, about 1,200 miles (1,930 kilometers) from Africa. The capital is Jamestown. Located at 15°58′ south latitude, longitude 5°43′ west. Discovered by Portuguese explorers in 1502, the island is a British dependency. St. Helena was the final residence of French Emperor Napoleon Bonaparte, who was exiled there 1815-1821 after his defeat by the British at Waterloo. The island's area is 47 square miles (122 sq. km.), and its highest elevation is 2,685 feet (818 meters). In 1994 its population was about 6,500.

Saint-Denis. Port and capital of the African island of RÉUNION. Located at the mouth of the Saint-Denis River. The population in 1990 was about 123,000.

Saint-Louis. Seaport and commercial center for the Senegal River Valley. Located in northwestern SENEGAL, on Saint-Louis Island at the mouth of the SENEGAL RIVER. Established by the French in 1659 as a trading post, it is one of the oldest European settlements in West Africa. Population was 132,500 in 1994.

Salonga National Park. Protected area in central CONGO-KINSHASA. Located halfway between KINSHASA and KISANGANI. Its two sections form the largest reserve in the country, covering 13,900 square miles (36,040 sq. km.). Created in 1970. Dense equatorial forest is the main vegetative cover. Among the park's animal and bird species are parrots, elephants, antelope, monkeys, and a unique species of pygmy chimpanzee.

Santa Cruz de Tenerife. Capital of the province of the same name in the CANARY ISLANDS, located on the island of Tenerife. The population was about 205,000 in 1995.

São Tomé and Príncipe. The smallest nation in or near Africa, consisting of two small volcanic islands lying just north of the equator in the Gulf of GUINEA. The capital is the city of São Tomé, with a population of about 57,000. A former Portuguese colony, São Tomé and Príncipe became an independent country in 1975. Its main exports have been cocoa, coconut, and coffee, but it began encouraging tourism to make up for failing production. It covers 372 square miles (964 sq. km.), an area less than one-third the size of Rhode Island. Its population in 1999 was about 144,000, mostly descendants of slaves brought from mainland Africa.

Semliki River. River in northeast CONGO-KINSHASA. Starts from Lake EDWARD and runs 130 miles (210 km.) north to Lake ALBERT. Part of its course is entirely in Congo-Kinshasa; the rest forms the border with UGANDA. Most of its course lies in VIRUNGA NATIONAL PARK.

Senegal River. West African river forming the boundary between SENEGAL and MAURITANIA. It has two main sources, the Bafing and the Bakoye Rivers. It is 990 miles (1,600 km.) long and empties into the Atlantic Ocean near SAINT-LOUIS in Senegal.

Senegal. French colony in West Africa until 1960. It covers an area of 75,951 square miles (196,713 sq. km.) with a population of 9.4 million in 1997. DAKAR is the capital. French is the official language. It achieved independence in 1960; in 1982, it began fighting a separatist movement in the southern part of the country. In 1982 formed the Confederation of Senegambia with GAMBIA, but this was dissolved in 1989. Administered within the federation of FRENCH WEST AFRICA during the era of colonial rule.

Seychelles. Nation consisting of 115 islands in the INDIAN OCEAN northeast of MADAGASCAR. The capital is VICTORIA. The major islands are granitic, rising from a large undersea plateau and reaching no more than 3,084 feet (940 meters) above sea level. The rest of the islands are low-lying coral atolls. The climate is tropical monsoonal. The country covers only 156 square miles

*Senegal
Page 1104*

*Sierra
Leone
Pages
1092, 1097*

*Seychelles
Page 963*

(404 sq. km.), making it one of the world's smallest countries. However, because the islands are spread across such a broad area (about 746 miles/ 1,200 kilometers between the farthest points), Seychelles claims fishing and mineral rights over 521,235 square miles (1.35 million sq. km.) of the Indian Ocean. The population was about 72,100 in 1994. Seychelles was a colony of Great Britain until 1976. Tourism has become its major source of income.

Sfax. Second-largest city of TUNISIA, located on the MEDITERRANEAN SEA, halfway along Tunisia's coastline, with a population of nearly 250,000. Known for the excellent olive oil it produces and exports around the world.

Shatt al-Jarid. See CHOTT DJERID.

Sidra, Gulf of. Indentation in the MEDITERRANEAN SEA, at whose eastern end is Benghazi, LIBYA. Libya claims the entire 150,000 square miles (388,400 sq. km.) of its territory. However, most other countries have recognized only a small fraction of this territory as belonging to Libya. Strained international relations between the United States and Libya worsened when a U.S. naval fleet held maneuvers there and clashed with Libya's armed forces in 1981.

Sierra Leone. West African country, founded in 1787 by a British antislavery group as the first colony for freed slaves in Africa. Total area of 27,925 square miles (72,326 sq. km.), with a population of 4.9 million in 1997. Capital and largest city is FREETOWN. English is the official language. An ongoing civil war has displaced a third of the population, who fled to neighboring states for safety.

Sinai Peninsula. Triangular land mass connecting Africa with Asia. It is arid, as the Mediterranean coastal plain gradually rises to a central plateau, with jagged mountains in its extreme south. Sparsely populated but rich in mineral resources, including oil, natural gas, and metallic ores. Its western border houses the SUEZ CANAL. Controlled by EGYPT since antiquity.

Sirte, Gulf of. See SIDRA, GULF OF.

Skikda. Major Mediterranean port city in northeastern ALGERIA. Serves CONSTANTINE, 50 miles (80 km.) to the northwest. Formerly Philippeville.

Slave Coast. See Bight of BENIN.

Somalia. Country in Africa. Total area of 246,216 square miles (637,700 sq. km.), slightly smaller than Texas, with a 1990's population of 7 million, primarily rural. Capital is MOGADISHU. Almost exclusively desert, with some irrigation agriculture possible in the south along the Jubba and Shebele Rivers. Despite more than 1,865 miles (3,000 km.) of coastline, it has few natural harbors. Encompasses the geographic feature known as the HORN OF AFRICA. More than 70 percent of the population engages in nomadic or seminomadic animal husbandry. The people are socially organized by clans, which establish status and the type of obligations their members have to one another and to outsiders. Warfare between clans competing for political and economic power in the 1990's led to anarchy.

South Africa. A republic and the most important country in Southern Africa. Total area of 471,445 square miles (1.2 million sq. km.). The 1990's population of 40 million was 75 percent black, 14 percent white, the rest mixed race. Administrative capital is PRETORIA; legislative capital is CAPE TOWN; judicial capital is BLOEMFONTEIN. Most of the country is covered by a large plateau, with the DRAKENSBERG MOUNTAINS on the southeast. Part of the KALAHARI

DESERT is in the northern area on the border with NAMIBIA. The Orange, Vaal, and LIMPOPO Rivers flow through South Africa. Its temperate climate is mostly regulated by trade winds from the INDIAN OCEAN. Has vast mineral resources; the gold mines in WITWATERSRAND are the richest in the world. Main cities are JOHANNESBURG, Cape Town, and DURBAN. The two official languages are Afrikaans (a local language based on Dutch) and English.

South African Mountains. The main mountain ranges in the interior of SOUTH AFRICA are the DRAKENSBERG, Stormberg, Nuweveldsreeks, Roggeveld, Berge, and Bokkeveldberg. Several peaks are more than 10,000 feet (3,050 meters) high. To their east is the High Veld, with elevations of 2,000-6,000 feet (600-1,800 meters). In the southwest part of South Africa lies the Little Karoo; farther north is the Great Karoo, which ultimately merges with the KALAHARI DESERT.

Southern Rhodesia. Colonial-era name of ZIMBABWE.

Spanish Morocco. Two tiny North African communities—CEUTA and MELILLA—surrounded by MOROCCO, which Spain retained when it gave up its claim to its Rio d'Oro colony south of Morocco in the 1970's. Ceuta is located on the MEDITERRANEAN SEA on the northern tip of Africa, 14 miles (20 km.) from GIBRALTAR. Melilla, on a spit of land that juts into the Mediterranean Sea, is close to the Algerian border. Spain has considered granting them autonomy.

Spanish Sahara. See WESTERN SAHARA.

Sudan. Largest country in Africa. Total area of 967,489 square miles (2,505,800 sq. km.) with a 1990's population of 33 million. Capital is KHARTOUM. The northern third of the country is located in the section of the SAHARA known as

Somalia Pages 973, 1103

South Africa Pages 962, 1102, 1156

the Nubian Desert, pierced by the White Nile and Blue Nile Rivers, which join in the middle of the nation to form the NILE RIVER. The middle third is occupied by a semiarid plateau and mountainous region, which gives way to the massive swamp region along the White Nile known as the As Sudd. The extreme south is tropical rain forest. More than two-thirds of the people engage in cultivation or animal husbandry. Cotton lint and cotton seed are the major exports. Eighty percent of the world's gum arabic is produced here.

Suez Canal
Page 1100

Suez Canal. Connection between the MEDITERRANEAN and RED Seas, located in northeastern EGYPT. It is 121 miles (195 km.) long, at least 197 feet (60 meters) wide, and able to accommodate ships with 52 feet (16 meters) of drag. An earlier canal was excavated in this area in the thirteen century B.C.E. and maintained irregularly until the eight century C.E. The modern canal was completed in 1869 by a French company.

Lake
Tanganyika
Page 1165

Surt Desert. North African desert that runs across the Mediterranean coast of northern LIBYA, from TRIPOLITANIA to the Tunisian border.

Swaziland. Small, landlocked state in Southern Africa. Total area of 6,705 square miles (17,366 sq. km.) with a 1990's population of 700,000, most of Bantu origin. Capital is Mbanane. Most of it borders SOUTH AFRICA, with the exception of a border with MOZAMBIQUE in the north. Economy is dominated by subsistence farming, although it has significant iron and asbestos mines, as well as sugar-processing facilities. A British protectorate until 1968.

Table Bay. Important harbor on the western side of SOUTH AFRICA. CAPE TOWN is located on its southern shore. Table

Table Bay
Page 962

Mountain, one of South Africa's main peaks, is nearby.

Table Mountain. Mountain overlooking CAPE TOWN, South Africa, that dominates the view from the city center and harbor and provides an excellent view of the city. A cable railway carries visitors to the top.

Tahat, Mount. Highest mountain in ALGERIA, rising to 9,852 feet (3,000 meters). Located in the AHAGGAR MOUNTAINS, almost precisely on the tropic of CANCER. Frequently snow-capped for extended periods in winter.

Tanga. Port city in northeastern TANZANIA. The terminus of a railroad to the interior, it gives access to plantation crops such as rubber, tea, and coffee. It also has coastal highways connecting it with DAR ES SALAAM and the Kenyan cities of NAIROBI and MOMBASA. Developed as a port by the Germans in the 1890's. Population was 187,000 in 1988.

Tanganyika. Name of the mainland portion of TANZANIA when the country was under British administration.

Tanganyika, Lake. Lake straddling CONGO-KINSHASA's borders with BURUNDI and TANZANIA in the GREAT RIFT VALLEY. Second-largest lake in eastern Africa, and the longest freshwater lake (410 miles/660 km.) and the second-deepest (4,710 feet/1,435 meters) in the world. Its width varies from 10 to 45 miles (16 to 70 km.); it covers 12,700 square miles (32,930 sq. km.). Has a large number of hippopotami and crocodiles. Its ports include BUJUMBURA, BURUNDI; KALEMIE, Congo-Kinshasa; and Kigoma, Tanzania.

Tangier. International port city on the Atlantic Ocean in northern MOROCCO. Population in the 1990's was more than half a million. Morocco's closest large city to Europe, located less than 40

miles (65 km.) from the Iberian Peninsula.

Tanta. A major city and railroad center in the NILE delta of Africa, situated on the main highway between CAIRO and ALEXANDRIA. Tobacco, food processing, and textiles are the main industries. Population was 380,000 in 1992.

Tanzania. Country in Africa. Total area of 364,903 square miles (945,100 sq. km.) with a 1990's population of 30 million. Capital is DAR ES SALAAM. Dominated by a plateau averaging about 3,940 feet (1,200 meters) in height, there is also a coastal plain, and mountain ranges in the northeast and southwest. Site of Mount KILIMANJARO, the highest point in Africa. The GREAT RIFT VALLEY runs along Tanzania's western border, demarcated by the lakes formed in this fault. Most of Tanzania's people live on the volcanic soils near Kilimanjaro and the fertile land around Lake NYASA, nearly 85 percent engaging in agriculture, fishing, or forestry. The islands of ZANZIBAR joined with TANGANYIKA in 1964 to form the United Republic of Tanzania.

Taroudant. Ancient walled town in NORTH AFRICA, located west of QUARZAZATE. It has been a desert outpost and trading center for more than a thousand years. Many Berbers live here and engage in trade with those who wander the SAHARA.

Tassili-n-Ajjer. Site in the southeastern SAHARA in ALGERIA, where prehistoric artifacts have been found, including the jawbone of a human who lived half a million years ago. Some four thousand sandstone engravings that are more than five thousand years old have been collected here, the largest collection of its kind. Primitive rock paintings also have been found in rock formations near there.

Tawzar. See TOZEUR.

Tell Atlas. One of two North African mountain ranges that divide ALGERIA into three physical regions. Located near the MEDITERRANEAN SEA, stretching from west of ORAN to ALGIERS. The fertile coastal area running from Algeria to TUNISIA is known as the Tell. The Tell Atlas to its west draws moisture from the air that provides the area with an abundant supply of water for irrigation.

Tétouan. Tourist resort in northern Morocco that faces onto the MEDITERRANEAN SEA. Its population of nearly 900,000 swells considerably during tourist season and holidays.

Tibesti Mountains. Volcanic-formed mountains in northern CHAD, extending into southern LIBYA and northeastern NIGER. Emi Koussi, the highest peak, has an elevation of 11,204 feet (3,415 meters).

Tobruk. Mediterranean port in northeastern LIBYA. Intense fighting occurred there between British and German forces during World War II.

Togo. Tiny West African nation that is divided physically and ethnically. Total area of 21,925 square miles (56,786 sq. km.), with a population of 4.7 million in 1997. Capital is LOMÉ. French is the official language. The Muslims in the north are separated from the southern Togolese by a mountain range. It has a large deposit of phosphates. The country was a colonial creation formed by Germany as Togoland during the 1880's. After World War I, the administration of Togoland was partitioned between Great Britain and France. Most of the original colony was reassembled as the independent nation of Togo in 1960.

Toubkal, Mount. Highest mountain peak in MOROCCO, located in the High AT-

Tanzania Pages 965, 1025, 1037

las Mountains in south central Morocco, it soars to 13,670 feet (4,100 meters)—an altitude about 500 feet (150 meters) lower than that of Pike's Peak in Colorado.

Tozeur. North African oasis in southwestern TUNISIA near the Algerian border. Located on the shores of SHATT AL-JARID, Tunisia's largest lake, which is often virtually dry because of limited rainfall and desert conditions. Also called Tawzar.

Transvaal. Region of SOUTH AFRICA between ZIMBABWE in the north and the FREE STATE—from which it is separated by the Vaal River—in the south. The higland region is mostly grassland and hilly savanna. The DRAKENSBERG MOUNTAINS are a main feature of the Transvaal. Kruger National Park is in the eastern portion, near the border with MOZAMBIQUE. Afrikaners (Boers) who settled the region in the mid-nineteenth century created an independent republic. In 1886 gold was found in the WITWATERSRAND area around JOHANNESBURG, and a massive gold rush ensued. Conflict between the Afrikaners and new residents sparked the South African (Boer) War, which the British won. After a period of colonial rule, the Transvaal joined the Cape Colony, the ORANGE FREE STATE, and Natal as a province in the Union of South Africa. During the early 1990's the province was split into two provinces: Northern Transvaal and Eastern Transvaal, with their capitals at Pietersburg and Nelspruit.

Tunisia Page 1095

Tripoli. Largest city and capital of LIBYA, located on the MEDITERRANEAN SEA in the western part of TUNISIA. It had about a million inhabitants in the 1990's, about one-fifth of the country's total population, and grew rapidly during Libya's oil boom of the 1960's.

Tripolitania. Productive agricultural region in which TRIPOLI, the capital of LIBYA, is located. Covering 16 percent of Libya's land mass, its Mediterranean coast extends 186 miles (300 km.) from the SURT DESERT to TUNISIA in the west.

Tristan da Cunha. Archipelago in the South ATLANTIC OCEAN. Its only inhabited island has the same name. Located at 37°15′ south latitude, longitude 12°30′ west. Since 1938, Tristan da Cunha has been a dependency of ST. HELENA. Eruption of the island's volcano (elevation 6,760 feet, or 2060 meters) in 1961 forced the island's 300 inhabitants to flee, but most returned to the island in 1963. Tristan da Cunha covers an area of 38 square miles (98 sq. km.).

Tropics. See CANCER, TROPIC OF and CAPRICORN, TROPIC OF.

Tunis. Largest city and capital of TUNISIA. Its population was approaching 850,000 in the 1990's. Built on low, chalk-white hills that extend toward a salt lake, EL BAHIRA, close to the harbor. In 1893 the French built a 20-foot-long (6-meter) channel across the Lake of Tunis to the MEDITERRANEAN SEA, opening Tunis as a port.

Tunis, Gulf of. Large, deep-water gulf in northeastern TUNISIA, located 65 miles (104 km.) from Sicily. Connected to TUNIS, the capital of Tunisia, by a 20-foot-wide (6-meter) channel that has turned Tunis into a port.

Tunisia. Smallest country in NORTH AFRICA. Total area of 63,170 square miles (163,610 sq. km.) with a 1990's population of about nine million, more than half living in its six largest cities. Capital is TUNIS. Bordered on the north and east by the MEDITERRANEAN SEA, on the west by ALGERIA, on the east by LIBYA, and on the south by Libya and

Algeria. Halfway between GIBRALTAR and SUEZ, and 85 miles (137 km.) south of Sicily, Tunisia was an important stop for ancient traders. Its highest point is Jabal Shanabi at 5,066 miles (1,544 meters).

Tunisian Dorsale. Branch of the ATLAS MOUNTAINS that extends from ALGERIA into TUNISIA. Numerous ranges of the Atlas Mountains continue from Algeria to Tunisia.

Turkana, Lake. One of the chain of lakes in the GREAT RIFT VALLEY, Africa. Having no outlet, it is brackish and has a high rate of evaporation. Nevertheless, it supports several species of fish, as well as hippopotami and crocodiles. It is at the center of one of the richest areas of hominid fossils. Covers 2,740 square miles (7,100 sq. km.).

Ubangi River. Right tributary of the CONGO RIVER in the north and west of CONGO-KINSHASA, along the border with the CENTRAL AFRICAN REPUBLIC and CONGO-BRAZZAVILLE. About 660 miles (1,060 km.) long. It results from the union of the Uele and Bomu Rivers and joins the Congo River about 60 miles (100 km.) southwest of the town of BANDAKA.

Ubangi-Shari. Colonial-era name of what beame the CENTRAL AFRICAN REPUBLIC.

Uganda. Landlocked nation in Africa. Total area of 91,459 square miles (236,880 sq. km.) with a population of more than 22 million in 1998. Capital is KAMPALA. Land includes swampy lowlands in the south, a fertile plateau covering most of the country, and a steppe and desert area in the north. The GREAT RIFT VALLEY is found in the western section of the country. The RUWENZORI Range forms the border with CONGO-KINSHASA, and has more than a dozen peaks over 13,000 feet (4,000 meters) in altitude. The highest, Mount Stanley, is Africa's third-highest peak, at 16,763 feet (5,109 meters). Seven peaks have permanent snowcaps, despite being located near the equator. Eighty-five percent of the labor force is engaged in agriculture; sixty-two percent are literate. Main exports are coffee, fish, and gold. There is access by rail to the Kenyan port of MOMBASA, and by boat and rail to the Tanzanian port of DAR ES SALAAM, by way of the southern Lake VICTORIA port of MWANZA. AIDS has been an enormous drain on the economy of Uganda, but infection rates have dropped to under 10 percent of the population.

United Republic of Tanzania. See TANZANIA.

Upemba, Lake. Lake in southeast CONGO-KINSHASA. An expansion of the CONGO RIVER, it is about 16 miles (25 km.) long and 18 miles (30 km.) wide, covering 190 square miles (500 sq. km.). Much of the lake is overgrown with papyrus. Its eastern side is in Upemba National Park.

Upemba National Park. Protected area in Katanga province in southeast CONGO-Kinshasa. Established in 1939 and covers 748 square miles (1,940 sq. km.). Extends eastward from Lake UPEMBA on the CONGO RIVER. Vegetation includes savanna and papyrus swamps. Fauna include zebras, peccaries, buffalo, antelope, crocodiles, and hippopotami.

Upper Volta. Former name of the West African nation of BURKINA FASO.

Victoria. Capital and only city of the nation of SEYCHELLES, located on the island of Mahé. Its population was about 24,300 in 1987.

Victoria, Lake. Largest lake in Africa and the world's second-largest, after Lake Superior in North America. Located in

*Uganda
Page 1164*

*Lake
Victoria
Page 1167*

Devil's Cataract, Victoria Falls. (PhotoDisc)

Victoria Falls Page 1166

Upper Nile Page 1164

KENYA, TANZANIA, and UGANDA. Ringed by productive agricultural districts, it also supports a sizable fishing industry. Around this lake is one of the densest population belts in Africa. It is one of the sources of the NILE RIVER. A dam constructed in 1954 where the river leaves the lake is a major source of electricity for Uganda. Covers 26,830 square miles (69,490 sq. km.).

Victoria Falls. One of the world's most beautiful waterfalls, located in Southern Africa. Part of the ZAMBEZI RIVER, located on the border between ZAMBIA and ZIMBABWE. There, the river is 1 mile (1.6 km.) wide and falls 400 feet (120 meters).

Virunga. Range of volcanic mountains extending across Africa's GREAT RIFT VALLEY, along the border of CONGO-KINSHASA with RWANDA and UGANDA. The highest of its eight volcanic peaks is KARISIMBI, at 14,787 feet (4,507 meters); the others are Mgahinga, MIKENO, Muhavura, NYAMLAGIRA, NYIRAGONGO, Visoke, and Sabinio.

Virunga National Park. Protected area in east CONGO-KINSHASA, near the UGANDA border. Created in 1925 and called Albert National Park until 1966. Covers about 3,900 square miles (10,100 sq. km.). Includes part of the SEMLIKI RIVER basin, the RUWENZORI range, the western shores of Lake EDWARD, and the VIRUNGA volcanoes. Variability in elevations results in a diversity of climates and vegetation, including marshes, savannas, lava plains, steppes, and several forest cover types. Some of the mountain peaks are permanently snowcapped. Wildlife is abundant, includes elephants, lions, mountain gorillas, and okapi. Designated as a World Heritage site in 1979 and placed on the list of World Heritage in Danger in 1994.

Volta Dam. See AKOSOMBO DAM.

Volta River. River system that drains 75 percent of the West African nation of GHANA. The Black Volta and White

Volta flow southward from BURKINA FASO to form the Volta River in Ghana. Along with its tributary, the Oti River, it feeds Lake Volta, which has a surface area of 3,270 square miles (8,480 sq. km.).

Wagadugu. See OUAGADOUGOU.

Western Sahara. Desert region of NORTH AFRICA, with a land mass of 97,344 square miles (252,120 sq. km.). Most of its 1990's population of about 165,000, lives in two of the region's cities, EL AAIÚN, just south of the disputed border with MOROCCO, and DAKHLA, two-thirds of the way down the Atlantic coast toward MAURITANIA. Both of these cities are international ports. The ownership of the area directly south of Morocco and east of ALGERIA and Mauritania has long been disputed, although it is generally considered to belong to Morocco, which currently occupies it. Western Sahara was a Spanish protectorate until 1976, when Spain transferred the country to Morocco and Mauritania. In 1979 Mauritania abandoned its claim to the area, ceding it to Morocco. An Algerian-backed guerilla group, the Polisario Front, has demanded independence for the area. Morocco's claim to it remains disputed.

Windhoek. Capital and commercial and transportation center of NAMIBIA in Southern Africa. Population in the 1990's was 104,000. Located on a dry plateau in the central part of the country, surrounded by hills, at an altitude of 5,400 feet (1,650 meters). Receives most of its rain between December and March. This area has some of the richest diamond fields in the world. Established by German soldiers in the late 1880's.

Witwatersrand. Mountainous part of SOUTH AFRICA that contains some of the richest gold mines in the world.

Gold was discovered there in 1886 and created a major gold rush. The immigrants, mainly British, were known as uitlanders (outlanders), and soon outnumbered the local farmers of Dutch ancestry, called Boers. The Boers' attempts to keep the uitlanders from participating in government led to the Boer War.

Yamoussoukro. Capital of CÔTE D'IVOIRE in West Africa since 1983. Located in the south central part of the country. Birthplace of the country's first president, Felix Houphouet-Boigny. Yamoussoukro Basilica, the largest Christian church in the world, is located here. Population was 120,000 in 1990.

Yamoussoukro Page 1168

Yaoundé. Capital and commercial center of CAMEROON. Located on the forested plateau between the Nyong and Sanaga Rivers in the south central section of the country. Founded in 1888 when the country was under German rule. Population was 712,089 in 1997.

Yorubaland. Region of southwestern NIGERIA historically inhabited by the Yoruba-speaking people.

Zaire. See CONGO-KINSHASA.

Zambezi River. Fourth-longest river in Africa. Begins in ZAMBIA and flows 2,200 miles (3,540 km.) to the INDIAN OCEAN, passing through ANGOLA, BOTSWANA, and MOZAMBIQUE. Partially controlled by the Kariba Dam, which has created Lake KARIBA. Barely navigable because it is shallow and has many rapids that interrupt its flow. Its main tributaries are the Lungwebungo, Luenal, Kafukwe, Loangwa, and KWANDO Rivers. Its best-known feature is the great waterfall known as VICTORIA FALLS. The Zambezi and its tributaries were first explored by David Livingstone, who published a description of it in 1865.

Zambezi River Page 1166

Windhoek Page 1167

Outer wall of the hill ruin in the Great Zimbabwe complex, after which the modern nation of Zimbabwe is named. (R. Kent Rasmussen)

Zambia. Republic in south central Africa. Total area of 291,000 square miles (753,000 sq. km.) with a 1990's population of 9 million. Capital is LUSAKA, with nearly 1 million residents. Located mostly on an elevated plateau. The ZAMBEZI, Kafue, and Luangwa Rivers run through it. Much of the northern part of the country is swampland surrounding Lake Bangweulu. A main feature is the impoundment created by the Kariba Dam on the Zambezi River. The country is mineral-rich, with large deposits of zinc, tin, copper, and cobalt. Copper provides 80 percent of Zambia's export earnings. Most of the country is made up of grassland, and most residents are peasant farmers who grow corn, cassava, and sugarcane. The plateau is broken by the Muchinga Mountains in the northeast. It has a temperate climate, with the hot season lasting only from September to November. Ancient volcanic activity has left the area with rich soil, but only one-third can be cultivated due to mountains, forests and rough savanna. The GREAT RIFT VALLEY runs the length of the country from north to south, and Lake NYASA fills most of the valley. Zambia was formerly under British rule and a colony of then NORTHERN RHODESIA. It became independent as Zambia in 1964.

Zanzibar. Low-lying island off the east coast of Africa. A British protectorate until gaining independence in 1963, it merged with the mainland nation of TANGANYIKA in 1964, to become part of the UNITED REPUBLIC OF TANZANIA, Situated 25 miles (40 km.) from the mainland; covers 640 square miles (1,660 sq. km.). Long a stop for Arab traders, Zanzibar was a major center for the slave trade before British rule came in 1890. Best known for its clove industry; also produces citrus crops and coconuts. Its population in 1994 was about 800,000. Chief city, also named Zanzibar, is on the main island and had a population of 157,000 in 1988.

Zimbabwe. Republic just to the north of SOUTH AFRICA. Total area of 150,873 square miles (390,759 sq. km.) with a 1990's population of 11 million. Capital and largest city is HARARE (called Salisbury in colonial times), with 700,000 residents. The composition of its population has shifted because of the emigration of white residents after independence and the installation of a black majority government in 1980. Economy is largely based on agriculture, although it is a leading supplier of chromium and produces several other minerals. Formerly known as Southern Rhodesia and as Rhodesia. Named after the megalithic Great Zimbabwe Ruins in the southeastern part of the country.

Femi Ferreira; C. James Haug; Grove Koger;
Kikombo Ilunga Ngoy; R. Baird Shuman

Zanzibar
Page 1168

Zimbabwe
Pages 966,
1034, 1038

INDEX TO VOLUME 4

See volume 8 for a comprehensive index to all eight volumes in set.

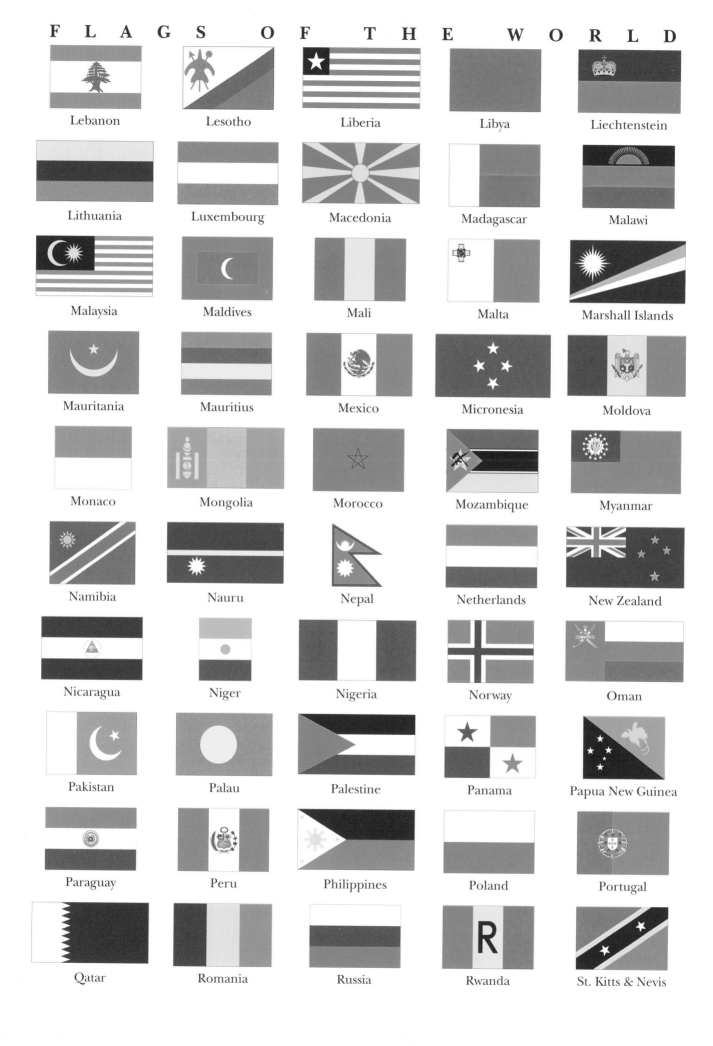

F L A G S O F T H E W O R L D

Lebanon

Lesotho

Liberia

Libya

Liechtenstein

Lithuania

Luxembourg

Macedonia

Madagascar

Malawi

Malaysia

Maldives

Mali

Malta

Marshall Islands

Mauritania

Mauritius

Mexico

Micronesia

Moldova

Monaco

Mongolia

Morocco

Mozambique

Myanmar

Namibia

Nauru

Nepal

Netherlands

New Zealand

Nicaragua

Niger

Nigeria

Norway

Oman

Pakistan

Palau

Palestine

Panama

Papua New Guinea

Paraguay

Peru

Philippines

Poland

Portugal

Qatar

Romania

Russia

Rwanda

St. Kitts & Nevis